Dr Howard Chilton has been a babies' physician for over 35 years, following training in London, Oxford and the United States. For much of this time he was Director of Newborn Care at the Royal Hospital for Women in Sydney, while also gaining invaluable experience not only as a neonatologist but also as a working father to his two daughters, Georgina and Isabella.

Dr Chilton continues to work clinically at the Prince of Wales Private Hospital and the Royal Hospital for Women. He is one of Australia's leading baby doctors. His previous book, *Baby on Board*, now in its third edition, is revered by parents for its rigorous evidence-based information couched in a reassuring, easy-to-read style.

www.babydoc.com.au
www.facebook.com/howardchilton
yourcherishedbaby.com

Also by Dr Howard Chilton

The New Baby Book

Babies from Top to Bottom

Baby on Board (three editions)

Your
Cherished Baby

Sleeping, settling and feeding strategies
to nurture your child's long-term health
and happiness

Dr Howard Chilton

MACMILLAN
Pan Macmillan Australia

First published 2014 in Macmillan by Pan Macmillan Australia Pty Ltd
1 Market Street, Sydney, New South Wales, Australia, 2000

Cataloguing-in-Publication entry is available
from the National Library of Australia
http://catalogue.nla.gov.au

Chapter heading images, except pp. 39 and 192, are sourced from Shutterstock
The chart on p. 107 is reproduced with permission from *Pediatrics*, vol. 29,
pp. 579–88, copyright 1962 by the AAP.

Typeset in 11/14.5 pt Sabon by Midland Typesetters, Australia
Internal text design by fisheye design group
Printed by McPherson's Printing Group

Papers used by Pan Macmillan Australia Pty Ltd are natural, recyclable
products made from wood grown in sustainable forests. The manufacturing
processes conform to the environmental regulations of the country of origin.

For Tamara

Contents

Introduction

I'VE READ MANY BABY BOOKS OVER the years (and indeed, have even written a few), and I am delighted to say that this one is different.

It does discuss most things that new parents need to know, but it's coming from a different perspective. This book isn't just to help you through the process of looking after your baby; it also tries to put the information into a longer time frame.

What you do with your baby in the first months and years rings down through the decades into their adulthood. If, when they get there, they can open themselves to give and receive love, and at the same time stay strong and independent, then we have succeeded.

That task, upon which all human happiness is based, is elusive. It starts with an inner core of security put there by parents and carers and is consolidated by layers of lovingness, consideration, compassion and empathy nurtured by repeated experience and example.

It's easy to push your children into being like you but better. It's harder and takes more discipline and restraint to make your children the best version of themselves.

This book lays out the nuts and bolts of the first two years of your child's life. What your baby learns now about love, relationships and their value in the world will last them a lifetime.

It's really not that hard – but it might be different from what you have in mind when you leave the hospital with your new baby.

The other aspect of this book (like my previous book *Baby on Board*) is that it looks at the science behind how we should care for babies. Overwhelmingly we find that it supports what parents' instincts tell them to do anyway.

The book starts with the lead-up to entering the labour ward, and continues to the birth itself and the big arrival; then it moves onward to the postnatal ward where all the little worries surface about your newcomer and the changes that seem to happen hour by hour. There is a 'quick guide' to carry you through these first few days, answering all the little and big questions that crop up.

A lot of the questions in this period are about breastfeeding, so there is also an easy-to-read, but comprehensive, section on this.

There is general baby information – the things that all new parents need to know, just so they won't treat their baby like a fragile object that can break if they don't do it exactly right.

Perhaps the core of the book lies in the subsequent chapters. These are about how, and under what influences, our babies wire up their brains in their first months. About how the parenting decisions we make in the early years of our babies' lives mould and shape their perceptions about life, love and their world.

Over the years I have seen so many mothers lose themselves in their parenting, both to their own and their baby's detriment. It is easy to do and the wider community encourages it. It doesn't have to be that way. We'll describe how that might be avoided.

Then, for when the baby gets a little older, there's a section on getting babies to sleep, or sleep longer – the overriding concern of parents worldwide – and a lot on the crying infant. There have been entire forests felled to provide paper upon which to write about this subject: numerous scientific papers, thousands of books and magazine articles, and oodles of myth, magic and just plain weirdness. I present a distillation of this information filtered through biology, common sense and my experience.

I'm also concerned about feeding and food for infants and kids. Something went wrong with our eating habits and what we fed our children a generation ago and it's time to address this before obesity and diabetes become the new normal.

Over the years a few mothers have asked me for suggestions about how they should play with their infants of various ages. Good question! I had such fun researching and writing a section for them.

There is also a toddler section for all of those parents who find that stage 'a bit of a challenge', which is the majority of us. It's just a matter of understanding what is going on in their minds so you can mould their behaviour, and avoid the pitfalls. Then you can both enjoy life together!

Read on.

Navigating the birth

FIRST, A QUICK WORD ABOUT THE lead-up to the birth. Before you go into labour, it is a really good idea to get all your ducks in a row:

- Make sure your attendants know your preferences regarding labour and its aftermath.
- Get your birth plan in order and negotiated.
- Pack your bag carefully well in advance, mostly with items for you. You will need only a couple of changes of clothes for the baby but check what the hospital supplies. They usually supply nappies, basic baby clothes and blankets, so don't bring your own unless you want to.
- Take a lamb or sheep skin to lie on in the hospital bed. This is very helpful especially if you have stitches. As you will have some bleeding for a few days after birth, maybe have a couple so they can be washed alternately.
- Make sure you have access to cabbage leaves/ice packs for your breasts, especially on day three when the milk first comes in.

FOOD SUPPLIES FOR LATER

In the last weeks of pregnancy, cook extra-large servings of meals that can be frozen to use when you bring the baby home.

Let family and friends know in advance that you would prefer food to flowers and chocolates after the baby is born.

The delight of a frozen casserole or curry in your freezer later when you're tired and hungry is hard to appreciate until after the baby has arrived!

GET A CLEANER IF YOU CAN

Tell your friends that enormous bunches of flowers are nice but a really thoughtful postnatal present might be the hiring of a weekly house cleaner. Maybe they could all chip in for the first six weeks.

You can also ask your friends when they visit if they could help with household chores. You'll be surprised by how everyone wants to feel helpful and contribute to the baby's wellbeing in a concrete way. They also need to know in advance that after the baby arrives the visitors will be making *you* the cup of tea when they arrive, not you.

HOW MUCH TIME CAN YOUR PARTNER TAKE OFF WORK?

Try to plan this ahead of time; however, there are a number of variables:

1. The kind of birth experience you have. If you have a caesarean or difficult vaginal birth, you will need extra support. It is likely you cannot drive for about three to six weeks after a caesarean section.

2. How demanding your baby is. Some babies slip into your life easily and spend a lot of time asleep. But these are usually other people's babies.

3. How quickly you recover. This is also hard to predict.

4. If you have a small or challenging baby who does not feed well, extra help can be essential to settle the baby or change nappies, while you do the feeding or expressing of your breasts.

CHAPTER 1

Beyond birth

LET'S TALK ABOUT ALL THE WORRYING things that you encounter when you've just had a baby. All the waiting is now over. Even better, the last trimester (the uncomfortable one) is over.

This is a quick dot-point guide with things you need to know about the baby at birth, and in the first few days after, and what you can do to avoid the pitfalls of the postnatal period.

It can be a worrying time unless you are prepared for all the contradictory advice, unexpected anxieties and conflicting emotions swirling around and in you during this time.

AT BIRTH

Babies can look blue at birth

Remember during the birth, babies are designed to remain healthy for quite a while without any oxygen supply either from the placenta or from breathing.

1

Every time the uterus contracts in labour, the baby is cut off from the oxygen supply from the mother's circulation. It's okay. Babies have wonderful ways to withstand periods of time without supplied oxygen. They have good stores of energy molecules that keep all their cells healthy during this time. Actually, their ability to do this is much better than when they are older. You and I could probably manage for only a few minutes, but our babies are usually good for at least 20 minutes without oxygen before they start running out of options. These options are called compensatory mechanisms: they are chemical pathways and alternative sources, to give the cells enough energy to stay healthy in the absence of circulating oxygen.

So if your new baby looks a little blue and even somewhat limp at birth, don't worry too much. She will probably recover quickly with a bit of encouragement from the staff and is in no danger.

Occasionally a baby can be pushed a little further than she is comfortable with, so her breathing drive may be depressed and she may need 'resuscitation'. This is normally achieved by hand-inflating the lungs using a tight-fitting mask (or, more rarely, a tube placed through the larynx), and a ventilation bag of air or oxygen. This usually rapidly kick-starts the process so the baby starts breathing on their own soon after, and all is well.

So don't wonder what the staff are talking about if they say that the baby was 'hand-bagged'! That's just what we call this form of resuscitation.

Important point

If your baby recovers from resuscitation quickly and completely, they have come to no harm.

You will know very soon if the lack of oxygen has pushed your baby too far and if she has the possibility of brain problems later, because these babies do not immediately recover. They get worse before they get better over a 12 to 24-hour period. During this time the stressed brain accumulates fluid ('cerebral oedema') and swells, making the baby very unwell and requiring intensive care. The doctor will then explain to you the potential problems and risks your baby faces.

But if she just gets better, starts breathing and fully recovers, you can bet she is fine and there is no need to worry about her future.

ANNIE'S STORY

Annie went into labour normally at full term. After six hours of contractions, the membranes ruptured and things went a little faster. The foetal heart rate was monitored and two hours later, as the cervix was becoming fully dilated, the heart rate started to dip from 120 beats per minute down to 60 beats per minute. Recovery to 120 was slow, so the obstetrician was called urgently. Between contractions, the heart rate was normal and steady, but with each contraction, again the heart rate dropped.

The obstetrician decided to hasten birth by using gentle traction, on a vacuum cup applied to the baby's head, during each contraction.

Three contractions later the baby, a good-sized girl, was born. The cord was noted to be around the neck and body.

At birth she was quiet, pale and floppy. She made no breathing effort. The cord was quickly cut and she was moved to the resuscitation trolley. She was rapidly dried and her airway cleared. Her heart rate was about 50 beats per minute. A tight-fitting mask was applied to her face and a few inflations of air made with the ventilation bag. No chest expansion was noted so it seemed the lungs were stiff and hard to inflate. Her heart rate remained low. The paediatrician used a laryngoscope to look down the throat, cleared it further with a sucker and then passed an endotracheal tube (about the size of a drinking straw) between the vocal cords into the trachea. He then fitted the ventilation bag and tried to inflate the lungs again. This time the chest expanded nicely. Immediately the heart rate increased and within seconds the baby pinked up and started moving her limbs. Soon she was breathing on her own, opening her eyes and trying to cry. The paediatrician then removed the tube from the baby's throat and she howled lustily. After a quick check-up, she was then carried over to her parents and placed, still damp and squirming, between Annie's breasts. Though the baby looked a little surprised at the whole business, within minutes she was rooting for the nipple and trying to feed.

She went to the postnatal ward with her parents and never looked back, although her parents remained a little anxious about her for a few days until it was obvious to them that she was just fine.

Baby's body at birth

At birth the baby's body has to make a number of important changes:

- Instead of obtaining oxygen from the placenta and the mother's bloodstream, it must start absorbing oxygen from the air in the lungs. As the breathing expands the air sacs, it also causes a complementary expansion of the blood vessels, increasing the blood flow to the lungs. The blood in the lungs avidly absorbs the oxygen from the air and supplies it to the body.
- The connections that allow the circulation in the foetus to bypass the lungs, when within the womb, have to close.
- The lungs, which in the womb are filled with fluid, have to either expel or absorb this, and then inflate with air.

These changes are made within seconds of birth. So although babies might appear rather blue at birth, they will rapidly pink up as the oxygen levels rise. The lips and tongue should be a glowing pink colour within seconds. Many babies will gasp and cry at this time, though some make the transition with little fuss or noise.

The Apgar score

Your baby will be given a score for how she's coped with the transition to life outside the womb.

In the past, the Apgar score was useful. The one-minute score showed how well the baby had coped with the birth process, and the five-minute showed her likely prognosis into the future. Since the introduction of modern neonatal resuscitation techniques it is less relevant. With good resuscitation, even babies with low Apgar scores tend to do very well in follow-up.

Physical signs	Score 0	Score 1	Score 2
Heart rate	Absent	Less than 100	More than 100
Respirations	Absent	Slow and irregular	Good and regular
Muscle tone	Limp	Some flexion of limbs	Active motion
Colour	Blue	Pink body, blue extremities	Completely pink
Reflex response	Nil	Grimace	Cough or sneeze (to nasal catheter)

- This scores five features of the baby's functioning at exactly one minute and five minutes after birth.
- Each feature gets two points, making a complete score of ten.
- Most babies don't get ten because their hands and feet remain slightly blue for some time after birth. This is quite normal.

Skin to skin

A few years ago, straight after birth babies were removed from their mother, weighed, measured, bathed and dressed, before being given back for their first cuddle and feed.

We now realise that this is not helpful for a few reasons:

- A cascade of hormones kicks in at birth and from close contact between mother and baby, especially in those early hours. They help the breastfeeding to go smoothly and allow the baby to adapt more gradually to life outside her mother.

- As soon after birth as possible it is good to put your baby on your chest with her ear against your heartbeat to reassure her that, although life has changed, you're still close.

- The parents have a need to gaze at their baby, especially early on, when she has the 'face-searching' reflex (see below) and gazes at them.

- Babies prefer the smell of the amniotic fluid on their skin rather than soaps, cleansers or antiseptics. The smell reminds them of the womb and their mother, and it comforts them. This is why we tend not to bath babies straightaway after birth anymore. They cry less.

However, if you miss this time because your baby needs to go to the nursery or you are in the recovery ward after a caesarean section, your relationship with your baby will come to no harm. It just might not be as smooth or might take a little longer to feel relaxed with her, but you'll end up in the same place anyway within a short time.

'Face-searching' reflex

When a baby is first born, despite the fact that she has never seen the human face before, she has a powerful desire to search for the 'eyes, nose, mouth' pattern and gaze at it. This is highly reproducible in studies – you should try it with your baby. If the baby is presented with a picture of a human face where the pattern has been swapped around or distorted, it will not hold her interest.

Babies also have a preference for a smiling rather than a frowning face. So the way to attract the attention of a baby (or anyone else, now I think about it) is a big smile.

Vitamin K

Almost every baby gets an injection of vitamin K at birth nowadays.

- Vitamin K is necessary for the baby's clotting system to work efficiently and babies who do not receive the injection have an increased likelihood of bleeding from their bowel, umbilicus or even within their brain.
- There is very little vitamin K in breastmilk and not enough can be transferred to the baby even if the mother's levels are good.
- Babies who are on formula usually can get enough vitamin K from the cow's milk but it is still an unreliable source.
- In 1991 a group of researchers in Bristol, UK, thought that they had found a relationship between the injection of vitamin K given to babies at birth and childhood cancers. Not only that, the information first appeared in a daily newspaper two months before it was published in the *British Medical Journal*. What a brilliant way to scare millions of parents! Many further detailed studies showed that this conclusion was completely wrong, but two decades later we are still dealing with the fallout from this mistake.
- You can give your baby vitamin K by mouth and not by injection. However, this takes multiple doses (three or four over the first three months) and it is still not effective for a small group of babies.
- My sincere advice is to stay with the 99 per cent and opt for the injection of vitamin K.

Temperature control

After a baby has had a long cuddle and a breastfeed with her mother, she is generally wrapped in a couple of blankets if she is put in her bassinette.

- At birth, babies are covered in fluid, which evaporates from their skin and this can cool them down.

- Hence they are well wrapped and kept warm during this time of transition to life outside the womb.
- After 24 hours babies are better at keeping themselves warm so generally don't need 'double wrapping'.

EARLY DAYS IN THE POSTNATAL WARD

Mucusy babies

- Most babies are mucusy on their first day. The baby dribbles and pukes clear fluid from the mouth.
- Occasionally a big vomit of the sticky stuff will make the baby hold his breath until his airway is clear and he might go blue in the face. It's okay; he can manage this by himself and his airway doesn't need sucking out. It lasts about a day or so.
- Later, after the milk comes in and he starts siphoning the milk into his sinuses and back of his nose, he'll get mucusy again. No, he doesn't have a cold and hasn't become allergic to the flowers in your room.
- He might even cough a little as the mucus drips back down his throat.
- This phase can last for weeks and parents notice it more at night.

The skin has red spots like mosquito bites: 'Toxic erythema'

- This rash develops in the first day or so and is a response to contact with clothes for the first time.
- It is completely harmless, doesn't hurt, needs no treatment and is not due to allergy.

The baby's got pimples on her nose!

- These are called 'milia' because they look like millet seeds.
- They are the pores of sweat glands that are not yet open.
- They will go away in a few weeks.

The baby is shivering!

- Babies are 'jittery'; that is, they make jerking movements of their arms and legs, like they are cold and shivery.
- They also make similar movements of the jaw.
- It is not likely that the baby is cold. It is due to the immaturity of their nervous system.
- If it is excessive in the first few days, the staff of the postnatal ward would normally check that the calcium and the blood sugar levels of the baby are normal, as low levels of these can make it worse.

She's so red!

- Most parents comment about how red their baby looks soon after birth. Babies have high haemoglobin levels (the substance that carries oxygen in the red cells in the blood) because they were foetuses. In the womb they need more haemoglobin to carry enough oxygen from the placenta, as it's less efficient than breathing air. Their colour will be less red every day, until by six weeks of age they will look rather pale.

Except her hands and feet are slightly blue!

- This is called 'acrocyanosis' and it's normal. The baby's circulation is just settling down from being warmed by the mother when in the womb.

But she actually feels cool to touch

- As mentioned, babies are born wet, so it's a little like stepping out of the shower after birth. The water evaporates from the skin and takes energy with it, cooling the skin. That's why babies are dried after birth and, hopefully, put on their mother's chest to maintain their body temperature.

- Alternatively, wrapping them snugly in a couple of blankets for a few hours will also keep them warm. If they do get cold, a short time under an open warmer (with an infra-red warming element) with the temperature carefully monitored will usually rapidly fix the issue.

Early weight loss

- Babies are waterlogged from floating in the womb when they are first born. They 'dry out' in the first few days and can lose up to 10 per cent of their birth weight. That's why our mature milk takes three or so days to arrive. Other animals' milk comes in with the birth, but humans need the delay to dry out. Don't worry about the weight loss. It's normal, and it's only water and 'meconium' (foetal stool).

A slight fever on day two

- Many babies get a temperature of up to about 37.7°C between the second and third day. Let the staff know. The baby should still be vigorous and healthy, not listless or pale. If things are not right, the baby should be checked for infection.
- It's usually due to the slight dehydration in the baby's body as the milk isn't quite in yet. To conserve fluid, the blood supply to the skin is slowed, so heat isn't as easily dissipated through it. Hence the baby warms.

There is no such thing as overfeeding your baby

- In the early days your baby sucks avidly to try to get your breasts to produce milk. That's how the system works.
- Once the milk comes in the baby controls the supply by draining the breast. How much he sucks is up to him. Don't worry. If he gets too much he will vomit. It's okay.

You can't cuddle your baby too much

- Your baby has just left the warmth and security of your womb. He wonders where he is. He can't hear the familiar sound of your heartbeat that filled his life when nestling inside you. When he's upset, pick him up, cuddle him against your chest and put his ear against your heartbeat. He will settle.

You can't spoil your baby at this age

- Babies can't have too much contact with or be too close to their mother. They can't have too much attention. They cannot learn bad habits for months yet. Disregard all advice to the contrary.

Hiccupping is normal

- Don't you remember that your baby hiccupped in the womb?
- Now that he's out he still does, but you can see it! Each hiccup jolts his little body and sounds alarming, especially after a feed. Relax. It's okay.

Early vomiting

- Regurgitation is normal for the baby. It doesn't mean he will suffer from reflux or that he is unwell. However, if he vomits bile (bright green vomit), he might need attention – call the staff.

It's not blood in the urine

- Most babies pass pink crystals of 'urate' in the urine in the first few days. The red stain in the nappy is not blood and is quite normal. It will go when the baby gets more fluid after the milk comes in.

NEVER give up breastfeeding and start formula at 2 am!

- Things often seem terrible in the middle of the night – in the light of day, they don't seem so bad. If you give up at night, when you're tired, upset and in pain, and your baby's screaming non-stop, the next morning you may well wish you hadn't. Make the decision in the cold light of day – this gives you a much better chance to make sure it's the right one!

Babies often develop 'dry lips' and a thick pad of skin in the middle of the upper lip

- The pad is called a 'suck blister'. But it's not a blister and isn't caused by sucking! The cells in the skin of the lips just reproduce faster than normal to start with.
- The baby is not dehydrated, or thirsty. The pad may peel off, and there may be another one underneath. They're normal and harmless.

Jaundice

- Most babies have yellow skin (jaundice) by day three.
- The jaundice colour is a substance called bilirubin. It is the end product of the breakdown of blood, which is happening normally in the body all the time.
- When the baby is in the womb, the mother's liver processes and deals with both her bilirubin and her baby's.
- After birth, the baby's liver takes a few days to learn to process this breakdown product and excrete it into the gut as bile.
- It is very yellow in colour and this can be seen in the baby's skin and in the whites (now yellow!) of the eyes.
- After three to five days it will settle.

Umbilical cord

- The umbilical cord is clamped and cut at birth, separating the baby from the placenta. After birth the stump will wither and dry up. The clamp can be removed usually after 48 hours.
- There are no nerves in the umbilical cord, which is why we can cut it at birth without causing discomfort. When you clean the cord you will not cause your baby discomfort either. Clean the cord with a dry cotton bud, especially in the gutter at the base.
- The cord separates due to the action of white blood cells in the blood dissolving the cord at its base. These cells can be killed by the action of surgical spirit or antiseptics. So unless the cord is smelly, just keep it dry with a cotton bud around the base as above. However, use alcohol or spirit if it becomes smelly or where there is a danger of cross infection, such as in multi-bed wards. If the skin around the cord becomes red and inflamed, go and show it to your doctor or midwife.
- A few drops of blood on cord separation is not unusual but should be closely observed. Usually it is from the clot in the separating cord stump, not from the baby.

Grunting and groaning in the cot

- Some babies, especially those who were born prematurely, can be really noisy sleepers. They grunt, groan, strain and arch their backs in their cot, even when they are asleep. This can be completely normal and they will settle in a few weeks.
- It can worsen when they start getting a little stressed after six weeks of age – when they take more interest in the world and get overstimulated. Take it as a sign to keep them calm and offer them a quiet life until they are more settled.
- Having them close is ideal but some are so noisy you have to get pragmatic and put them in their own room, with a monitor that you can turn down!

Meconium and baby poos

- In the first hours and days, babies pass meconium, a thick, treacle-like, odourless stool. It occasionally follows a white mucus plug.
- Babies will usually pass their first stool in the first 24 hours. If they don't, be patient but get your baby examined to see that all is well.
- It is okay to use wet baby wipes to clean their bottom.
- When the colostrum turns to milk the stools will become 'transitional'; that is, softer, lighter in colour and develop a slightly milky smell. This is a great sign that your lactation is progressing! Once your milk is in, the stools become frankly milky in smell and yellow in colour. They can be frequent, gassy and liquid. Your milk is in!
- In the early days after that the stools usually maintain this appearance, and depending on your milk supply can be with (and between) every feed and become 'seedy' (the indigestible curds left over from your milk).
- Also in the stool is bile, excreted from the baby's liver and containing the jaundice pigment from her normal blood breakdown. It can make the stools more greenish (even fluorescent green).
- If the stools are white or colourless, let the staff know as this is important.
- Babies will then settle into their particular stool frequency, which depends mostly on your milk supply but also on the gut's absorption rate. Some babies will have 20 stools a day and after a few weeks sometimes this number will drop to one stool every couple of weeks or so.
- Occasionally in fully breastfed babies, streaks of blood and blobs of mucus appear intermittently in the stools. This is caused by irritation to the mucus lining of the large bowel. As it can be due to the baby being sensitive to cow's milk protein excreted in her breastmilk, it is a good idea for the mother to stop consuming all dairy products (that is,

anything with cow's milk protein in it) for a couple of weeks. Most likely, though, this will make no difference, in which case, after seeking medical advice and checking that the baby is well in every other respect, it can be safely ignored.

Constipation

- Constipation in babies is not infrequent stools. It is hard, dry stools.
- Don't worry about constipation in breastfed babies. Even after two or three weeks with no stool, when it eventually comes it will be fluid.
- With the formula-fed baby, the stools tend to be firmer, more greenish, and smell less milky than those of the breastfed.
- In the formula fed you should expect a stool every day or two and not wait to take action if there is a delay, or if it emerges dry and pellet-like. If this happens, it may be necessary to soften the stool using dietary means.
- In this case, the old-fashioned remedy of a teaspoonful of brown sugar in each bottle works very effectively; however, it should not be used regularly as this enhances the baby's attraction to sweet tastes. If stool softeners need to be given regularly, it is better to use a small amount of lactulose (2–5 ml) in the bottle. This can be obtained from the chemist. After a few weeks' time, diluted prune juice (10 ml of 50 per cent juice with boiled and cooled water) can also be used now and again to soften the stool. Giving the formula-fed baby with hard stools small quantities of extra water (10–20 ml) is also reasonable.
- For constipation after the introduction of solids, see Chapter 19.

Starting breastfeeding

- Get a midwife to help you attach the baby to the breast.
- Babies (and you) need to learn the correct breastfeeding

technique – how to 'latch' on to the breast, with mouth wide, enveloping the areola.

- If babies 'nipple-suck', they can quickly damage the skin of their mother's nipples.
- Milk comes in at about two and a half days. Before that, some babies feed constantly, some sleep for long periods. You go with the flow, but check with a midwife if you think your baby's behaviour seems a little extreme.
- Your breasts produce only a dribble of colostrum for the first couple of days. So, for some babies, there's not a lot to wake up for. Let him do whatever he wants to do. The milk will come in anyway. Your job is to protect your nipples from damage from your baby's little mouth.
- When you feel your breasts changing, getting heavier or hotter, and filling, it means there are about 12 hours until the arrival of the milk. Then your baby will start to feed insatiably (this is the 'feeding frenzy'). He'll be on and off the breast continually for 24 hours. Let him feed. Despite the way he behaves, he does not have a pain in his tummy, and he does not have wind. He just wants to feed and induce your milk flow. Let him.
- Babies Prefer to Feed at NIGHT in the first few days (and sometimes beyond). Your baby knows that night feeds induce the hormone prolactin (which boosts milk supply) better than day feeds do. When the milk is in and the supply is secure, the baby will get day and night sorted out.
- The breast is never 'emptied'. One can always squeeze some milk out of the lactating breast, because it is constantly being produced. However, there is a reservoir of milk that you should aim to drain, to boost or maintain your supply.
- Smaller babies often wish to grow faster than average to catch up, and should be allowed to do so. So don't worry if these babies seem to be hungry all the time. They probably are!
- Babies enjoy the act of sucking; it induces the blissful beta-endorphin hormone into their circulation, which calms

them. Hence if you have a 'sucky' baby and an excellent milk supply, your baby may put on more than average weight gain. This is fine. By the time he gets to six months of age or so, it will sort itself out.

IMPORTANT POINTS FOR MOTHERS

Baby and your sleep

Babies often sleep best in the early morning so try to have a nap after breakfast.

Remember, if you can: sleep when the baby sleeps. You might need to sleep in the middle of the day, a pattern which will have ramifications for your visitors.

Babies are nocturnal

For the first week or so, babies tend to be awake and fussy especially between 9 pm and 3 am. Night feeds induce more prolactin – that milk-boosting hormone – in your body so these feeds are not to be missed. It's okay to put your baby in the nursery if you are totally exhausted on the first night but think carefully about doing it on subsequent nights. Night nurses will do as you wish, including taking the baby to the nursery at night and giving formula. This may not help your breastfeeding at all, so think about this in advance.

Visitors

Let your friends know that you need daytime sleep and to keep their visits short or delay them until after you get home.

Let them know that you will be switching your phone off. Invite them to text you and you'll call them back, or your partner can handle the calls.

Babymoon

Think of the first few weeks after the birth as your babymoon, just like your honeymoon; that is, a quiet time when you get to know each other.

Food

Have some nutritious snacks available to eat when you're hungry. Breastfeeding mums are often hungry; after all, they are eating for two people and it's a long time between hospital dinner and breakfast.

Water

Have a bottle of water next to you where you feed the baby. As they get the 'letdown' reflex, where milk is expelled forcefully from the breast, many women find they get an intense hormone-induced thirst.

Don't drink more than you need to quench your thirst.

But if your urine is concentrated, you are not drinking enough.

Oxytocin

This is a hormone that causes the letdown reflex. It also causes the uterus to contract (and expel the baby). After birth when you breastfeed you will probably get contractions from the uterus. This will expel blood from your vagina and soak your maternity pad, so change it before the feed. These contractions, especially in mothers with second or third babies, can be very strong and cause great discomfort. If so, you may need to ask for a painkiller before a feed.

Feeding posture

Make sure you are comfortable during the feed.

Ensure your back is well supported, perhaps with a pillow.

Your arms and shoulders should be relaxed and comfortable. It is a good idea to have a firm pillow under your elbow and arm for support, and this will also allow your shoulders to relax while holding your baby.

Get a small footstool to support your feet and this will also take the pressure off the small of your back.

Local mothers' groups

As you leave the hospital, make enquiries about a mothers' group in your area. Do this sooner rather than later. Check with your early childhood centre or family doctor for the ones in your area. Meeting and talking to other mothers is an important part of your journey into motherhood. You can learn from other people's experience and meet some new friends at the same time. It can be very isolating to be a new mother at home with her baby, and this is a great way to get out and about.

The Australian Breastfeeding Association is the peak body for supporting breastfeeding in Australia. It trains breastfeeding counsellors and helps support thousands of mothers with their breastfeeding. It runs local mothers' groups that are especially useful for first-time mothers but experienced mothers can benefit from their meetings too. They also provide free telephone support on breastfeeding and mothering, and have an excellent website with lots of reliable, evidence-based information on breastfeeding. (Also see Chapter 2 on breastfeeding.)

Postnatal depression

If you start feeling really depressed after giving birth to your baby, don't be ashamed or hide the fact. Postnatal depression (PND) is common, with 20 per cent of mothers being affected. It occurs all over the world and has done so throughout history. It is caused just by being pregnant and may occur in subsequent pregnancies.

PND can occur up to a year after the baby's birth. Some fathers can get it too.

PND is not to be confused with fourth-day blues or baby blues. Most mothers feel low at that time after the birth due to the change in the hormones in their body in the transition from being pregnant.

Postnatal psychosis is also a completely different disease. It is rare. In this the mother loses touch with reality and has a disorder of the thinking process itself. She has no insight that she is unwell. She may be depressed, paranoid or anxious but may also be happy and active. However, she has delusions, hallucinations and disordered thoughts as well. She can be a danger to herself or her baby and needs hospitalisation. With treatment, most recover over a few months.

PND symptoms include:

- deep depression
- anxiety, obsessive thoughts and concerns, fear even of being alone
- guilt and loss of self-esteem
- irritability or anger
- chronic fatigue and inability to cope
- poor appetite and sleep
- inability to concentrate or think clearly.

It may be triggered by a number of factors:

From the mother:

- genetic tendency
- previous depression
- perfectionistic or anxious personality
- difficulty in communicating
- unresolved grief
- previous abuse or psychological trauma.

Outside factors:

- difficult pregnancy or birth, or disappointment with the process or the baby.
- anything that puts a heavy strain on the mother: fretful baby, breastfeeding difficulties, poor support from family, money troubles, isolation, relationship problems, and so on.

Diagnosis:

The most difficult part is the mother admitting that a problem exists. Many mothers battle through and hide it or think it is their own fault, as society expects new mothers to be happy. Very often the mother's bond with her baby is normal but for some this can be affected. PND is a disease state that cannot be overcome by will alone. We do not 'battle through' when we have pneumonia. This is a similar situation and it needs treatment.

Treatment:

Talk to your doctor or healthcare worker. Very often psychiatric advice and anti-depressant medications are needed. It is not necessary to stop breastfeeding during treatment. Counselling is also important and there are self-help groups to help you get through. Generally with treatment the problem is controllable and disappears after a few months.

Chapter 2

Breastfeeding: your baby made entirely of you

THIS IS MOSTLY A BOOK FOR parents, especially mothers, about the emotional and psychological aspects of looking after babies. It is, if you like, about settling babies and getting mothers to take care of themselves. Of all the activities that mothers and babies do together, breastfeeding ticks both these boxes.

Once the process is underway most feeds will last 20 minutes or so. On average there will be six to eight feeds a day, so let's say seven. That means on any given day you are spending about two and a half hours feeding, holding and hopefully gazing at your baby as she gazes back at you. She drinks in your milk, your smell, your gaze and your touch.

So if you breastfeed her for a year, you have spent over 900 hours, or 38 solid days, connecting with your baby at the deepest level possible.

As explained elsewhere, this first year is a time when critically important and lifelong changes to the baby's brain are being made, which relate to her ability to feel secure and loved. There is no better mediator for this process than breastfeeding. When your baby gets distressed there is no greater sedative than the breast. Nothing reduces stress hormone levels faster.

The fabulous food content is only part of it!

Maureen Minchin, author of one of the best, most comprehensive books on breastfeeding, said that formula feeding was the 'largest uncontrolled in vivo experiment in human history'. The message has still not been heard. Formula is food; that's all it is. It does not have the same emotional and hormonal power to enhance the baby's development, intelligence and emotional stability like breastfeeding.

And on top of that, it is easier, more convenient, and has more important health benefits to the mother than the alternative. It also brings satisfaction and joy. What's not to like?

Sadly, some mothers, no matter how hard they try, or how much they want to, are unable to breastfeed. If that is the case, the baby will thrive regardless, but make sure during bottle feeds that she gets the same loving closeness, the same eye contact and murmured words as if she was breastfeeding. (See p.36 for details.)

WHY BREASTFEED?

Human milk is designed specifically and perfectly for the human baby. The components are appropriate for a smart primate. It is the milk of a continuous-contact animal, has low protein (for slow, gradual growth), high lactose (to grow a large brain), a fat level that is low to moderate (also appropriate for the slow-growing foetus living in a warm environment) and high water content (for good hydration even in hot conditions).

Breastmilk contains 100 per cent of the daily requirement of everything a baby needs to grow perfectly. It is also filled with biological agents that work for the baby's benefit, helping her absorb trace elements, keeping out infections, improving brain growth and intelligence, and giving lifetime protection from many chronic diseases and cancers.

Babies believe breastfeeding is ordinary and normal. To them it is not special, not reserved for those mothers who have time on their hands or the need to give their babies something extra. Only cats and humans drink the milk of another species and generally if this is attempted in other species, the young will not thrive.

It is impossible to be too enthusiastic about this wonderful tissue fluid and the numerous still-unfolding qualities it brings to our new babies.

Not only is it the most perfect, complete food that money can't buy, but it also helps babies regulate their appetite, enhancing it when necessary, and suppressing it when intake is sufficient. This decreases their likelihood of obesity and all its associated diseases later.

And in addition, it tastes good. Every time a baby breastfeeds he partakes in his mother's last meal, tasting the odourants from her food and storing them away in his brain in a file labelled 'This is Good Food (because my mother eats it)'.

It is excellent 'desert' milk, perfectly designed for the hottest climates. All the water in breastmilk is 'free' water; that is, water available for evaporating from the skin to keep the body cool. This is because the salt level in the milk is low so little fluid is wasted to excrete excess salt through the kidneys. So breastfed babies never need extra water even in hot weather; they just need access to the breast to quench their thirst.

The breastmilk is also customised to the baby's environment. As her mother is exposed to the germs around her, she makes antibodies to protect herself, and these she passes on to her baby who gets this personalised mixture of local germ protection when she feeds.

Even the act of feeding is beneficial, for as she feeds she receives a cocktail of pleasurable chemicals (hormones and neurotransmitters), which course through her body, invoked by the sight, smell, touch and sound of her mother's body, breast and voice. Prominent among these agents is oxytocin, which as mentioned elsewhere creates a feeling of calm and connectedness both in mother and baby, and enhances their attachment and close bond. In addition, prolactin, dopamine, beta-endorphin and other feel-good hormones enhance the experience and make it almost addictive for both participants. Nature knows how to encourage useful behaviour – by creating intense pleasure.

HOW TO DO IT

Breastfeeding is like riding a bicycle: hard to start but once you figure it out, you can't believe how easy it is.

It is critical to get the 'latch' right. Many babies, especially the ones who were thumb-suckers in the womb, tend to try to suck the nipple like a bottle teat, mouth half closed, tongue rubbing against the nipple. This hurts and traumatises your nipple and gets the baby little colostrum.

In a good latch the baby's mouth is wide open. The nipple goes way into the mouth and the tip sits at the junction between the hard and the soft palate.

Where is the junction of the hard and soft palate?

Put your finger on to the roof of your mouth and run it (slowly – don't gag!) down towards your throat. The first part is hard bone, then near the back it becomes soft muscles only. It is at that junction that the tip of the nipple should be placed for a good latch.

Small chins are common in babies and are normal. Actually all babies' chins grow faster than the rest of their face – a small jaw gives babies their 'infant' face. But the smaller the chin the more you have to be sure that it is well tucked into your breast so your nipple points to the roof of her mouth.

Gripping the back of the baby's head with your hand to put her on the breast will tend to make her close her mouth and raise her shoulders. This inhibits a good latch.

Numerous studies have shown that early skin-to-skin contact between mother and baby enhances the likelihood that the breast-feeding will go well.

Things you need when breastfeeding

- a glass of water (the hormones of breastfeeding may give you a sudden thirst)
- your phone
- a book, iPod or TV remote (once you get experienced)
- an extra cushion or pillow
- a box of tissues.

The technique

- Try to get him on the breast before he is so hungry he is howling and tense.
- Get comfortable either sitting or lying with the things you need around you.
- Talk to him gently and gaze at him. Use the same 'trigger' words whenever you start to breastfeed so he associates the two.
- Put him across your body, tummy to tummy, skin to skin.
- His head should be free to move from side to side and not be constrained, so don't have it in the crook of your arm, but on your forearm.
- Hold him so his nose is opposite your nipple, with his head slightly extended (back) in the 'sniffing' position.
- Gently rub the pigmented area of your breast (areola) against his lower lip.
- In early feeds, or if your breast is tense and full, place the forefinger of your free hand in the same plane as the baby's mouth on top of the areola. The third finger should go underneath, also on the areola. By gently squeezing them slightly, the areola and nipple will be flattened to enter the baby's mouth.

- Allow him to root for the nipple, continuing to give his head enough freedom to move side to side to try to find and engulf the nipple and much of the lower areola.

- When he opens his mouth and has a wide gape, move his whole body towards the breast by moving him back closer to you.

- Move his chin gently into the breast to clear his nose and point your nipple towards the roof of his mouth.

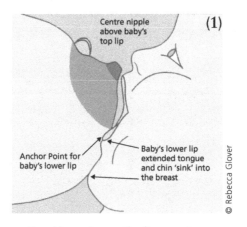

Good breast–mouth alignment

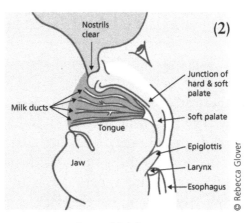

A good latch

Graphic used with permission, from 'The Key to Successful Breastfeeding' pamphlet by Rebecca Glover, available at www.rebeccaglover.com.au

His position is right if:

1. He 'chomps' with his jaws, without sucking in his cheeks. You will see the muscles below his ears moving as he does so.

2. There is lots of tongue action. Actually, he drops his tongue in his mouth and thereby creates a vacuum that sucks the milk out of the breast. Once the flow is going it then tends to 'siphon' almost continually.

3. You can only see a little crescent of pigmented areola above the baby's mouth and none below.

4. You may feel some initial discomfort as the nipple stretches but this should settle down as milk flow improves during the feed.

Once he's settled, remove your fingers, release your shoulders (don't hunch!) and relax.

At the end of the feed when you withdraw your nipple, check its shape is not flattened or distorted.

HOW LONG SHOULD THE FEED TAKE?

Once the milk supply is established and a good latch is secured, milk transfers very quickly from the breast to the baby, the majority of the feed transferring in the first six minutes after the feed starts. The baby will attempt to drain your reservoir of breastmilk with big gulps, and as the flow diminishes so will his suck-swallow frequency. All breasts are different of course and some may take longer to drain, but the way to monitor this is to check the baby's suck pattern, not the clock.

So to start: suck – swallow – suck – swallow.

As the volume decreases: suck – suck – suck – swallow. This is a reliable way to determine whether the breast is emptying because, as mentioned earlier, squeezing the breast can always obtain a little milk. Watching his suck-swallow rhythm will enable you to switch breasts at the appropriate time. If you are unsure, express a few drops of milk; if it is rich and creamy or sticky, you know the baby may be ready for the second side.

FOREMILK AND HINDMILK

The fat concentration of the milk doubles from the beginning to the end of the feed, making the hindmilk thicker, creamier and more satisfying for the baby (you can see it: the foremilk is thin and watery, the hindmilk thick and creamy). However, the sugar in the milk (lactose) remains at exactly the same concentration throughout the feed. It has been shown that it is the fat load that switches off the baby's appetite, not the fullness of his stomach.

So for a baby to have a satisfying feed, he should stay on the breast until the reservoir is low (suck – suck – suck – swallow – pause) before going to sleep, or moving on to the next breast if he is still unsettled.

The letdown reflex

The hormone oxytocin acts on the muscle of your uterus to cause contractions during the birth, and later to keep it contracted to seal the blood vessels that are connected to the placenta. It also acts on the muscles around the milk ducts in your breasts, which cause the milk to be ejected. This is why you may get quite intense uterine contractions when breastfeeding. The hormone is produced in your body by things that you associate with feeding, such as the cry or smell of your baby, or even just thoughts about him. It explains the rapid transferral of milk from breast to baby, and hence why feeds can be so rapid. The letdown is sensed by a 'tingling' sensation in the breast and is inhibited by pain or anxiety.

MAINTAINING AND BUILDING UP YOUR SUPPLY

There is a substance secreted by the breast into the milk that acts as its own milk production suppressor. If too much milk is left in the breast after a good feed, the breast assumes it's made more than the baby needs and the suppressor in the leftover milk decreases the milk supply. And when the breastmilk reservoir is low, the suppressor is all removed, and this induces maximum supply. Babies know this. That is why demand feeding is such a good idea.

Remember, one can always squeeze some milk out of the lactating breast, as the milk is being produced all the time, so the breast is never 'empty'.

HOW OFTEN SHOULD THE BABY FEED?

Before the milk comes in

In the first few days, babies' feeding can be quite erratic. Some feed constantly, while others sleep most of the time. Most of them do tend to feed much more at night than during the day as night feeds induce more prolactin than day feeds, therefore boosting the milk supply. In these early feeds babies get a small amount of colostrum (2–12 ml), which is all they require.

Many parents become very concerned about the lack of milk in the first few days, and some get so worried that they give the baby formula during this time. This is generally very inadvisable and unnecessary. By taking only the gel-like colostrum, the baby's bowel is 'sealed' so the lining cannot be invaded by harmful bacteria and the bacteria that are encouraged to grow are healthy ones. In addition, the colostrum contains antibodies, prebiotics, probiotics and many other bioactive substances, which set the bowel up for optimal functioning. By introducing formula, which has none of these factors, the wrong proteins encourage the wrong bacteria to grow and we miss out on so many of the advantages designed into the system by nature.

After the milk comes in

At about two and a half days, the breasts start to change. You will notice they become heavier, hotter and somewhat uncomfortable. About 12 hours after this sensation starts, the milk starts to flow and the baby starts to feed voraciously. As mentioned earlier, this is the 'feeding frenzy'. It can be very intense as the baby may feed almost continuously for 24 hours. Don't worry, the baby is merely trying to boost your milk supply, so this is no time to put the baby into the nursery at night, even with the incessant feeding.

Once the feeding is established it is appropriate to demand feed the baby, as only he knows how much he needs, and how much you have. So he should be left to control the business.

For those of you who are used to controlling things, this can be tough. It's not often that we have to just trust our bodies to work things out, and the baby seems so helpless . . . However, that is the way the system works.

It's all superbly evolved to function optimally under the baby's direction. All you have to remember is which breast to start the feed with, as both should be kept comfortable, and your breast size and capacity may be unequal in the beginning.

You might even find that this unequal situation continues down the track and you have to deal with it by making sure the smaller capacity breast gets as much attention as the larger. This will keep the supply at an ideal level in both.

After a few days

Soon babies generally sort themselves out to feed somewhere between every two to four hours around the clock.

Some babies feed more frequently:

- if they are born small and need to catch up with their growth.
- if they are 'sucky' babies that need to suck frequently to keep themselves calm (see below).
- if they are carried next to the breast constantly. If the breast is right there, why not feed?
- if the mother has small breastmilk reservoirs.

Comfort sucking

Of course sometimes babies also feed for comfort. Babies enjoy the act of sucking, as it induces the blissful beta-endorphin hormone into their circulation, which calms them. In the early days, as long as the attachment to the breast is correct (so there is no nipple trauma), if they wish to comfort feed, let them. Later, over the days and weeks, you can negotiate a more time-efficient pattern.

> The baby's stomach, when filled with breastmilk, empties within 30–40 minutes, so overfeeding is hard to do.

If you have such a 'sucky' baby in combination with an excellent milk supply, your baby may put on more weight than average. Expect some frowns from the early childhood nurse and some praise from Grandma. But generally it's okay. When he gets to six months of age or so he will become more interested in his surroundings rather than in your breast, and his weight will plateau and then settle down.

DAY/NIGHT RHYTHMS

To get day/night (diurnal) rhythms established, make the first feed of the day in the brightest room you have. This will tell the baby's brain that it is morning and encourage the correct hormone rhythms.

ISSUES

Painful breasts

I'm sure there is a connection between the verb 'graze', meaning feed for hours, and 'graze', meaning skin damage – there certainly is with babies. Many mothers get learning grazes in the first few days, when the baby's technique is not quite right and the breasts are unused to all the attention. Luckily the nipples learn to stretch and have very copious blood flow so they heal quickly as soon as they are allowed to do so. Other than fresh air, there are no remedies such as creams or lotions that can help this process, as the healing is from within. If the nipple is very cracked and painful, expressing that breast (to maintain the milk supply) for 24 hours is usually enough to heal it.

Engorgement

When the milk first comes in, often the breast can appear overfull (it could be called 'the beach ball syndrome'); this can be either from too much milk in the ducts or congestion of the veins. The management is much the same.

- The breast may be so tight that you will need to express a little milk first so the baby can attach. If the areola is puffy, ease the puffiness back into the breast so the nipple is more flexible.

- Make sure your bra is comfortable. There should be no straps or any areas that can compress the breast.

- Apply cool compresses. For some reason cooled cabbage leaves seem to work better than the equivalent cool pack. Put the washed and dried inner leaves into the fridge, and then transfer them into your bra, avoiding the nipple. Keep them there for at least two hours, replacing if necessary.

- Don't warm your breasts under the shower during this time as this increases blood flow and congestion.

- Usually the problem sorts itself out in about 24 hours, by the milk suppressor reducing your supply and your baby drinking more efficiently.

Mastitis

If you start feeling like you're coming down with the flu, and you have a painful lump or red area in your breast, you may be getting mastitis. This is a condition where there is a blocked duct in the breast and milk products become reabsorbed into the circulation. The blocked duct also rapidly becomes colonised with bacteria, which thrive in the warm milk, and their growth can accelerate.

Don't waste time. Get to your doctor and get some flucloxacillin antibiotic into you. This medication specifically targets the germ that causes the problem.

At the same time it is important to drain the blocked duct if you can. Get the baby to feed on that side. (Don't worry, he can deal with the germs very well – breastmilk has germs in it at the best of times.) Alternatively, hand express, or use an electric or hand breast pump.

Often mothers get mastitis when they are not looking after themselves enough, and become run-down. Take your attack as a wake-up call to try to get some help, plan your day better, catnap, and do less and care for yourself more.

Drugs in breastmilk

Generally there are few substances that mothers consume that impact on their baby adversely. That is because when they absorb substances in their bodies, these are usually diluted into all the water inside them, then excreted at that very low concentration into the breastmilk. Hence the amount that the baby gets is incredibly small. However, there are a few exceptions.

ALCOHOL: At the best of times alcohol is a tissue poison, and although the amounts getting to the baby are small, it is still a poison. It will clear from your body in two to three hours, so delay feeding until after that and take no more than one standard drink every 24 hours.

CIGARETTES: Cigarette smoke gets into your breastmilk and makes the milk taste smoky. Also there are thousands of nasty components in the smoke, which get into your milk. It's been implicated in SIDS, leukaemia, respiratory infections and lowered IQ in the children of smokers. Having said that, we know that it is still safer to smoke and breastfeed than to put the baby on formula in order to continue smoking. If you can't quit, cut down, but keep feeding. See the Contacts chapter for iCanQuit contact details.

CODEINE: Babies find it hard to excrete codeine once it gets into their body so completely avoid it and its big brother HEROIN. Other analgesics like paracetamol and ibuprofen are fine in the correct dosage.

RECREATIONAL DRUGS such as cannabis, amphetamines and cocaine all tend to accumulate in the baby's body, so completely avoid these.

TETRACYCLINE causes staining of the baby's teeth and bones.

ANTICANCER drugs attack the baby's growing cells.

ISOTOPES: Ordinary X-rays are harmless to the milk; should you need a special scan for bones or lungs, though the dose to the baby will still be very small especially if the dose of radiation is less than 3 milliCuries, perhaps you should 'pump and dump' your milk until most of the isotope has left your body. Seventy-five per cent has gone in twice the half-life of the isotope (for example, technetium has a six-hour half-life, so delaying for 12 hours after the scan will be enough). However, check with the radiologist and ask your doctor whether the test could be delayed or done in a different way (such as an MRI or CT scan).

ANTITHYROID DRUGS AND IODIDES: that certainly includes Iodine 131 (radioiodine), which is used for thyroid scans.

ORAL DIABETES DRUGS like Metformin and others.

SOME SEX HORMONES such as the high-dose contraceptive pill. Alternatives are available.

SOME POWERFUL STEROIDS, though prednisone is okay.

SOME ANTIRHEUMATISM DRUGS such as gold salts, indomethacin or phenylbutazone.

ANTI-MIGRAINE DRUGS containing ergot.

If you have any queries about drugs in breastmilk, please check with the Mothersafe Service. Please see the Contacts chapter at the back of this book for details.

Bottle-feeding formula

If you cannot breastfeed your infant, here are a few tips that you might not get from the tin of your formula:

- Try to bottle-feed as you would breastfeed. Don't use the clock – use the baby to determine feed frequency and amount, at least to start with. What it says on the can is what the average baby needs in an average feed on an average day. Babies are hungrier at some feeds than other feeds and should be fed accordingly. If there's something left in the bottle and his little mouth is shut, he's had enough.

- Always make the formula exactly as it states on the can; never add more powder or more water unless it is under careful medical supervision.

- Always use a 'gold' formula. These contain long-chain omega-3 fatty acids, which occur in high concentration in breastmilk and are incorporated into nervous and brain tissue.

- Milk is a very good bacterial medium and will support a heavy growth of germs if not prepared in a sterile manner and kept chilled before the feed. Mixed formula can be kept for 24 hours in the fridge (below 4°C). Any feed not used, or allowed to get to room temperature after this time, should be discarded.

- Though it is actually unnecessary, it is usual to warm formula before giving it to the baby. It should be warmed to around body temperature or below in a water bath or formula-warming device. Beware if microwaving as there can be inadequate mixing, with some of the milk very hot and some cool, and the bottle may not warm up as much as the liquid inside. ALWAYS test the temperature of the feed before giving it to the baby.

- When the baby is breastfed he gets a different-tasting feed every time, depending on his mother's diet. To give him variations in the taste of his formula, occasionally add small amounts of alcohol-free vanilla essence, cumin, cinnamon, nutmeg and so on to his feed. There is more on this subject in Chapter 19.

- For the same reason, you might want to change his formula on a regular basis. So try him on a soy, hydrolysed or goat's milk formula. The usual advice is 'once you find a formula he enjoys, you should stick to it', but that means he gets an invariant taste for the first four to six months of his life. Very boring.

- When you bottle-feed him, use both sides as you would if you were breastfeeding. So sometimes hold him on your right arm with the bottle in your left, and sometimes hold him on the left with the bottle in your right. This will give him two perspectives on his mother/father/helper when he is feeding.

- If possible, replicate the closeness and contact with your baby during the bottle-feeds. Where you can, hold him against your skin, even against your breast, as you feed. Try to give the baby your full attention during the feed times. Feeding is a time of closeness and communication.

- For the bottle-fed baby it is important that solids are not started younger than four months of age, as this leads to a greater likelihood of obesity later. Start spoon foods when the baby is very keen on the idea (see Chapter 19).

DOING BOTH

If you're finding exclusive breastfeeding too gruelling, or you need to take some time off for whatever reason, before you move on to formula feeding try expressing some breastmilk and getting your partner or helper to feed the baby with the breastmilk in a bottle.

The best time to express is in the morning when your breasts are more full than at other times. Use hand expression, or a hand or electrical device, and make sure the whole process is very clean and the milk is stored in sterile containers. Keep the milk carefully refrigerated (at about 4°C) until it is used, and use this milk in the 24 hours after collection. If it is to be stored longer it should go straight into the freezer, and then thawed just before use.

Breastfed babies will often take a few feeds to get used to the physical act of sucking the bottle. It is a very different technique for the baby than emptying a breast, quite apart from the fact that it feels, smells and tastes different.

The first bottle-feed should be when she is not wildly hungry and in a good mood. It should be given by a familiar person, but not the mother, so the baby is not distracted by breast aroma.

Some babies, especially those whose first introduction to a bottle is at the age of several months, resist for long periods of time but can be overcome eventually by persuasion and hunger.

If expression does not work for you because of poor supply, work commitments or illness, then doing both breast and formula feeding is a good option. Your baby still gets the wonderful bio-active agents in the breastmilk and adequate food from the formula.

It is true the formula dilutes the good things from the breastmilk but the end result is better than no breastmilk at all. Indeed there is some evidence that the presence of breastmilk enhances the absorption of the nutrients from the formula.

One of the major problems is the fact that it's more time consuming for the mother to do both all the time, but if you're sharing the feeds, especially with the father, then it can work well.

Chapter 3

Out and about with your baby

AFTER YOU GET BACK FROM HOSPITAL there will hopefully be friends, relatives and your partner to help start your life at home with the baby.

Soon the grandparents will go home, and your partner will have to go back to work. To some, this is a great relief. They can get on with looking after their baby in peace. They can spend time in bed with the baby, resting and feeding. If they have thought ahead, there is a lot of food in the freezer and they can get by with the minimum of housework. In some cultures a new mother barely gets out of bed for the first six weeks, and for some, this can work for them.

But for others, this can be a difficult and stressful time. Suddenly the relentless responsibility shifts into sharp focus. At a time when sleep is short and everything is new, it is easy to spiral into worry and even panic at the prospect of a ten-hour day alone coping with the little baby.

There is no doubt it gets better day by day and week by week, but if you haven't had much practice being on your own, and are somewhat daunted by the prospect, it is a good idea to plan for these early weeks to ease the stress. Get a relative or friend to come round each day to help.

If you are going stir-crazy, you need to get out of the house. However, if you've had a caesarean section or a difficult birth experience, this should be attempted in small steps, and carefully.

- As you leave the hospital make enquiries about a mothers' group in your area. Do this sooner rather than later. A good mothers' group can provide support and company, even new friends. It can also supply you with lots of advice and help you avoid becoming confused by it all.

- If you find you are too tired to get out, try to make progress slowly by setting realistic goals. Start with having a shower and something to eat before trying to make it to the park.

- It might be more important that you rest rather than go out. Ensure your priorities are right.

- For your first trip out, see if you can have a friend or relative accompany you.

- For a short trip, put the baby in a sling and just take a spare nappy and some wipes. If the trip is for longer, say, to a mothers' group, you will be staggered how much luggage you need. A checklist is a very good idea, especially as you will find your memory takes a hit in the weeks and months after childbirth.

- Remember that everything takes longer with the baby. That is, preparation for the trip, the trip itself and tidying up after the trip.

- Before you have to do it on a trip, rehearse opening and closing the pram and using the brake. You actually don't have enough hands to do everything necessary to get you on and off a bus, for instance. Ask for help. People will always respond to a mother and a baby.

- If you intend to breastfeed while you are out, think ahead and try to find a baby-friendly location. There is no need to wear special clothes; hiking up your T-shirt is perfectly okay. With a little practice, you will soon stop being embarrassed and will often find wonderful support from people around you in public places. Ignore the leerers and starers. Remember that it is illegal for people to ask you to stop breastfeeding in public.

CAR TRAVEL

- Obviously babies should only ever travel in a properly fitted car seat – always rear facing for the first months. Actually, studies have shown that it is safer up to the age of four to face the rear – but we can't convince the children of this (and you can't blame them to prefer to face the front).
- All babies and children should be restrained, even for the shortest trip.
- Tether everything you can, but especially dummies and favourite toys for the older child. Always carry spares.
- Have some new toys and lots of pit stops for longer journeys.
- Try to travel at the baby's nap time if you can.
- Some babies love the car and fall asleep quickly. Some hate it and cry. For the latter, get a mirror for them to see themselves in, try to travel with a companion, or walk instead!

AIR TRAVEL

- This is best when children are young.
- Toddlers can be a menace in a plane. They actually feel just the same as we do, but are uninhibited enough to express themselves. You can't blame them! Get the grandparents to visit you instead.
- With a young baby, always book as far ahead as possible so you can get a bulkhead seat with a bassinette.

- Many babies settle very well on aeroplanes, as the drone of the engines and the womb-like interior of the cabin can soothe them.
- As the plane descends, make sure that the baby or child is sucking on something – your breast, a dummy or drink – to clear the ears. Ear pressure is usually not a problem on the ascent.
- Like in the car, always tether dummies and important objects to the baby's clothing or cot. Scrabbling around under the seat while the baby howls is a challenging experience.
- For long-haul flights a big bag of new toys and games, to be revealed gradually during the flight, is a must.
- Don't sedate. Firstly, because it is unreliable and may not work, and then you end up with a confused, addled child who won't sleep. The drugs may also have a paradoxical effect and hype your toddler up. For a long flight the child will eventually wake up halfway through but have a hangover and behave worse than ever.
- There is always a chance the children will behave beautifully!

SLINGS

Slings are like mobile swaddles. It's hard for a baby to stay awake when held next to her mother's body in the snug containment of a sling. They also free your hands so you can pick up and carry bags and nappies when you're both out and about. Just make sure that you look after your back, especially when you bend down.

Make sure that they are correctly sized for your baby and the head is not held in a too flexed position with chin on chest, especially if your baby is an ex-premature or small baby. They can kink their airway and have difficulty breathing.

BABY CARRIERS

My two-week-old daughter has been in a von Rosen splint since day two for left hip dysplasia and I am hoping she is in it for no more than 6–12 weeks. Do you have any thoughts regarding whether it is safe to put her in a baby carrier when she comes out of it?

Babies are designed to be carried and until recently in our evolution we were carried most of the time for most of our first two years. When a mother or other carer carries a baby they generally do so on their hip, which positions the legs in the right position for the best hip development.

Babies' hip joints are entirely made of cartilage, a soft malleable substance which gradually changes to bone over the first year or two. During this time the head of the leg bone (femur) is pressed into the socket. At birth this socket is relatively shallow, containing only 50 per cent of the head of the femur, but over the first year under the influence of the pressure from the head of the femur, the socket becomes deeper. By the end of the first year it is deep enough and bony enough to support the toddler's weight as they start to walk.

It is critical during this first year that their legs are in an appropriate position so that the head presses into the socket. The way to do that is to have the hips flexed at about 90 degrees from the spine with the knees splayed at around 30 to 45 degrees from the midline.

The worst position is to have the legs stretched out (in extension); this causes the head of the femur to press up against the upper margin of the socket.

Essentially, any baby carrier that keeps the baby's legs in the appropriate position and does not allow them to extend down will be fine. So the question is: when the baby is in the carrier, does the seat of the carrier keep the hips in this flexed position, allow the knees to splay out and, most importantly, support the *whole of the back* of the leg up to the back of the knee?

Some carriers have a relatively small seat area that concentrates the weight on the baby's buttocks and crotch, and this allows the legs to flop down unless you have a small baby. Beware also when you carry your baby facing outwards. Again, as the legs are not wrapped around your body they will tend to extend down with such carrying.

In contrast some carriers are now appearing with a nice big support area for the bottom and legs, keeping all babies in an excellent posture but especially those with hip dysplasia.

Hip dysplasia

Just about every baby nowadays will get their hips examined soon after they are born. What the nurses and doctors are looking for is a condition known as 'developmental dysplasia of the hip' (DDH). This condition is often known as 'clicky hips'. It used to be called 'congenital dislocation of the hip' but now we realise that babies are not necessarily born with it and it may develop over the first few months, and actual dislocation of the hip is just the severe end of a condition that has a spectrum of severity. The range of the condition can be from a slightly shallow socket that rights itself on its own, to the severest form that, if left, can lead to a lifetime of disability.

That is the reason we are so obsessed with diagnosing it. If it is missed it can have prolonged, painful, lifelong effects. Dysplastic hips can end up with severe arthritis, which can cause pain and seriously affect mobility. So it is really important to not only get the examination done correctly but to keep an eye on all babies' hips, especially in the first year.

As mentioned, when babies are born, the ball and socket of their hip joint is entirely made of soft cartilage and the socket of the joint is rather more like a saucer than a cup. Over their first year or so, as a result of the pressure exerted by the ball of the femur the socket deepens to form a nice stable joint. By the time the baby is walking the joint is very stable and strong.

There are a few factors that can interfere with this:

- Being female – girl babies are more affected by the hormones from the placenta whose job it is to soften the ligaments in the mother's pelvis to help the birthing process. Consequently there is more 'play' (or laxity) in the ligaments around their hip joints.
- Breech babies, especially ones delivering naturally – these babies' hip joints are put under strain when they're in the womb and during the descent in the birth canal, and this stretches the ligaments.
- Family history – there is definitely a genetic factor in some with this condition. So if anyone in your family was in a harness or in double nappies after their birth, let your doctor know.
- Other factors – firstborn baby, big babies, and a reduction in the amount of amniotic fluid all mean less room in the womb and hence more strain on the hip joints.
- Swaddling – when the legs are extended with the knees together, the head of the femur is pulled slightly out of the socket so the pressure to deepen it is reduced. Not only that, the head then presses on the soft cartilage on the top of the socket and this can cause a problem. In Japan swaddling babies with their legs extended was common until the mid-1970s when a nationwide campaign to cease this practice resulted in a fivefold reduction in the incidence of DDH. This issue may be emerging again in all countries with the use of tight zip-up sleeping bags where the legs are stretched out. Babies prefer to be in a position with both arms and legs flexed (just like in the womb), with the legs spread, and it is much healthier for their hips to be in this posture.

These factors are all cumulative so, for instance, if you are a firstborn female breech baby, you have about a one in eight chance of developing hip dysplasia.

Testing for hip dysplasia

The doctor or nurse will test your baby's hips within the first week or so after birth.

With the baby lying on their back, the knee is raised so the femur points straight up. The hand is placed to grasp the femur and the leg is pushed towards the mat in an attempt to push the head of the femur backwards out of the socket. The leg is then hinged outwards into a frog position. If the head of the femur was dislocated by the first movement, the second will relocate it. Both movements can be detected as a 'clunk' (hence the 'clicky hip').

For the less severely affected hip, backward movement can be detected between the head and the socket of the joint when these movements are applied (the so-called slippery hip).

If there is any doubt about the clinical examination as above, or any of the risk factors are present, then the baby's hips will be examined by ultrasound imaging. Unless there is severe dislocation this study is usually delayed for a few weeks to allow the normal laxity of the ligaments in newborns' hips to settle down and the hips to stabilise.

After six months or so there is enough bone in the joint to show what's going on by using X-ray. In fact at this age and beyond, X-ray shows the configuration and shape of the joint more clearly than ultrasound.

Later on

If the newborn baby's hips pass these tests it is still important to examine them as the months roll on. As well as dislocation, which can be detected at any time, another sign as the baby gets older is a limitation in the ability of the hips to move to the side into the frog position. Mothers often notice that they have increasing difficulty spreading the baby's knees to put on the nappy. Under these circumstances it is worthwhile getting the baby re-examined as it can occur any time in the first year or beyond.

The signs to look for as the baby gets older are:

- asymmetrical creases in the fat of the buttocks or thighs (this can also be completely normal, especially in chubby babies).
- difficulty spreading the legs apart to put on a nappy.
- visible shortening of one leg from knee to hip.
- clicks in the hip joint. Remember joints other than the hips in babies commonly tend to be mobile and 'clicky'.
- asymmetrical posture when starting to walk.

Treatment

If the hips are only mildly affected with the socket showing some shallowness but the head of the femur nicely applied, often it is enough to follow the progress of the hips with regular ultrasounds and it will usually resolve.

If the hips remain unstable then the baby is put into a splint or harness, which does two things: it causes the hip joints to be held in the flexed and splayed outward position. This applies the head of the femur firmly into the socket, which helps mould the joint towards a normal depth and shape. Often the baby will stay in their harness day and night for a few weeks and then, once improvement is seen, they can be removed for bathing and increasingly longer periods of time. Usually with newborns there will be so much improvement within two to three months that the harness can be removed completely. This treatment works extremely well for nearly all babies who are diagnosed early.

If the baby is diagnosed later, different devices are required to correct them. The nearer the initial diagnosis gets to one year of age, the more likely the baby will need operative intervention to correct the joint and the more likely the result will be imperfect.

All babies diagnosed with this condition will of course remain under close follow-up, both clinically and with ultrasound, until their hip joints are completely bony and they are in the clear.

See this site for further reading: www.hipdysplasia.org.

HOLLY'S STORY

I have an interesting tale to tell about hips.

A little while ago a nine-month-old baby girl called Holly was brought in by her mother to see me at my office. She had previously been seen twice in the neonatal period by her paediatrician and was found to be completely normal at that time.

Holly was an ideal baby for her first seven months, breast-fed and contented. Then she started vomiting, frequently and copiously. Her mother added solids, propped her up, and varied the frequency and volume of feeds, but nothing made any difference. She vomited almost continuously day and night.

When I saw her she looked fine, a chubby, contented nine month old. I had no idea why she was vomiting. After a discussion with her mother I then examined her. She was completely normal, except for one important aspect. Holly's left hip was completely dislocatable; gentle pressure on the hip joint dropped the head of the femur out of the socket. I sent her for an urgent X-ray and found she had severe dysplasia of the hip; that is, the socket of the hip joint, instead of being cup-shaped, was flattened like a saucer.

When I told Holly's mother about the diagnosis she was most upset. I reassured her by saying that as Holly was only nine months old and the hips were still immature, there was every likelihood of a completely normal outcome. I sent her to an orthopaedic surgeon that afternoon. I also suggested that perhaps she should celebrate tonight, as it was extremely lucky that she had brought Holly, for whatever reason, to seek medical attention now. The alternative was a child with a limp for life.

The vomiting was almost forgotten in all the excitement. But I ordered a barium meal X-ray to see whether the baby had reflux, or a partial malrotation of the bowel, or some other reason why she should vomit so copiously. I started no treatment.

The mother brought her back to see me two weeks later. Her little girl was due to go into hospital for a waist-to-knee plaster of paris spica cast the following week, with an excellent prospect of a normal hip after three months' treatment.

She brought the barium meal result with her, and a remarkable tale.

Since her visit to me two weeks before, Holly hadn't vomited once. Not even a wet burp. Nothing else had changed. The barium meal was completely normal.

I have always believed babies have a certain knowingness, but I've never met a baby who knew something was wrong and induced a symptom so that her mother would take her to a doctor . . .

CHAPTER 4

Baby brain 101

AFTER MONTHS OF ANXIOUS ANTICIPATION, YOU finally have your baby in your arms. Your mind floods with relief that both you and your baby are safe.

This feeling may last for all of ten minutes. Then the realisation dawns that you are now completely responsible for this little being, who seems to embody only helplessness, directionlessness and vulnerability.

Until now, when confronted with such a puzzle most people would dig out the manual, ask an expert or, nowadays, google it. There's a problem with that in this situation. Dealing with your particular baby is not necessarily a process helped by others' experiences. It is likely that all the information you obtain, and all the experts you consult, will get you no closer to the real answers you think you need.

To understand why that is, we must go back in time to the origin of humans on this planet. It is a counterintuitive fact that we, the smartest placental mammal on the planet, are born the most helpless and immature. Our babies are born completely dependent, with very little ability to survive without their parents or adult carers. Even chimpanzees, when newly born, can at least hold on firmly to their mother's coat by their arms and also toddle about, but human babies cannot. Sure, human babies have a grasp reflex – try tickling a baby's palm and the little hand will grasp your finger – but the grip is unreliable and weak, and toddling is a year away. From the start the chimpanzee baby can run rings around our baby, and climb and jump on him too. It will be 18 months before our baby can do similar things.

The reason for this hopeless inefficiency was brutal necessity. When our pre-hominid ancestors climbed down from the trees to live on the ground, they decided it was a good idea to stand upright and walk on two legs. This gave them a better view of the surrounding countryside and freed up their forearms for more useful tasks than supporting the body. But this decision came with a cost. To take the weight of the body on two legs, not four, changed the anatomy of the pelvis. It became stronger and the wing-like bones at the back flared to contain the internal organs, and, more significantly, the birth canal was narrowed.

Early on, these changes had little impact as their babies' brains remained small, and being born, even through the convoluted narrow birth canal, was easy. But as the species evolved into *Homo sapiens* a major dilemma emerged. The modern human's claim to fame was a big brain and intelligence to match. But how do you deliver a big-brained baby through a narrow birth canal?

Evolution's answer was to have the babies earlier in pregnancy – when they are still small enough to fit.

There may be another reason why our babies are born so 'premature'. Quite apart from the pelvic size issue was the issue of energy capacity. Biologists have worked out that our babies cannot stay inside their mothers any longer than they do now, even if the pelvic outlet was bigger. Our babies are born when the mother's capacity to metabolise energy, and supply it to the baby for growth, has hit a limit. This amount of energy is a function of body weight. At term, the baby is of a size that his rate of growth will be compromised if he stays inside and continues to depend on the placenta for growth any longer. It is more efficient for him to deliver and start using his gut to absorb food for growth!

So the human baby emerges in a state described by biologists as an 'extero-gestate foetus' – a foetus on the outside. In contrast, many four-legged animals can have up to 80 per cent of their brain formed by the time they are born; that is, they are really just miniature adults at birth. After a few months with their parents they can disappear into the landscape and lead an independent life.

In comparison the human baby has only 25 per cent of his brain formed at birth. Brain scanning studies have shown that this amount represents all of the brain cells – all one hundred billion of them. What the baby's brain lacks and what makes up the other 75 per cent of the potential brain mass is the connections between the brain cells.

THE BRAIN CONNECTIONS

Brain connections, the wiring if you like, are laid down as rapidly as possible in the months and years following the baby's escape from the birth canal. As a consequence, the baby's brain weight actually doubles in the year after he is born. Billions of connections are made, each single brain cell being capable of making up to 10,000 connections to adjacent and other more distant cells. It is these myriad connections and how they are configured that represent the 'code' that programs the brain's incredible computer-like functioning. With this amount of complexity the human brain develops into a supercomputer of unimaginable processing capacity and power.

Such immense potential, starting with such helpless immaturity!

How and where the connections go within the brain is largely a function of our genetics – that's our potential. But how we actually end up connecting certain critical parts of our brains is, we now know, greatly determined by our environment. And the relevant environment is our upbringing: it's how we are managed by our carers. This is one of the reasons why humankind is so efficient at adapting to all the varied ecological niches on the planet.

High up in the topmost branches of the evolutionary tree, humans are born very immature and helpless, and we have a very long period of childhood when we slowly develop and learn. During this time we are completely dependent on our parents and carers for everything – food, warmth, protection and education.

Much further down the evolutionary tree, insects, by contrast, are born with a full set of instinctive behaviours. They have nothing to learn, and soon after birth can start functioning efficiently in an adult capacity. That is because everything they do is driven by inborn, instinctive programming. This works just fine as long as all their behaviours and actions are well adapted for their environment and, just as important, the environment doesn't change. If it changes, they die like flies – as the saying goes – for that reason.

Humans, however, are born with the bare minimum of instinctive behaviour. This extends to such activities as finding the nipple, suckling, cuddling, calling for help if a threat is perceived, and others. The presence of our parents and carers, but especially our mother, starts the learning process that shows us the world and allows us to adapt to it. It is our very immaturity and lack of instinctive behaviour that gives us the ability to learn so much and adapt so well to our environment.

The first thing a baby has to learn, and it ideally comes from her mother, is how safe, secure and loved she is. This is in the form of food, warmth and the close presence of a loving protector. This is rooted in our basic biology and will never change.

In the following pages I will describe how this process works and emphasise how vitally important it is. The process of mothering infants, and the infants' response to that process, has been perfected over at least 60 million years, when mammals were evolving on this planet. Over that time the basic mechanism has remained pretty much exactly the same, unchanging because it works really well.

The ability of our brains to develop in an adaptive way depending on our environment is what neurobiologists call 'brain plasticity' and humans have it in spades. Once we have developed our basic security and self-image, during the rest of our childhood (up to about the age of 25 years) our tribe or society can continue to mould us to be appropriate members, and this varies depending on which ecological niche we occupy. So coastal fishing people living in large tribes connect their brains up in one way, and jungle dwellers living in tiny groups connect their brains in a subtly different way.

But this is the icing on the cake. It is the first year or two of the baby's life that determines her future happiness and determines how secure and safe she feels for the rest of her life. It tells her how valuable she is to her parents and her society and, most importantly, tells her what love is, and how to give it and feel worthy enough to fully receive it.

To say that love makes the world go round is trite yet entirely true on many levels. But even on the most superficial level the scientific evidence is very clear. After a good food supply and shelter, the one thing that reliably allows people to experience happiness and contentment with their lives is having fulfilling relationships with other people and the experience of mutual love. All the striving we see in our world, mostly for money or power, is merely a substitute for the emptiness and insecurity felt by those who, during the first couple of years of their life, did not acquire this fundamental programming. They then spend a lifetime searching for something to replace it and fill their void.

WHAT THIS MEANS TO YOU – AND YOUR BABY

This has enormous implications regarding babies' development. It means the parents, and especially the mother, of a baby have the power to enhance (or impair) the baby's outcome by the way they manage her during her early upbringing. With this information they can make informed decisions regarding how to interact with her, deal with her behaviour and manage her day-to-day living. In this way, by giving her a protected, enriching and supportive environment, they can help their baby achieve not only her genetic potential, but also go through life with a calm, loving and happy worldview.

WIRING YOUR BABY'S BRAIN

A good analogy for our brain is an incredibly complex computer. Nothing created by Silicon Valley comes anywhere close to the computing power of the human brain. However, when babies are born, the computer is unfinished. Not only are many of the circuit boards not connected, but the code that runs the computer is largely unwritten. The baby's brain is all potential, not much processing.

As the baby gazes out on the world, she sees clearly, but has little idea what she's looking at. Similarly with her other senses, she can hear, smell, feel and touch, but only a few of these senses mean very much. She is born with enough computing power to cry when she's hungry or when she is tired, and snuggle in when she is cuddled, but her understanding of the world is very rudimentary.

The structure of the brain

Our primate brain is constructed in three main layers.

The most primitive, the 'reptilian' brain, lies at the base of our brain and runs our basic functioning and physiology, our blood pressure, breathing drive, muscle movement and bodily sensation. On an evolutionary scale it is the most ancient part of our brain and any animal with a backbone has something similar.

The next layer is called the limbic system or midbrain. This part is also called the 'emotional' or 'mammalian' brain. It evolved, particularly in mammals, to protect us from harm. It is involved also in memory, motivation, and monitoring and maintenance of stability in our body. It is our subconscious. It scans constantly for threat and is the origin of our feelings, many of them deep and powerful, such as fear, rage, separation anxiety (to keep us safe), love, kindness and joy (to reward us). This part of our brain is perpetually vigilant, always aware, monitoring our body and our environment. If it perceives something new, especially something that could be threatening, it reacts instantly and powerfully in order to protect us. It does this through the 'stress response'.

The top layer, and most evolved and advanced part of our brain, is the neocortex or 'new brain'. This was added most recently in our evolution and is mostly our frontal lobes. It was the development of this part that separated us from lower animals. It is the imaginative, thinking and intellectual part. It can also remember and use experiences both to reassure us and also allow us to plan ahead to avoid danger and keep ourselves secure.

And here's the crunch. Brain scanning studies (summarised by Allan Schore) have shown that newborn babies have under-developed limbic systems, and this and other lower brain parts have no connection at all with the neocortex. So newborn babies have no 'thinking' brain online at all. Their brains have neither the physical connections between the lower and higher levels nor the cognitive code to understand the world. Essentially the babies are functioning at a very unsophisticated level, at best at the midbrain level – the level of love and joy mixed with fear and separation anxiety. How like a baby!

As soon as the baby is born and escapes the birth canal, she starts to make connections and hence write the code to program her brain, both within the limbic system and out to the neocortex. How well, or in what configuration, she makes the connections is determined by her interaction with the people in her environment, especially her mother. Second to food, this interaction is vitally important to help the baby's brain grow and develop.

The right side of the brain

Interestingly, nearly all of these connections made in the first year or so are on the right side of the brain, from the right side of the limbic system to the right cerebral hemisphere up in the neocortex. The right side of the brain is considered the more intuitive, imaginative and holistic side of our brain: it is said to be the more 'female' side. The left or 'male' side is more concerned with logical processes such as language acquisition, mathematical calculations and forward planning. This left hemisphere's maximum time of connectivity will be a year or so later when the baby starts acquiring language at a fast rate.

It is not only the baby's brain that is making these right-sided coding connections. After having a baby, the mother's brain also develops a growth spurt of connections to prepare the brain for the more demanding environment of motherhood. So despite the temporary lapse that comes with the feeding and the fatigue, the so-called baby brain that mothers have is actually a more complex and efficient organ, with many more brain connections than before!

The driving force that enhances the connections in these early months and years is the interaction between the mother and baby. Their talking, gazing, singing, cuddling and playing together forms the wonderful and dynamic process of attachment. Attachment is not just emotional interaction, a sentimental process of falling in love, but the very engine of brain development in the baby, as well as a booster of the mother's ability to care. (And withstand the relentless fatigue!) In the absence of this emotional link, vital connections within the brain are not made and the baby runs the risk of going through life without a full repertoire of emotional responses and feelings.

As a process it is very much a two-way street, with the mother and baby's interaction stimulating a response in the other. As these responses go between them, so each one amplifies and loops back to the other, intensifying the response and deepening the relationship.

It is these back and forth interactions that cause the burgeoning brain growth and development in them both, but especially the baby.

The mechanism of brain development is this day-by-day, minute-by-minute interplay between the participants. They use their eyes and faces, hands and bodies, laughs and tears to induce joy and love in each other, tempered and strengthened by a self-sustaining stability and confidence in each other. Over the months and years this intense relationship of playfulness, joy and love deepens and expands, driven by the rewards each derives from the other.

We've all seen the process. The baby is a few months old and sits propped up in a little chair in the corner of the room. He spies his mother on the other side of the room and starts to make cooing noises to attract her. She stops what she's doing, looks over to him and approaches him, replying to his coos with her own. He gazes into her eyes and his face breaks into an enormous gummy smile, and his mother's whole face and body soften as she gazes and smiles back at him.

The baby waves his arms and pulls a face. Mother imitates him. The baby is so pleased by her response that he starts kicking his legs and saying 'nah, nah'. Mother grasps his thighs and says 'nah, nah' back. The baby is delighted and chuckles and laughs. Mother laughs too. Back and forth, back and forth the interaction goes, increasing in intensity with each interchange.

Suddenly the baby frowns and looks away. He switches off, looks away to the window. He calms himself while he digests what has just happened. His mother also looks away and wanders back to what she was doing before. The baby rests and gazes at his hands in his lap. Slowly he relaxes, and now he's ready for another game.

He glances at his mother, waves his arms – and it starts all over again . . .

CHAPTER 5

The new baby's tasks

THE NEW BABY ARRIVES WITH TWO fundamentally conflicting impulses.

1. to explore the world using all of her senses. But at the same time.

2. to keep calm and regulate her stress.

The main carer, ideally the mother, needs to teach her baby how to balance these conflicting impulses. Not *all* stress is bad, of course. In fact it is through the stress of novel experiences and change that all new things are learned. But, right from the start, babies need to be helped so that they can explore their world with enthusiasm and openness and not get overwhelmed by too much arousal.

Mother's gaze and closeness, her hands and voice, all offer the stability the baby needs to stay centred. At eight weeks there is a dramatic increase in the baby's capacity to communicate visually as new connections are made to her visual cortex in the brain. Most babies will then start gazing fixedly at their mother and the responsive mother cannot help but gaze back. It is this powerful process that cements the emerging bond between these two and creates a love that lasts a lifetime. For many mothers it is the first time in their lives that they love anything so selflessly or intensely. As the baby basks in her mother's gaze and embrace, this provides a rock-solid base that the baby can use as a jumping-off point to find out how the rest of the world works.

The creation and maintenance of this calming centre is critical to a baby's stability and an antidote to the stress response.

The stress response

The stress response has two components in the human body. The first is the so-called sympathetic part of our autonomic nervous system. This system reacts to stress instantaneously, pumping out excitatory hormones, such as adrenaline, from our nerve endings. When secreted these hormones cause us to stop whatever we are doing and deal with the problem. They give us a fright and we freeze, as our bodies are prepared for fight or flight. Our eyes dilate, so we can see clearer, and the blood vessels to our muscles dilate to gather strength. They also direct the circulation away from organs not needed in the response, such as the gut, kidneys and skin, and towards important organs, such as the heart. They also boost our blood sugar and get us ready for action, all with the aim of protecting us from whatever caused the initial response.

The other component is from the limbic system or midbrain. This system reacts slightly slower and in a slightly different way. At the base of the midbrain there is an organ called the amygdala. This organ receives impulses from the parts of the limbic system that scan for threat and when it perceives a problem, having already initiated the sympathetic response, it then sets off a further, more attenuated and longer term stress response. The amygdala communicates to the pituitary gland at the base of the brain and, in response, this secretes a hormone which circulates in the blood and induces the adrenal glands near the kidneys to secrete cortisol. When cortisol enters the circulation, it enhances the changes already started by the sympathetic nervous system.

This produces a body focused on defeating the stress, ready for battle and raring to go.

Cortisol is also produced within the brain, not in its usual form of a circulating hormone but as a neurotransmitter. This directly causes the mind to focus on the problem at hand and dampens all distractions.

This is a useful and powerful mechanism, which over hundreds of thousands of years has saved us many times, keeping us out of trouble, and depriving many a sabre-toothed tiger of his dinner.

Modifying the stress response

As you get older, the thoughts and experiences remembered within the thinking part of the brain can modify the emotions from the midbrain and the sympathetic nervous system. If your body perceives a threat that you have met before and which you have found by experience is not actually dangerous, your neo-cortex (the thinking brain) can modify the response and keep you calm. This is how we manage in our day-to-day life. Our thoughts modulate and modify our subconscious feelings and fears.

But what of our poor little newborn? As her neocortex is not yet connected, she has no way of modifying the unpleasant response from her midbrain provoked by stressful events.

What would stress a newborn? At a deep level, as an immature primate they understand how vulnerable they are and are aware they need the full-time help of their parents to stay alive. So any adverse circumstances, such as hunger, cold, discomfort or anything they can't fix will invoke a cry for survival – but most and especially, the absence of the parents.

Without a carer, our frightened baby, stressed for whatever reason, can do little to help herself other than cry for help. Without a loving response from outside, she cannot modify her reaction herself and so remains mired in boundless fear, her whole universe filled with dread.

Happily, nature has allowed for this situation, by giving the baby access to not one but two fully programmed neocortices – they belong to her parents. They, unbeknown to them, have had their brains trained over hundreds of thousands of years to deal with this exact situation.

The parents are instinctively driven to help their baby with protection, loving arms, soft voices and reassurance. Their innermost feelings tell them that this is the right thing to do.

What a pity there are often so many uninvolved and ignorant bystanders around when this happens! The 'spare the rod and spoil the child' brigade arrive, finger raised, and tell hair-raising cautionary tales about how spoiling the baby will have awful consequences later. This advice is seriously uninformed by biology or the rudiments of baby brain development and should be courteously but studiously ignored. Your instincts to calm and protect your baby are there for a purpose, so let those feelings rule!

How the parents, especially the mother, respond to the baby in this situation determines many important things.

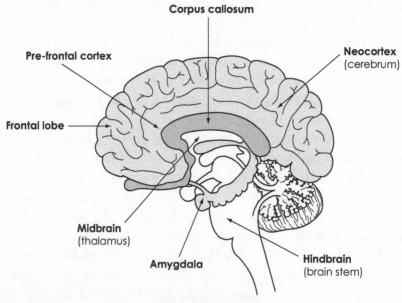

Anatomy of the brain

If the baby is calmed successfully, the cortisol level in her blood drops into a low, comfortable zone and warm, soothing hormones wash into her brain, making her feel contented and loved. She uses this feeling as a template for later encounters with stress, because at the same time as this is occurring, she is forming the connections between her limbic system and neocortex. These first connections in her neocortex are to the 'prefrontal cortex' (PFC). This area in her forebrain has a number of functions, including managing the emotions generated in the midbrain, which are made in response to these stressful events. If she is loved and cared for, the connected cells in the PFC form many cortisol receptors. These mop up the fear hormones and neurotransmitters washing through her brain, and drop the level back into a comfortable zone. If instead she is constantly ignored – for instance, left unattended in a primitive orphanage – her brain's connections will not code for cortisol receptors and the brain accepts a high level of cortisol as 'normal'. As she's stressed all the time she thinks that is the way the world is. In contrast, by the end of the first year our loved baby has, in her PFC, a 'set point' for normal cortisol level that is low and calm.

These coded connections are formed deep in her hardware. They are difficult to unlearn or replace with a different response if the situation changes. They have the potential to last a lifetime.

There seems to be a critical period for the formation of many of these basic brain connections. Miss this period and the door closes. There is a lot of scientific information that this situation of a 'connection window' occurs with such functions as memory acquisition, intellectual capacity, social regulation and many of the other so-called executive functions for which the brain is designed. If the pathway is formed but then is underutilised as the brain develops, so these connections will be 'pruned' and will disappear, whereas well-used pathways will become wider, thicker and faster. With brain connections, it is a case of 'use it or lose it'.

Not only that, during this early rapid growth period, if babies' needs are not met and the functions relating to emotional security aren't bedded down, the capacities of *later* emotional, mental and intellectual health will not be able to flourish. It seems that this function is the bedrock upon which the later capacities are built. Without a feeling of security and confidence that she is loved, much of her later thinking abilities will be built on sand.

But the nurtured baby, whose needs for security, protection and interaction with loved ones are met, builds neural pathways optimised for learning and stability.

GETTING IT WRONG

Our babies are innately social creatures. By natural selection over millennia we have created a finely tuned, loving and interactive being. Solitude, to a baby, is a worrying, even threatening, condition. Naturally they will usually complain loudly if left without a loving protector and this protest often will bring the carer quickly.

If no carer arrives and the situation continues, a consistent pattern emerges. This pattern can be seen in a primitive form in the newborn to six months (we call it 'extinction' – see Chapter 14 Quiet nights, on sleep), and becomes more sophisticated as they grow into toddlers.

If the carer does not appear, the protests become louder and more panicky as the baby searches more intensely for the source of his security. He will have brief periods when he will fall silent as he quietly reassures himself that his mother will return in a moment, but soon he resumes his cries. Eventually he realises that his pleas will go unanswered, and he starts to despair. Intense misery overwhelms him and he finally falls silent. This is a situation for which he is unequipped to cope. He no longer searches for his carer, and stares despondently at his hands. He no longer cries.

Later, he gives up and descends into 'detachment'. He has realised that he has been abandoned. Even if his carer now returns, he will not respond to her. He no longer trusts her and he has no wish to return to the misery of despair.

Observations on babies who have been separated from their loved ones are absolutely consistent in showing this downward spiral from panic into detachment. This pattern of behaviour, which takes place over a matter of days in young children, represents a defensive response to what the infant perceives is an unimaginable tragedy: that of abandonment and separation. (See more detail in Chapter 20, Toddlers and Separation.)

These episodes form scars on the infant's psyche and undermine the confidence they have in the people around them to offer reliability and protection. They also undermine the infant's belief that they are valued and loved. Such scars can influence how they respond to later events. It gives them less resilience to deal with negative experiences and has the real potential to change their perceptions and attitudes not only to bad experiences, but also to the good. These influences over time can literally change the personality of the child from one who is outgoing and sunny to one who is withdrawn, suspicious and depressed.

This stereotyped behaviour occurs in the situation when the carer disappears for a significant time and there are no secondary carers to replace her. Such a replacement, though not ideal, can certainly mitigate the worst of the baby's fears, especially if the new carer is known to the infant and is committed and loving.

But what of shorter periods of deprivation, which lead only to loud protests and minimal despair?

There is reason to believe that even these briefer periods will have the potential to affect babies. As we develop, we are the sum total not only of our loves, our periods of happiness and our successes, but also the product of our traumas and disappointments.

Such studies have shown us that when children have a secure attachment history they tend to grow up emotionally mature, with an innate moral compass. They tend to lead, not follow. They are confident in their ability to deal with the world and have self-discipline. They also have the ability to love and be loved, and achieve their potential both in their work and their social and personal lives.

As we grow we tend to see and take notice of only those aspects of our lives that reinforce the beliefs we have about ourselves. These we embrace as true. Conversely, we tend to ignore those occurrences that send us messages which conflict. By filtering our experiences through our perception of ourselves, and ignoring input that disagrees with these deep beliefs, we try to live in a world that makes sense to us and only sends us messages that confirm how we feel about ourselves. This is what makes our personality. Personality is a subtle blend of our genetic endowment and the conditioning we receive, especially from the first two years of our lives.

In mitigation, there is no doubt that there is also variation in the capacity of a baby to deal with such negative experiences. Some are innately more resilient than others. Not only that, if a baby later has a number of positive experiences with his relationships, these can potentially replace negative views about how life works. The less resilient, however, do not have such flexibility and these babies, no matter how reassuring their life becomes, have real difficulty recovering from early loveless experiences.

We are a product therefore not only of our genetic resilience but also of how our environment treats us. Unfortunately, we often do not help ourselves in this way. The genetically unhappy baby is hard to parent and tends to evoke further unhappiness from his environment, whereas the sunny, beaming baby tends to attract happiness in his carers as he is rewarding and easy to manage.

But no baby is doomed by genetics. If difficult babies are managed patiently, consistently, and with care and love, they too will grow into contented, happy babies. They just take a great deal more work and require more consistency than their happy peers.

So if you want your baby to do well in a career, partner happily and not ignore you when you are old, don't give him a nanny and a 'brain-power' DVD. Give him your time and attention, and lots of cuddles.

CHAPTER 6

That's the 'how' – now let's talk about the 'who'

WE CAN ARGUE ALL WE LIKE about gender equality, and there is no doubt that brains and talent are handed out equally between men and women, but there is one aspect of our biology that transcends political correctness. In pushing for equality in the workplace, society strategically made something of an error here. It worked for the end that women should be treated like men, not more like complete women. It ignored the biological difference of having a uterus, which allowed for the propagation of the species. Having two X chromosomes also carried with it the programming to put the building blocks of baby development in place in the first months of a baby's life. The system was designed over millions of years to be done, ideally, by the mother. No one else is quite as good.

So the ideal workplace for women should allow for adequate time off to care for their young children, without losing job opportunity, seniority or status. It would allow for adequate paid parental leave in the first years of the child's life, and adequate extra sick leave to care for the inevitable childhood illnesses.

How interesting it is that this work of mothering, the nurturing of society's replacements, is not represented in the gross national product of the country. According to the economists, this work is worth nothing. The only time such an activity is considered valuable is when it is done by unrelated third parties, by childcare workers in day-care nurseries and by nannies. Once it becomes a commercial venture, business interests and governments get involved. You can then buy shares in companies involved in child care, and governments can legislate regarding child–staff ratios and staff remuneration. There remains a deafening silence about exactly the same activity (done more effectively) in the home.

If the mother is not available, next in line is a caring, involved member of the family who loves and has a personal investment in the individual baby, such as the father, grandma, or a cousin or aunt (an alloparent). It also goes without saying that a caring father or other relative is better than an overly busy and unavailable mother. Babies need time and attention, and the longer the time and the higher the quality of attention, the better.

Somewhat down the list of ideal carers are workers in child or day care. These operations are now a reality of our time. Too many mothers feel they have to return to the workforce in order to maintain a comfortable lifestyle; some have situations where it is essential for survival. Under such circumstances, of course the ideal is day care by kin, where an involved alloparent looks after the baby during working hours, as above. Commercial day care is a rather different matter. The introduction of such establishments has been described by Dr Peter Cook in his important 2011 book *Mothering Matters* as a massive 'disorganised social . . . experiment'.

It must be said that most parents who put their children into day care do so reluctantly, at least in the first year. Mostly it is because of financial necessity and it creates as much stress in the parents as it does in the baby. These parents are often persuaded that such an environment helps to 'socialise' their child and gives him or her access to early education.

Unfortunately for most of us, the data does not seem to back that up. Young humans are inherently social creatures anyway and do not need this enhancing in their first couple of years. Indeed, children up to three years of age tend not to play with each other, even when together. The early education of a baby is exclusively that of interaction with a loving, involved person whom they know and who enjoys their company. This can theoretically be achieved in day care, but it is expensive and difficult to achieve. It requires dedicated, loving staff in high ratio to the number of babies in their care. Recommended ratios of one carer to three babies is the bare minimum and, of course, one on one would be better. In addition, the staff should not change and move on to other jobs so that the babies can form stable relationships. This means the day-care staff have to be paid enough to stop them seeking more lucrative employment elsewhere.

With these parameters, it is clear that 'high-quality' day care is extremely difficult to achieve in an affordable commercial setting. It is just too expensive. If it was underwritten by government it would actually turn out cheaper to give mothers extended maternity leave instead.

This situation arose in Sweden a few years ago and the two alternatives were then offered. Interestingly, the vast majority of parents preferred to look after their babies themselves rather than availing themselves of the high-quality day-care option and re-entering the workforce.

While a large number of children in a society are looked after in industrial-size day-care operations, there is a price to pay. However, it isn't all bad. This situation, of course, definitely helps those children who come from deprived backgrounds with unavailable parents. For this group it boosts their cognitive and social development in comparison to those left in their homes and seems to give them a better future.

But for others with loving parents and secure backgrounds, a significant proportion of them have detrimental outcomes. A Swedish study by Dr Ingrid Harsman (1994) (also quoted in Cook's *Mothering Matters*) showed that up to half of the babies in their early months who entered day care had a slowing of their developmental progress. Some babies become overtly depressed, while others show biochemical and clinical signs of chronic stress.

Many other larger studies also showed that the harm that day care does seems to increase with the dosage, especially in the under twos. The earlier it is started, the more days a week, and the longer the days, the more the child can be affected, with significant numbers becoming withdrawn and sad, or becoming mean and anti-social. The children were not the only ones affected. The parents also missed out on developing a confident, loving relationship with their child, which gave both sides difficulties as time went on.

Later on when graduates of day care enter kindergarten, they tend to show increased aggression, disobedience and conflict with adults. Not only that, their presence seems to affect the non-day-care children around them, who start to copy them. (National Institute for Child Health and Development: Early Child Care Research Network report for 2007.)

TO DAY CARE OR NOT

There is no doubt that this is a significant issue for the career woman, most especially because many careers are not sympathetic to her plight. It's glib and untrue to say that money is of secondary importance to the health of the child. There are few worse environmental influences on a family than constant financial stress. Some mothers need day care in order to keep food on the table and the roof over their heads, and these families need a pragmatic solution to allow all adults to work. There are no easy answers in this situation.

It's not only money. Some professional careers do not tolerate long periods of time removed from the scene. Law, medicine, architecture, design, business management and sales, to name a few, do not allow members to cease constant striving. For most, regaining or maintaining a position on the ladder to promotion, status and seniority is difficult or impossible in the face of taking time out for children. This forces women into part-time or more lowly positions in their profession.

For these women, who are the majority of highly trained professionals, at present, there is little choice but to join in with the boys and make do with the best nanny or day care they can afford. I've seen valiant attempts with expressing machines in briefcases and babies at work, which can buy time, but when one tries to take toddlers into the workplace things rapidly go pear-shaped. Some professional workplaces are improving, for instance with on-site crèches, but the speed is glacial, with little more relief in sight.

Don't ask your working friends for their opinion. Many of them do not feel that work in the home is 'real work'. Some of them might feel you are 'letting the side down' by not contributing your expertise in the workplace and you should step up to support women's place in society. Theirs is a narrow prescriptive view of feminism which excludes choice and ignores biology.

For those who truly have the choice, and whose decision to use day care is based on such peer pressure, overblown personal ambition or the desire to boost an adequate family income even higher, I make the following observation.

When you become a mother, it is a good time to ask the question 'Who is the real you?' The high court judge, the obstetrician, the hairdresser, the business manager, the teacher, the sales assistant – all these women need to take stock of their lives with the arrival of their babies.

In the last few decades new mothers have been encouraged, by our materialistic society and by government, to do the bare minimum for the children, and then get back to the real work and real life.

This attitude needs serious personal scrutiny. When she dies, a high court judge will be replaced in three months, the doctor or teacher within a week and the sales assistant overnight. Few people at her work will be affected for very long by her passing. The surface of the river of life around her will ripple a little, and then flow on unchanged.

But to her children, a mother can never be replaced. Even a loving partner can possibly love again, but a child can never be re-mothered. It is the one role the mother will play for which there is no understudy.

It has been proposed by optimists that as our society changes so we as a species might evolve with it. In response to our plugged-in, digital world of instant information, our brains could change to accept new forms of information exchange, our relationships will evolve with social media, and therefore new forms of parenting will emerge. We are inspired to imagine a futuristic society where babies are looked after in idealised caring facilities to produce mentally balanced, stable, perfect humans. What is not appreciated by this view is that it would require a radical change in our fundamental biology. Evolution in that or any other direction can only be through natural selection. That is, those babies who could not adapt to it would die and not grow up to reproduce. Over many generations we would select those babies who could successfully cope and grow up to reproduce themselves. This is not only science fiction but a speculative dystopia.

Biology doesn't work like that. As I said earlier, the way in which mammals reproduce and bring up their young has basically not changed for tens of millions of years, biochemically, hormonally and neurologically. It hasn't changed because this method is efficient and produces the best quality offspring.

By embracing these few short years, at least until your babies are three years old, and putting other aspects of your life on hold, you will be rewarded by joy and love as you share with them, and contribute to, their blossoming. This is a time when babies learn about love – what it is, how it works and who to obtain it from. To have a third party usurping your place in this magical process risks later sadness, frustration and disappointment from all parties.

Imagine yourself in a few short years leafing through a photo album, or browsing through the pictures and videos of your little toddler on your computer. She is now home from school, playing with her friends in her room. The little girl in the pictures doesn't exist anymore. She's gone, completely replaced by her older version. But during the time she was an infant you were too stressed, distracted and busy to really notice her, or the passage of time. You were just getting by, postponing happiness, waiting for the pressure to ease.

We have to make a conscious decision to be happy now and give her our attention in the present moment. It's the only way to appreciate it, and her, fully. Then we don't feel cheated when it's gone forever.

There is another version of the old adage that 'on the way to the cemetery nobody feels that they didn't spend enough time at work'. I know of no mothers who, when taking their children to the first day at school, wish they had spent less time with them when they were younger.

SO WHAT DOES ALL THAT MEAN?

- Babies are born very early in their development and also have the longest childhoods on the planet. This is because they grow slowly, and need to have a complex culture passed on to them.
- Because of this our brains have plasticity and resilience; that is, they are constantly changed and moulded by their upbringing and the people around them, intensely for the first months and years, then at a more leisurely pace as they grow.
- How much resilience our babies have and how much poor parenting they can compensate for is genetic luck. Some babies can cope with poor experiences and adjust. Others cannot.
- Young babies are not so much interested in what we think, but what we feel and how that reflects in our body. They can read our body language. But if you want to call it telepathy, please do.

- An upbringing of love, acceptance, consistency, truth and security allows the child to be the best he or she can be.
- The old African proverb 'It takes a village to bring up a child' states that succinctly. The title carries a basic truth. From the early days of human society the care of babies was distributed among many in the tribe. So long are our babies' childhoods and so intense are their demands, it is hardly possible for just parents to give all that is needed. Involving alloparents – grandparents, relations and friends – in their lives is not only a great respite, but also beneficial for the children. They benefit from having a number of different carers in their life, as each child is different and each alloparent brings his or her own perspective to bear on the process, giving the child another aspect of the truth.
- To quote Professor Alison Gopnik, psychologist and philosopher, from her book *The Philosophical Baby*, 'We can't ensure that our children will have a happy future – there, all we can do is move the odds around. But we can at least try to ensure that they will have a happy past.'

CHAPTER 7

The woman who cares for herself

Don't be 'the best mother', be the best woman –
and then mother your children.

BY NATURE WOMEN TEND TO BE nurturers. This is part of their essence and their biology. Maybe as a response to the way society conditions females, the heavy domestic workload placed on her or the fact that motherhood can easily become all-consuming, such nurturing does not often seem to involve the woman herself.

She tends to disregard herself, especially when there is family to look after. She eats less and last. She cares first for the babies and children, then her partner, and her own needs come down the bottom. Many have been taught from childhood that, for a woman, sacrifice is not only a necessary but an essential part of their life. If they're not doing it tough, they're clearly not trying hard enough!

There's another aspect of the same phenomenon. This mother has always been in control of her life and has done everything well. There is nothing this woman cannot succeed in doing, as long as she puts her mind to it. Her baby is just another major project.

So she works and works. Her baby is clean and fed, her house is tidy, and she manages to be coiffed and groomed. Even her nails are perfect. She presents an image to the world of control and competence, but it's fingernail thin. As she strives to keep all the balls in the air, she's aware that she is bone-achingly exhausted.

It has to be said, especially with young babies, that there are times when it *is* very hard and, in actual truth, the baby needs his mother day and night. If the mother desperately needs time to sleep but the baby's needs will not wait, she has no choice but to attend to him. But as time goes on, and the demands diminish, many mothers will still keep going on autopilot. Continuing in the aviation metaphor, remember what the cabin crew say in the flight safety briefing? First fit your own oxygen mask, then deal with the child's. That remains an excellent principle.

THE SELF-NURTURING WOMAN

With a little thought it is obvious that, especially as the babies get older, self-nurturing is an essential pre-requisite to good parenting:

- As your children get older, you need to set an example for them. They are watching you, observing your every move. They need to see someone who respects and looks after herself. This is not selfishness; this is self-respect.
- If you disregard yourself, why should your children treat you any better than you treat yourself?
- And if you don't look after yourself, when the babies grow up they will have learned, by observation, to do the same with themselves.

So, right from the start, make space for your own needs. Practise nurturing yourself by doing something each day that *you* want to do. Make an effort to take things more gently than your usual pace. Things will not get out of control if you slow down a little and look after yourself along the way. By pacing yourself and accepting being less than perfect, you can even make things easier, as you are free to think more clearly without stress winding you up.

Many women actually lose themselves in the process of mothering. Their personal identity disappears behind a fog of parenting duties, responsibilities, tasks and expectations.

There are two main reasons why they can become so absorbed with their babies and children that it excludes many other important aspects of their life:

1. Evolution has designed mothering to be addictive. The feel of a baby against your body, her touch and her smell, and the very act of breastfeeding itself are all designed to create, in both participants, a wonderful cocktail of hormones. These include endorphins, prolactin, dopamine and oxytocin, among many others. The presence of these neurohormones swirling around in your body and brain gives a feeling of calm, contentment and connectedness, very often in a way previously only experienced when falling in love.

2. Bringing up babies and children is a wild ride. And wild rides are risky and uncertain. When we are single, we can work to control most aspects of our life. We can bury the raw parts of our temperament and avoid things that bother us. In order to deal successfully with our relationships, especially sexual ones, we need to have an inner core of security that allows us the strength and motivation to let go of this control, to be loving, spontaneous and take risks.

After we bring home a baby, for many of us that whole risk-taking side of our personality is considered too unpredictable and unsafe. Looking at our helpless infant we realise that we have to grow up and, often for the first time, be serious, stable and dependable. This can be a big leap into the unknown.

To give us a feeling of stability, we try to control the things in our lives that are fixable. We become obsessed with cleanliness, order and safety. We start to keep our home germ and dust free, and make our visitors wash their hands and produce their vaccine certificates. Such obsession is very time consuming and we end up doing almost nothing in our lives that does not involve the baby.

This is fine, even normal, for the first few months but, for the sake of the child and our partner, this situation needs to evolve as the baby becomes older.

Once babies leave the age when they are totally dependent and they start becoming mobile, mothers need to become more mobile too. Some find this is difficult as they are so enmeshed in their children and are reduced to becoming only their children's mothers as they lose their own sense of who they are as individuals. They can also end up relying on their little ones for the emotional satisfaction people all need to feel special and needed.

This issue is sadly not unusual. With some women, in order to bring an element of control into their relentlessly busy lives, they exclude all else but their children to a degree that their partner feels, and increasingly becomes, isolated from her. As the mother and father drift apart, mother into the nursery, father into his work, so the children start to carry the burden of their parents' emotional needs.

Children are very savvy at reading relationships and it is too heavy a burden for a child to bear to have emotionally dependent parents. Children must see that their parents, and especially their mothers, have an emotional and intimate life that does not include them.

One of the most critical components in infants' lives is to perceive that their parents have a stable, loving relationship with each other, to which the infants have no access. They need to recognise that not every corner of their parents' lives is available to them. In essence, there are clear limits to their territory within the family.

- Parents should therefore plan their lives so there is adequate couple time, which is without the presence of the youngsters. Only then can they reignite the mutual nurturing that they had before the baby came home. This is as essential as the hygiene, the housework, the breadwinning and servicing the bank loan.
- The parents should kiss and embrace each other in front of the children. The children need to see that their parents

love each other; they need a model of adult affection that they can use in their own lives. Nothing is as reassuring to a child as seeing this. And if you're becoming estranged from your partner because of the baby, this is even more important. Schedule it, and if you're shy, get over it! The children will not complain until they become teenagers and even then, they're only kidding – they still find it reassuring.

- Schedule regular time-outs from the time that your baby is a few months old. A babysitter is not a luxury; it's as important as a sturdy stroller in a family's life. Go to a movie or just for a walk together. Have a nice dinner at a restaurant where you can talk – perhaps about things other than the baby.

CHAPTER 8

Attunement to your baby

NOW WE UNDERSTAND HOW IMMATURE BABIES' brains are, we realise how little 'working memory' they have. With the thinking, evaluating and planning part of the human brain not yet connected, it is months before they can learn about altering their patterns of living, like sleeping longer and feeding less often, or responding to a routine. Young babies react only through their innate body rhythms. It is those body rhythms that parents, and the mother in particular, need to tune into in the first weeks and months in the anxious and delightful process of learning about their particular baby. This is the critical process of 'attunement' which is the very essence of sensitive and appropriate parenting.

Young babies do not have a concept of their identity as separate from their mothers, but their bodies do have a specific and innate rhythm that is unique to them and independent of their mother. By observing them without interference, we can recognise it and work with it.

Try to avoid having preset ideas about when to feed her or when to put her down. Whatever you do, it's likely to be okay.

Such is her adaptability, the baby will usually comply.
using the baby's own body to determine a program is m
to develop into a mutually satisfying and successful daily routine.

In practical terms it means observing your baby calmly and carefully and, by using trial and error and common sense, trying to respond to her cues appropriately.

In the early days many new mothers find merely watching their babies very difficult. They have too many bits of advice coursing through their brains to allow them to just see what works for their baby. Too many 'the baby ought to be doing this', or 'we should be doing that', or 'he isn't supposed to be doing the other'. It's hard to calm yourself and just concentrate on looking when you're googling 'whinging baby' on your iPad!

Essentially it is a process of noticing the little behavioural characteristics of your baby when she is, for instance, hungry, upset, over-aroused or distressed. Then deal with those emotions when they arise, using the Top Tools for Parents:

- Intuition
- Common sense
- Trial and error
- Confidence from knowing that babies are inherently pretty tough and adaptable.

In the early days, often you will get it wrong. That's part of the process. Good enough is fine; your baby is not expecting perfect parents right from the start. Also remember her memory is very short and you will be rapidly forgiven for botching it totally. Within a short time, when you get it right you will be rewarded by the happy response of a contented baby. The next time the baby behaves in a similar way, you plug in the right response and are rewarded again. Success breeds success and within a few short weeks you are the global expert on your baby.

The beauty of this process is it self-amplifies. The more often you get it right, the more confidence you have to experiment further. Equally, the more confidence your baby develops in her communication to you, the more confidence she has in you interpreting her cues correctly.

I had a nurse come to my home to help me with my baby, who was so unsettled and I couldn't seem to get him into any kind of routine. I had always been trying to get him to fall asleep on the breast. Then the nurse showed me what his 'tired signs' were. I had been looking for yawning but we could see that he got instead a 'vacant look' and started stretching and wriggling when he was tired and needed a nap. When he was put down immediately at that time, even though he was awake, he would put himself to sleep. Miraculous. Since then I've looked for and found other particular signs of his and acted on them. I now have a quiet, contented baby!

More than occasionally the connection will fail and the baby will become distressed. This minor wobble is not harmful and, as you both seek to re-attune, the connection is mended. This process will teach your baby how to negotiate distressing situations later. You do it by interacting socially! What a revelation and an essential lifelong skill for her to learn.

While you are observing, try not to think about cooking dinner, the shopping list or, if you're still working, your company's profit and loss report. The most common intrusive thoughts, of course, are all the helpful advice you are being given by family and friends.

Recognise that you come from an endless line of women ancestors stretching back into prehistory, every single one of whom must have had a baby successfully enough for that baby to have grown up and to have reproduced. Otherwise you wouldn't be here. So natural selection has selected you to do this job perfectly, without help from the lady over the road, a baby book or the internet. The relationship between you and your baby will blossom and be quite enough for both of you, if you let it.

Just be with her. Babies have an awareness of whether you are truly there or not. They know when your worries and thoughts intervene as you sit with them.

To start with, you will have numerous thoughts about how you are going and whether you are meeting your baby's needs. As you get more confident and attuned you will seek less and less advice and use more and more of your intuition and experience to deal with each new situation. Within a short time you'll find that your decisions about what to do become more accurate and instinctive. Practice makes perfect, or as near perfect as you both need.

These times of quiet attention are the best quality time. They are so much better than quantity time with the mind elsewhere.

BABIES, INFANTS, TODDLERS . . . TO TEENAGERS

Sooner or later it often occurs to parents that there is a lot of similarity between the behaviour of toddlers and teenagers. Now neurobiologists doing brain scanning studies have shown that there is more than a little truth to that.

We have discussed earlier about the massive brain growth and burgeoning connections in early infant life. In this process, the limbic system, the source of powerful emotions of fear and pleasure, makes neural contact with the processing capacity of the right-sided prefrontal cortex.

During adolescence these same tracts proliferate yet again, but now the brain is much more organised. This time the changes manifest in characteristic teenage behaviour. Attention is more scattered, sleep patterns are disrupted, the sensitivity to fear is diminished, producing risk-taking behaviour, and all appetites including sexual are increased. There is also an increased drive for immediate gratification from their behaviour. Our engaged and engaging child becomes a distant memory and an even more distant stranger.

But it's not all bad; on the other side, when motivated, there is a massive development of skills and improved thinking.

The point is that as teenagers are using the same brain pathways they laid down in infancy and toddlerhood, so the same underlying emotional atmosphere pervades the changes. The boisterous toddler leads the way for his later wilder teenage self.

Teenagers whose childhoods were secure and loving tend to get through this difficult time of adolescence with more ease than those whose early days were difficult. The loved group had the advantage of a core of security and love from parents or carers, and had formed high-quality brain pathways that they then start to reuse and enhance. So when the hormone storms kick in, they don't get knocked over by them. They have a stable centre they can hold on to and on which they can rely, using it as a jumping-off point to explore and develop during these tumultuous years.

So you want a nice, loving, not too rebellious 14-year-old? Another reason to give your baby lots of cuddles and love.

CHAPTER 9

Being there and staying calm

IT IS ALWAYS SAID THAT YOU mother as you were mothered. It happens, certainly, but equally we may see another dynamic of women who, after unsatisfactory childhoods, go completely the other way and run their parenting behaviour through a reverse filter. The over-disciplined girl becomes a laid-back earth mother; the child of the hippie becomes a relentless, high-achieving mum.

> Don't let your ideals and thoughts get in the way of your mothering.

Studies summarised by Gopnik show that the parenting styles of those people who had satisfactory childhoods tend to reflect those same values later when they have children. For the parents whose childhoods were difficult, how they deal with this when they have children seems to depend on whether they have thought about and processed the reasons behind why it didn't go well.

If they remembered their past clearly and had an 'internal narrative' about it – that is, they recognised the reasons behind the way it was, and acknowledged how it had shaped them – these parents were usually able to imagine an alternative, and better, way. They could bring up their children in a different way from their own experience. It was only the parents who suppressed the memories of their childhood and remembered very little about it who seemed destined to repeat the patterns.

But in addition to this, we all have issues, our imperfections, phobias, personal beliefs and lofty ideals derived from myriad life experiences and influences. These colour the way we see the world and drive the way we behave. We hold in our mind an idea of how we believe 'parents' should behave and how children should be treated and all too frequently don't let the individual child's needs and specific temperament interfere with this view.

I am by no means the first to suggest that parenting is a powerful self-realisation experience. Before we have children we develop a strong persona that works for us in our environment, in our workplace, our home and in our relationships. The arrival of a baby provokes a cataclysmic change in our priorities and our worldview – but not often our temperament.

With horror we notice we are saying exactly the same things our parents said! We discover feelings of responsibility and new anxieties that are completely foreign to us. How we react to this new situation depends on our distillation of the experiences and the beliefs that we have acquired to date. Our previously suppressed neuroses and fears become amplified by our concern for our babies and their future. If we were a little bit obsessive before, it can become a real issue after the baby. We may notice that we start to line up the nappies coded in colour and size, from left to right!

In struggling for control, what we may present to our children is our persona, that familiar artificial self that we are comfortable to portray to the world. Young babies don't have a sense of self. They think they are part of us and they can see clearly through our mask. But early on, they learn that the world works by everyone not digging too deep. As they grow, to get our approval, love and security, they learn to behave in a way we seem to like. They communicate things that please us, and over the years they learn to override their true feelings, needs and impressions. Eventually they create their own persona and their true self is left far behind. Their fully-fledged persona, like ours, is also not the real deal, and they spend a lifetime living within its constraints and limitations.

Avoiding this is no easy pathway. It is hard to calm our anxieties about the basic process of parenting, let alone raise our eyes to the horizon of their future. We are barely able to see ourselves clearly, let alone see the baby for the person she truly is.

Young babies may not have a concept of their identity as separate from their mothers but, as mentioned, their bodies do have a specific and inherent rhythm that is unique to them. So try to observe them from early babyhood without interference, and work with this, not with your preset ideas about what babies should do. Your daily routine with your baby should emerge from this. Don't think about anything else when you are watching her. Just be with her.

As she gets older, make an effort to recognise your baby as an individual, not an extension of your hopes and dreams. Spend time learning who your child is, by observing and listening to her. Avoid interrupting her when she is absorbed in something. Help this unique person to develop along a path that is appropriate for her to fulfil her destiny. This may or may not necessarily be your preferred path. In your day-to-day interaction you should attempt to bring an honesty to the process, by trying to separate what you want, to answer your needs, from what is appropriate for your individual child. Be careful of the tricks your mind plays as you try to direct her towards what makes you comfortable, not what is right for her!

So avoid pushing little round pegs into little square holes.

Love and respect

A philosopher once asked whether you love your children enough to let them break their legs. I'm not sure about the orthopaedic trauma but the main thrust of the remark is worth thinking about. There is no doubt that young babies need complete protection.

Toddlers need almost as much because they truly will break their legs if given the opportunity. But the truth of the question lies elsewhere, in what is often a lack of respect for our children as individuals. We insist that as we are older and wiser, we always know better. Their opinions, needs and wishes can be overridden because of the superiority of adult perspective.

It is worth considering that in many ways children are better at life than we are. They see the world in its freshness and innocence, unfiltered by our jaded sensibilities and experience. Small children will dawdle as they gaze in wonder at a flower or a tree, when we want to hurry them along down the woodland path to get somewhere. Perhaps if we took the opportunity to see the world as they do, we might learn (or unlearn) a great deal. Perhaps we should stop judging them and their perceptions and start merely being there for them, as they are with themselves.

Sometimes we need to get out of our children's way and let them get on with life, make a few mistakes and recognise that some worthwhile things in life are hard to achieve. Too often once they get out of babyhood we are tempted to smooth the way for them too much and even discourage them from trying difficult tasks, which demeans them and their abilities.

Do you listen to your children? Do you let them talk to you and tell you what is in their hearts? So many parents half listen, then, as quickly as possible, cut in to use the conversation as a learning experience for the child. They interrupt and talk at the child, to impart some piece of worldly wisdom in the hope they can improve them just a little. But what did the little one actually have to say? What insights did you miss as you stopped the flow of words that was coming straight from the purity of his worldview?

This is the gift that babies and children bring to their parents. The rewards of parenting can be subtle and have to be embraced to be appreciated. There is the feeling of love, the cuddles, the baby smell, the biteable shoulders, the soft skin and melting, gummy smile but, more profoundly, there is also the opportunity to see the world through the eyes of a child. Their presence gives us the chance to stop spinning as we try to make sense of the world, and instead settle quietly into stillness and see how it actually is.

Being there

When you are with your babies and children, they just want you to be right there and connected to them. As we've seen, they also know when you are not. Young children live their lives in the perpetual present and they have a handle on true reality that has long since slipped from us.

To join them there, we need to be able to calm ourselves enough to reside in the present moment too. Unfortunately it is our constant thinking that prevents us returning to such an innocent state. The process of logical thought and deductive reasoning grabs us at an early age and from then on never lets us go. We begin to believe that our thoughts represent reality and they are all terribly important. We spend the whole of our lives watching their ebb and flow, giving them power over us and our lives.

Some thoughts are helpful of course. Because of such a process humankind has made sensational advances in numerous areas of knowledge and technology. But they are not our essence. Our brain is designed to think, and that is what it does, all of the time, awake or asleep.

The constant random commentary of our minds keeps us from seeing our true selves. The useless chatter prevents us returning to that calm centre that lies within us all, which can nurture and replenish us in our busy lives.

This little-appreciated concept was demonstrated to me vividly a long time ago. For many years I studied Zen meditation under the direction of an older experienced Zen teacher, Joko (Charlotte) Beck, in the United States.

During a *sesshin* (a prolonged meditation retreat), after a few days in sitting meditation, something became very obvious to me.

It occurred to me that my thoughts were not mine; they barely belonged to me at all. As my practice (of counting the breath) settled my mind, so I achieved great calmness; however, my mind continued to think. As I had been trained, I merely allowed my thoughts and continued with my practice. I found I could tune in to my thoughts or tune out, like a radio. I once tuned in and realised to my surprise that I was thinking about cricket. I am not the least bit interested in cricket. Nevertheless my mind was doing what it was designed to do, which was think. But the thoughts had nothing to do with me.

Occasionally out of the calmness would come an emotion: amusement, anger, boredom. But these emotions were also unrelated to me as a person. They were merely further evidence of my mind's functioning.

Once demonstrated, this knowledge is extremely useful. I realised that our beloved or hated thoughts and emotions are not necessarily our own, but we give them respectability and power over us by assuming they are. We are never 'just angry' – we assume we are angry for a reason. We are often anxious and cast about in our mind looking for a trigger, and we can usually find one. Often, however, the anxiety is a free-floating emotion of no real significance to us, but we give it a hook that justifies it and we claim it as our own.

These thoughts and emotions intensify and become more frequent after having a baby. Anxiety, guilt and perceived shortcomings burgeon when the mother is home alone with her baby. There is more time for rumination and a limitless expanse of self-doubt that accompanies parenthood. Learning that just because you feel an emotion does not make it valid and appropriate is a valuable lesson. After a hard day looking after a toddler, few parents do not occasionally feel drained, tired and bored. Looking dispassionately at these emotions, accepting them for what they are but not accommodating them, is a very useful practice to survive the bumps in the rocky road of parenthood. By ignoring and not getting sucked into them, the unattached emotions soon evaporate and disappear completely.

Some of you may have already learned meditation techniques that can help you in this direction. If you have, now is a good time to dust off your technique and resume it.

The problem for most of these practices, especially when you have a baby, is setting aside a specific time and space each day to do it. Instead of being a practice to reduce stress and calm oneself, it becomes yet another stressful item on your to-do list. A better and truer way is a technique that you can utilise at any time, anywhere.

Gentle breath meditation

This is a meditation technique that we can all use every minute, anywhere, and it is based upon the premise of being there.

First you need to calm yourself and centre your mind. The most effective way to do this is to become aware of your breath.

You feel it at the tip of your nose as it gently moves in and out, stirring the hairs inside your nasal passages. You can do this when you are out and about, sitting at the computer or holding your baby while breastfeeding.

Just be with the breath. In and Out.

Then gently become aware of your thoughts. Just allow them. Don't try to stop them, calm them or engage with them, just watch them and then get back to observing your breath.

Awareness of your many thoughts while in stillness *is* meditation.

That's all there is to it. You can do it for a few seconds, a minute or two, or even settle down for ten minutes if you have the time or inclination. But there's no pressure and no timetable. Just whenever there is an opportunity, bring yourself back to the present moment.

Feel the breath.
Settle the mind.
Allow the thoughts.
If you find you're engaging with your thoughts (and you will), it's okay – but go back to observing the breath.

Then with a little practice you can start to feel a connection between your mind and a quiet part of yourself (in your heart, if you like) that is unruffled and calm in the midst of life. Your baby can read your body and will also tend to settle while you are in this state.

This state is the present moment. This is where children reside and where mystics seek to go. Indeed, it is all we have. The past has gone for ever, and the future doesn't exist.

Not being there

To deliver its joys, parenthood needs to be embraced. How many of us spend time with our babies or children, fantasising about being elsewhere and doing something more interesting? When things get tough, when the toddler's feeling antsy and won't leave the sandpit or the baby vomits everything yet again, it is easy to catastrophise. We should never have had a baby! This parenting business is too hard for me! I should've stayed in the company and pushed for a seat on the board!

We sometimes long for the life we had when we were single and fancy-free. Those were the days! Feel lonely? Ring up a friend. Feeling bored? Go to the movies. Feeling tense? Have a drink or two.

Fantasising about a different life is a profoundly useless pastime and entertaining the negativity only makes matters worse. These emotions are clouds across the sun and will pass if they are not given our energy.

Stop, feel the breath, and allow the thoughts and emotions without judging them. Accept them for what they are: our body's reaction to momentary discomfort. Accept that everybody's lives, even the ones that you are jealous about, have periods of discomfort, even despair. It's part of being human. Life *is* imperfect. Then return to the present moment and live the life you have.

Switch off the radio or TV when it's in the background. Many people use muzak to take them out of the present moment and distract them from their feelings. The silence can help you recognise how your mind tries to play games with you and stop you from living in reality. When you quieten your mind, where do you go? What other dimension do you try to live in?

Be here now, and don't miss this time with the children. When they are older and busy with their friends, you'll wonder where they are. When they move away and get married, you'll seldom see them except at Christmas. From the perspective of years you will see how short a time their infancy and childhood was.

The child you have today will not exist in a few years. He or she will be someone else, just as beautiful and just as loved, but quite different. What you have today is unique and irreplaceable. Only by experiencing it moment by moment can this short time be appreciated in its fullness.

This is why grandparents are the way they are. They dote over your children because they recognise what they missed the first time. Looking back, they can see they were not only too busy with the laundry and the housework but, more importantly, they were too much in their heads with anxiety, guilt and regret. The second time around, they do not want to miss a moment.

CHAPTER 10

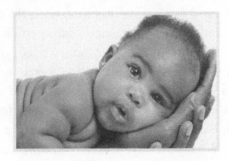

Helpful advice

HAVE YOU EVER WONDERED WHY THERE is so much advice out there for new parents? And it's not just the volume; the advice is also incredibly varied and often completely contradictory. It's not only about the big-ticket items like whether or not to feed to a routine or put pressure on babies to sleep through the night, but also every tiny detail of their management, from cleaning their ears, to using a dummy or not, to the four different way to sterilise it if you use one. It's a neat way to part parents from their sanity.

It's probably always been this way. Today, though, it is more conflicted than ever in the past. Even a few decades ago opinions were less divergent than today as most people held fairly similar views about how to manage a baby.

Back then, mainstream opinion in the West was dominated by the Church's view. It had determined that babies were born with 'original sin' (after all, they were the product of sex!) and were therefore inherently selfish and potentially evil. The only solution was to provide control, discipline and routine to break their spirit in order to purge them of sin and yield useful members of society.

To allow independence or show them too much affection would likely cause a downward spiral into spoilt indulgence.

Breastfeeding was also considered rather vulgar and formula feeding (the word implied such technical, chemical accuracy!) was the enlightened way to nourish a baby. A kiss on the forehead before bedtime was enough affection and, as the children grew, a handshake became preferable. To read the baby-advice books from around 1910 to the 1950s is to risk your hair standing on end and your head shaking in disbelief.

Happily a more enlightened view emerged in the 1940s and was later driven by doctors Donald Winnicott, John Bowlby and Mary Ainsworth among many others, including the ubiquitous Dr Benjamin Spock and his 1946 book *Baby and Child Care* (which for a while was a global bestseller, second only to the bible). They believed less in routines, dogmatism and discipline, and more in the biology of mammalian reproduction. Significantly, most of the initiators of this movement were trained in psychotherapy, psychiatry or psychology. With their training they were able to see that mental health issues in adults were often rooted in their infancy. They were interested in the interaction between mothers, babies and families, and believed that we were designed to care for our babies using our instincts. We were meant to love and keep them close, feed them when they were hungry and soothe them when they were distressed.

It was a profound, seismic shift in belief. It caused ructions in the paediatric and mothercraft communities and the aftershocks are still felt to this day. Even nowadays, some professionals still remain conflicted about the change and hold grimly to the old model. From this ambivalence emerge the endless debates regarding controlled crying, demand or routine feeding, the discipline of the toddler and the smacking of children.

Sadly, new parents are caught in the middle of these two schools of baby management. Professionals are still part of the culture, and culture can take generations to catch up with new scientific knowledge – even when that knowledge is overwhelming and meshes with what parents instinctively want to do. It isn't only professionals who extol the old methods, of course. Throughout society these methods are still used. By oral tradition and example, down through the generations, mother to daughter, and in peer groups, we still pass on the same ancient beliefs.

Another important reason that the old beliefs persist is the ability of the developing brain to minimise or cover up the effects of our mistakes. So, on the surface, either of these models appears to work.

It has been said that the development of a child is like a ball rolling down a valley. The ball may deviate up the sides of the valley from the forces of life but it tends to self-correct and continues down the valley. It takes an extraordinary force to drive the ball over the hill into the adjacent valley of such aberrant development that correction is not feasible. The human child generally has an extraordinary capacity to correct for problematic infant experiences if he is lucky enough to have been born with innate resilience. Unfortunately, some don't have that flexibility genetically, and they find it much more difficult to shake off the effects of those experiences.

There is, therefore, a growing appreciation that at the end of the valley there are a lot of different exits for different babies. Which one they emerge from depends on their genetic endowment, their environment, and their resilience. That is, you are the end result of who you are, how you were brought up and also how competently you corrected the mistakes of this upbringing.

Teasing out what childcare methods need the least resilience and correction has been the aim of a large amount of detailed scientific work by many sources. Enough knowledge has now been accumulated to work out which advice to believe and which to ignore.

There is an extra factor encouraging lots of advice. Just about everyone thinks babies are very cute and lovable. They have indeed been designed by evolution to be so attractive that everybody wants to get involved and help. This was useful in the past when there was a good chance that the baby's mother wouldn't survive childbirth; happily now that situation is excessively rare, but the impulse remains. Whether they know anything or not, complete strangers will stop you in the street and give you parenting tips. Even little old men will pontificate on the finer techniques of breastfeeding. Unfortunately, even some other mothers are also strangely competitive, believing their way of doing things is the only way and lambasting those who have other views.

The basics

It is clear that in the first weeks and early months, our babies need the same kind of care they got inside the womb. They require:

- absolute security
- feeding on demand
- very close contact care, skin to skin when available
- their needs met promptly.

Our instinct also drives us towards this kind of care, which is obvious when we appreciate how 'immature' our babies are. Equally obvious, judging by the success we've had on this planet, is that as a species we are incredibly resilient and adaptable. So even if our upbringing is not ideal, we will still survive and thrive.

It is this adaptability, the ability of babies to make do with a wide variety of parental styles (even some extreme ones), that has perpetuated the myriad mothercraft myths that inundate new parents when they seek advice from family and friends.

So find a trusted source of the information you seek, and don't worry too much about the rest. If you ask four people, you will get four different answers.

When you receive clearly useless or contradictory advice about managing your baby, remember the following:

- If the advice doesn't make sense, it probably isn't true.
- If the advice implies that the baby is a delicate organism who, if she isn't managed in exactly the right way, will come to harm, it's not likely to be true.
- Just because it worked for the adviser doesn't mean it's relevant to you.

- You have complex software written into your brain that tells you how to look after your baby. Use this through your intuition and common sense.
- Trial and error is a useful tool. Your baby will let you know soon enough if your strategy is not working.
- Remember that some strangers and friends want to help in order to make themselves feel good.
- Some people really want you to do it the way they did it. This is for two reasons: it reinforces the rightness of what they did and it makes them feel better about their personal choices. Smile and agree, then do what you feel is right for your baby.

CHAPTER 11

Fathers: a special relationship

FOR THE FIRST FEW MONTHS AFTER the birth of a baby many fathers feel somewhat excluded while the baby and mother huddle together, totally involved in each other. Nevertheless the presence and love of a father is ideal for every baby and child to achieve their optimal development.

Biologically this is a time of maternal engrossment, where the mother and baby get the breastfeeding and their relationship bedded down. Though you may feel a little sidelined, your job as a father is to support the process, your baby and the mother. There are many ways in which you can do this to enhance this critical time for your family.

Providing resources is certainly an essential part of your function as it is not possible for a mother to support herself, at least in the months after the baby comes home. This is why our species, *Homo sapiens*, evolved into pair bonds (and consolidated into groups of pairs called tribes). Human babies are extraordinarily dependent and helpless, and need the dedicated care of two parents (and an extended family, if possible) for them to survive and develop normally.

So the father's essential functions are:

- to love and care for his family
- to provide resources for mother and baby
- to be physically and psychologically available to them
- to engage directly with the baby
- to be patient with and support the mother
- to accept that they will not receive the same level of nurturing from their partner at least in the short-term, so
- to nurture himself.

Security flows from father, to mother, to baby, and this is critical for relaxed and fulfilling parenting.

Parenting works best when both partners work as a team and back each other up. Quietly negotiating differences of opinion in parenting beliefs and styles should be done out of earshot. Overt arguments should be avoided completely as children can sense even subliminal conflict in the family and this erodes their confidence and personal feeling of security.

Many mothers complain that their partners have no idea how relentless the demands and needs of a baby are. Indeed, until they have experienced it, most women cannot appreciate the minute-by-minute intensity and magnitude of the workload either. This shock is then compounded by the inevitable chronic fatigue that makes even normal day-to-day functioning difficult.

This, of course, emphasises the last essential function on the list. It is important to remember to be extremely patient with your partner. You need to forgive her if she stops behaving as she did when she was single and fancy-free for a while. Such is the stress and work of a new baby that she is allowed to be snappy and irritable, hard to please and even totally unreasonable. Hang in there and help as much as possible. Things will improve – the important thing is not to take it personally (or they might not).

It is hard to come to the realisation that suddenly you are not your partner's greatest concern and your needs start to come in behind the baby's. This is usually only for a short time but, without doubt, you make it worse by complaining!

It isn't only for this reason that fathers should get involved with whatever baby tasks they can. Fathers can look after their babies very well, and much better than they think, as long as they give it a go. Babies are pretty tough and resilient and they are adapted to cope with incompetence, and trial and error. Other than breastfeeding, there is little babies need that fathers cannot provide. Fathers who have close contact with their babies from the early days have very similar hormonal and physical responses to mothers. The mothering hormone oxytocin (often called the hormone of 'calm and connectedness') is available to men who hold, care for and love their babies.

So you can change nappies (it's really not that hard and poos of breastfed babies just smell milky), bath, hold, talk to, read and sing to the baby. The baby recognises your voice within a short time. Holding a baby skin to skin against your chest is a wonderful feeling and this can give you practice at being aware of and in touch with your feelings. And the warm touch of the baby can create a lifelong emotional bond if it is explored and maintained. So allow your natural tenderness to blossom and grow. Practise this and expand on it in your life. This is a small advantage of having a daughter first – it gives fathers permission to be soft. Boys need this just a much, of course, so ignore the conditioning that tells you to treat them more boisterously.

It is often necessary for a father to be proactive in handling his new baby, especially when the newcomer is surrounded by a group of needy female relatives who will happily push the father aside to get their hands on the baby. It is important that the father asserts himself and his baby-handling qualities early on.

Fathers should also be sensitive regarding the anxiety many mothers feel about others handling their baby. Mothers can often become quite aggressive about having the baby things done their way. Developing quiet diplomacy and avoiding dogmatism is a really good fathering (and life!) plan.

After a few months fathers find it much easier to get involved with their baby, who is often much more responsive to them by this time. Observations show that fathers tend to interact with their babies and young children in a different way to mothers and this difference is important to show the baby a different aspect of love. Fathers tend to be much more physical with the little ones. It's usually fathers who throw their babies into the air and catch them, not mothers. Also, as the child starts toddling, fathers allow them to stray further than mothers, who tend to want to keep their babies close. Essentially fathers tend to limit freedom only for safety reasons and this allows babies to become more exploratory and develop confidence.

Fathers are essential role models not only for boys (which is obvious) but also for girls.

Boys: the mere presence of a father in the house tends to improve cognitive learning and decrease the incidence of behaviour problems in boys. The father's regular and active engagement with the child also tends to reduce aggressive behaviour later.

Boys use their father as a model for how males behave so with this comes great responsibility. It is important that fathers treat their sons gently, softly and show affection. Indicating to them that boys are tough people who hide their emotions and are wary of physical touching tends to yield dissatisfied and emotionally immature men.

The baby's father must treat his partner kindly, and lovingly and respectfully show overt affection to her in front of their children of both genders, but especially boys. This shows him that women are to be treated as equals, and are to be respected and nurtured.

Girls: the presence of a father tends to decrease psychological problems in girls later; it also boosts their cognitive development. Girls who are emotionally close to their father have fewer weight and food problems later. They use their father as a role model for all males and as the template by which others are judged. Fathers should: teach their daughters to honour and respect themselves; be emotionally supportive; avoid negative criticism; and not get too involved with their mistakes. Rough and abusive fathers tend to lead their daughters to form relationships with similar men.

Both: For children of both genders, it is important that fathers set aside time when they are alone with their child, and during which they give them their undivided attention. No newspapers or computers around. Children need their fathers to listen to them, understand and empathise with them.

It is also tempting to teach children by giving them lots of information. For the younger child it is important to give them only enough information to get them started with their own deductive and processing abilities, then help them along with just enough information to keep them going, meanwhile staying involved (but ignoring their mistakes). Give praise and encouragement where appropriate.

It is often not necessary to provide solutions to their issues. Listening is usually enough. Then respect the child enough to allow them to find their own solutions with minimal guidance.

'Daddy fix it', although tempting, can be a response that diminishes the child.

CHAPTER 12

The unsettled baby, Part I: myths and making sense

IN THE WOODY ALLEN FILM *ANNIE HALL*, a young married couple ends up in family counselling. They are interviewed separately.

'Do you have sex often?' the counsellor asks the woman.

'Constantly,' she says. 'I'd say about three times a week.'

The counsellor asks the man.

'Hardly ever,' he replies. 'Maybe three times a week.'

It's a similar situation with the unsettled baby. I have mothers who swear their babies are really unsettled 'all of the time' (but they sleep all night and have two naps). And there are others who have a baby who seems to scream nonstop and they manage very well.

Unsettledness is often in the ear of the beholder. But there is little as demoralising as a baby who cries too much, and that begs the question, 'How much is too much?'

The answer is: 'More than you can stand.'

But first, a few important facts:

BABY

- Over 90 per cent of excessively crying babies have no organic disease. That is, no pain, no physical cause, no parental deficiencies.
- Babies normally cry quite a lot. It is their only way of communicating everything in their lives. It might mean, 'Hi, I'm here', or 'Fix this, I'm uncomfortable', but it does not necessarily denote misery; nor does it mean you are failing as a parent.
- Some crying is part of the normal development of their brain. As they make brain connections their response can be to cry. It's a sign of progress!
- All babies are born with different temperaments and some babies cry more than others. Some are laid-back babies who can calm themselves; others are wired, jumpy and hyper-alert since birth. This aspect has nothing to do with the parents (other than they donated the genes and provided the womb). The parents have to work around their baby's personality and do the best they can (more advice on this soon).
- Babies' cries have different notes and intensities. I've heard some babies whose cries could shatter glass – 120 decibels of pain in the ears. These are hard to listen to for even a short time. Others have a gentle burble – these are other people's babies!

PARENT

How much crying you can tolerate depends on a number of personal factors:

- Your confidence level – first-time parents are often less tolerant than the seasoned ones. Naturally, the confidence of first-timers in their ability to deal successfully with the whole scenario is lower, and their expectations usually higher.

- Your temperament – do you insist on control, or do you go with the flow? People who come from very structured professions like teaching, accountancy or management sometimes find it more difficult to let go of the need to 'fix' everything. They find it hard to just admit that 'this situation is not ideal, but it's okay'.

- Your expectations – it is harder for you to cope with the noise if you have a fantasy that babies sleep all night, only chortle and coo, and never vomit or poo on your silk blouse.

- Your past – how well do you remember your childhood? How did your parents behave with you and your siblings? This gives you the basic beliefs about what is normal.

- How tired you are – fatigue undermines your ability to deal with adverse events. This aspect is a tough and vicious cycle. The more exhausted you are, the shorter your fuse.

- The background stress in your life – if you've got depression, or too many debts, or a stressful marriage, then everything is harder to deal with. But everyone experiences a level of stress from the massive change of having a new baby in their home, and that can be overwhelming.

'NORMAL' CRYING

It is really worth knowing just how much a normal, average baby cries in a day. In 1962 Dr T. Berry Brazelton conducted a study of a large number of babies to see how much they cried. (See the data chart on the next page.)

As you can see the babies cried a lot. It started for most of them at about two weeks of age, rose to a peak at about six weeks, when, on average, they were crying over two and a half hours a day, and then fell gradually to be much improved by three to four months.

Most of them had a peak of crying in the evening and at least one-fifth of babies cried enough to worry their parents sufficiently to see a doctor about it.

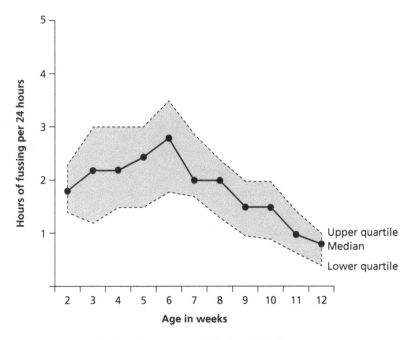

Total crying time in infants studied

By the way, the upper and lower borders of the chart only represent half of the babies. A quarter of the babies cried more than this and a quarter cried less. That is a lot of variability in 'normal' crying.

This study has been repeated many times with larger numbers since then, with exactly the same results.

The bottom line is that this period of crying, mostly in the evening, peaking at six weeks and diminishing by three months, is an issue rooted in the normal development of a baby. The young of other breastfeeding animals from guinea pigs to monkeys exhibit the same crying pattern. Consequently the old belief that it was mostly caused by pain in the stomach or from heartburn is just not true. It used to be called '6 o'clock' or 'evening' colic (according to its time of occurrence), or 'three-month' colic (according to the time of its disappearance). Those timings suggest a behaviour, not a pain.

When it was realised that this problem was not caused by tummy ache, it was suggested that the word 'colic' should be used as an acronym – 'Cause Obscure, Lengthy Infant Crying'. Somehow this never caught on, but it remains absolutely true.

FIVE TYPES OF CRYING

However, there seem to be FIVE components to the cries a baby makes – all for different reasons and with a different solution. If you lump them into one catch-all bag, it will lead to confusion and more crying – both from you and from the baby.

1. Crying and irritability from a physical cause, such as hunger, cold or loneliness, or discomfort in particular from reflux or cow's milk protein allergy
2. 'Fussy' crying
3. Whinging in light sleep
4. Inconsolable crying
5. Crying from overstimulation, mostly visual.

Once a baby is crying for whatever reason, he doesn't necessarily have an off switch, unless his carers help him. Tension and stress then build up in the baby's body from the cause and as he tries to cope.

Causes

1. Physical causes

Obviously, first off check that your baby is not too hot or too cold, the nappy is dry and clothes not too tight. Most parents will also give their baby a cuddle and some close contact to see if that is their need.

The most common organic cause for a lot of unsettledness is hunger. One of the advantages of breastfeeding is you don't know how much milk your baby is getting (so he learns to regulate his

> Our little baby Annie cries a lot. She is fully breastfed and never seems to be satisfied. If she's not on the breast, she's crying. I took her to the early childhood centre and they said she had put on only 100 g this week, and though she is now four weeks old, she hasn't yet got back to birth weight. How do I know if I've got enough milk?

own appetite). However, when there isn't enough, or the baby is not attaching to the breast correctly, this can be a disadvantage.

Babies should put on about 200 g a week on average and usually 160–180 g is satisfactory as long as everybody is happy and the baby settled.

However, weight gains below 160 g need to be addressed before anything else.

Go and see a lactation consultant to check that your technique of breastfeeding is right. Make sure the breasts are being drained properly, as this will boost the supply so they refill fully. Consider medication such as Domperidone or the herb fenugreek, both of which can help boost milk production as long as the breast is also draining properly. (See Chapter 2 on breastfeeding for information about dealing with low milk supply or a poor latch to the breast during feeding.)

With the formula-fed baby, at least you know the supply is adequate. Just be sure you're mixing powder to water in the correct proportion of scoops to water (this is vital).

You can find more information about reflux and cow's milk protein allergy in the next chapter.

2. Fussy crying

Over a 24-hour period this is the most common kind of crying. It is the incessant low-key unsettledness that can go on and on. It can occur any time of the day or night.

It is amenable to parenting practice, so warmth, feeding, and closeness from cuddling or breastfeeding work well to diminish or

> We read this British book that said we should put our
> baby into a routine as soon as we got him home. We
> tried this and found that it really is difficult. He seems to
> whinge most of the time and I've been picking him up as little
> as possible and sticking to the routine, but it doesn't seem to be
> working. Whinge, whinge, whinge, hour after hour; it's driving
> me crazy!

eliminate it. In one study by Professor Ian St James Roberts and others, there was 50 per cent less crying from the babies whose parents carried and cuddled them ten to fifteen hours a day than the group who held their babies as little as possible (an average of about six hours a day). These timings were at five weeks of age, which was the age when the babies were at their noisiest.

At this age babies are still missing the environment of the womb, but are also becoming more communicative and therefore they express their displeasure more competently and loudly.

So to diminish this unsettledness at this age, don't worry about 'spoiling' your baby, don't try to 'teach him to settle himself' and do what your instincts tell you: hold, kiss and cuddle him, and revel in his smell, touch – and the eventual silence!

3. Whinging in light sleep

As a baby moves from the phases of deep to light sleep (which they do every 50 minutes or so), they will often thrash their arms and head, and whinge. Beware, they are not awake! If you erroneously think they are distressed and interfere with them, they soon will be. Generally the baby will murmur and cry out for a few minutes, then fall back into the deeper realms of sleep, and quieten. So if you feel your baby is stirring within sleep, wait a few minutes before going in to them, as they may well settle themselves.

4. Inconsolable crying

> Just last night my three-week-old baby screamed like he was in excruciating pain for about half an hour. We held him, walked him and tried to feed him but nothing would make him stop. Even my mother (who is a mothercraft nurse) couldn't do anything with him. Then suddenly he stopped and seemed happy. He's done it before. What is it and what can we do?

There is no doubt that a small proportion of the crying that occurs in the first two to three months bears no relation to parenting practice, feeding issues or the baby's environment. It happens to about half of babies and when it does, it makes up about 5 per cent (that is, less than 15–20 minutes a day) of their total crying. For this kind of crying there is nothing the parents or anyone else can do about it except hold them and comfort them, and try not to get too concerned about it or take it personally. Nobody is quite sure why these bouts of intense crying occur but it is speculated that it is part of babies' neurodevelopment; that is, the effect on the baby's mood when brain connections are being made. When we are older we know that Rapid Eye Movement (REM) sleep is a time when brain connections are made, and this type of sleep produces dreams and images. So maybe this is like having an intense daydream.

The study mentioned above also showed that across all caring regimes, from full-contact carrying, through to low-contact, routine-based parenting, there is no difference in the amount of this kind of crying. It peaks at six weeks and tends to diminish greatly beyond eight to ten weeks.

5. 'Colicky' crying

Here we are in true 'colic' territory.

Babies are defined as having colic when they cry more than three hours a day for more than three days a week. By that definition it

> Jack was the perfect baby until he was four weeks of age. From then on he spent most of his waking hours crying, but he was much worse in the evening. Starting at about 3 o'clock in the afternoon all he wanted to do was feed and whenever the breast was not in his mouth, he would cry. This would go on for the rest of the evening till he fell into an exhausted sleep about 10 or 11 o'clock. He would then wake every two hours and want to feed again. The only thing we could do to settle him was feed and carry him. Leaving him alone was just not an option.

occurs in up to 20 per cent of babies. But similar crying to a lesser degree probably occurs in most babies.

It's certainly been part of parenting for hundreds of years. It was lucidly described in the first English paediatric textbook ever published, in 1544. In his *Boke of Chyldren*, Thomas Phaire describes babies with 'colycke and rumblynge in the guttes'. This problem is not new.

Most parents are familiar with the picture, as are many listeners to talkback radio, or readers of the correspondence columns of parenting magazines and websites. Everybody has an idea of what a colicky baby is like.

Starting at about four weeks of age, the baby has increasingly prolonged periods of agonised screaming, drawing up his knees, screwing up his face, and looking for all the world as if he has a terrible tummy ache. These bursts of crying wax and wane without apparent cause or pattern. In the throes of an episode the baby's movements are jerky and erratic, his stricken gaze darts about the room, his hands grasp the air, fists tight, and his screams cut the air like a knife.

The unsettledness usually starts to build up in late afternoon to be in full voice by early evening (hence why it's called 6 o'clock or evening colic). Occasionally after going to sleep the baby will wake up with a start and this can herald more hours of crying.

There's no doubt that my baby has wind. Especially in the evening she tenses up and screams, passes wind and then relaxes. She's been doing this for the last couple of weeks and it seems to be getting worse. About the same time she also started vomiting a lot when she feeds. You can hear the milk hitting her stomach and she often pulls off the breast and screams during a feed. She is often unsettled after a feed and will cry until she vomits and then settles down a bit. We tried burping a lot after a feed but it doesn't seem to make any difference. She also passes a lot of wind from the other end and it appears to make her very uncomfortable. Her poos are very soft but she strains and strains when she passes them, with her tummy tight as a drum. She is fully breastfed and I wonder whether it is something I am eating but I put myself on a very restrictive diet (no dairy, chocolate or coffee) and it really hasn't changed anything.

Very soon the whole focus of the family is centred upon trying to fix this problem. Dad finds that driving the baby around in the car can calm him down (but the baby still screams at the traffic lights), Mum finds that turning on the vacuum cleaner next to his cot seems to improve matters temporarily.

After a couple of weeks, with the family strung out and sleepless, the marriage looking shaky, the vacuum cleaner burned out and the car out of petrol, the parents cast around for help.

As mentioned, this is not always a good idea. The lady over the road says the baby has 'The Wind' and they're 'not burping him enough'. Talkback radio participants suggest everything from gripe water, massaging his stomach (in a clockwise direction) with warm olive oil (which he enjoys when he's calm but it makes him worse when he's screaming), right through to (and I kid you not) 'putting him face down on a rolling pin and ro-o-o-ll-ll-ing the wind through his tummy'. They're all trying desperately to help but none of this information does.

And the worst piece of advice: 'Just you let him cry it out!'

Eventually the parents find themselves in the consultation room of a professional. And here things don't necessarily improve. Now the medical diagnoses start. The baby has wind, reflux or lactose intolerance, or, very fashionable of late, cow's milk protein sensitivity.

As mentioned earlier, there is now no doubt that over 90 per cent of babies with excessive crying have no organic disease whatever. Even so, under pressure from the need to do something, most babies who see most professionals for this problem still leave the consultation with some kind of physical diagnosis.

Very often when these screaming babies and exhausted families were in crisis the baby would be admitted to a mothercraft hospital where skilled and experienced nurses would help mother and baby. Usually these babies would rapidly improve, without medicines or investigations, and within 48 hours most of them were calm, the parents were reassured and they would go home. And there things might deteriorate again. It was therefore wondered whether the work put into consoling the babies at home by the parents was in fact over-stimulating them; it was also observed that many of these parents, as the problem worsened, increasingly misinterpreted the baby's cries and consequently their responses became less and less effective.

Interestingly, this condition is also called three-month colic, because at three months the condition miraculously disappears in most babies. And, most tellingly, it is at three months old that most babies develop the ability to 'self-soothe'. That is, if they are being over-aroused by their environment (from too much visual input, for instance), they develop the ability to 'switch off', ignore the input and calm themselves.

So quite apart from the clinical experience, logic tells us that the colic syndrome is a mostly behavioural matter, not a physical one.

The way it works goes like this:

- As mentioned earlier, our babies emerge from the womb in an immature state. Within the womb they are cocooned in a warm, snug but, it must be said, visually boring, environment.

- Suddenly they emerge into the light of day. (Or more often the lights of the delivery suite at night!) From a quiet, meditative state they emerge to the screams and smiles of delighted parents, grandparents and assorted relatives all trying to see whether their personal genes are represented in the little newcomer. How babies cope with this transition depends, mostly, on their temperament.

Like most biological matters, the range of variability of babies' temperaments can be fitted into a bell-shaped (normal distribution) curve.

About 15 out of 100 babies are 'self-soothers'. These are wonderful babies who sleep when unattended, feed enthusiastically when their mother has the time, and generally are laid-back and calm. These babies get taken enthusiastically to mothers' groups, where their mothers can be a bit of a menace. It's hard not to brag about such an easy baby who is quiet and amenable – 'MY baby's sleeping through – isn't yours?'

At the other end of the scale there are 15 per cent of babies who are 'supersensitive'. These babies emerge from the womb and immediately react to their environment. Their eyes dart around, they frown a lot and find it hard to relax, and if they meet one other person besides Mum and Dad, they scream for the next several hours. You won't see this baby at any mothers' group: Mum can barely go shopping without inducing a crying jag.

Right from the start Elsie was a 'wired' baby. Her eyes were always darting around the room and her body would clench whenever she wasn't being held, her little face would screw up, and her hands were little fists. She would scream for hours if we let her. I thought I would go mad. Then my mother came round and she managed to settle her better than me, but Elsie's still hard to manage. I had no idea that having a baby was this hard.

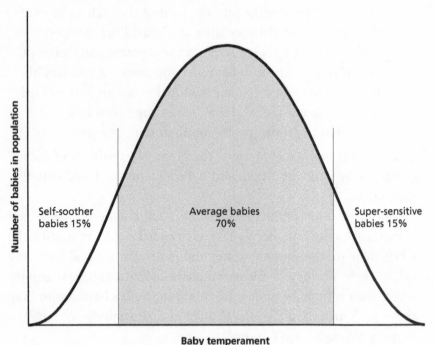

Most babies, however, lie within these two extremes. In the early weeks, they are usually upset about two days out of seven. But as their parents slowly tune in to their needs, they instinctively recognise that there is a limit to the amount of environmental stimulation that their baby can cope with. Early on, the baby is mostly interested only in his mother's breast, her warmth, milk and smell, and over the days and weeks the parents learn to maintain the household at a calm level that keeps their baby settled. After a few weeks these parents come to believe that perhaps they have a little 'self-soother' too. Time to go to the mothers' group and start bragging!

Bad idea. At about four or five weeks of age the baby develops the ability to look around and, perhaps for the first time, to take notice of things and people around him. This is about a week before he starts to smile. Once he starts to smile, of course, it's game on! Everybody from grandparents to total strangers jumps in, goochy-gooing and gazing at him intently, trying to get him to smile.

Suddenly the amount of visual stimulation in this baby's life increases rapidly and so his behaviour shifts to the supersensitive end. It is for this reason that 'colicky' crying peaks at around this age.

Premature babies have it earlier and more intensely. It was through the study of just this group of babies that developmental psychologists started to unravel the problem in the full-term infant. As premature babies approach term they can become very distressed when their environment presents them with even minimal increases in stimulation. If you pick up such a baby, look at him and talk to him, he will often start straining, crying and arching his back as his nervous system overloads with the increased input on his senses. With babies such as him, you can pick them up, or you can look at them, or you can speak to them. You just can't do all of this at once.

The full-term baby psyche is much more resilient than that. But this baby still has his limits. So, to explain, let's start at the end and work backwards.

THE SELF-SOOTHING BABY

At and beyond three months of age babies usually develop an increased ability to self-soothe, and calm themselves. You can see this at work in a four to five-month-old baby who is fed and happy and sitting in a little prop-up chair. He wants to play with his mother so he gazes at her across the room, chuckles and waves his arms to attract her. She can't resist and approaches him, their eyes lock and soon they are talking nonsense, looking deeply into each other's eyes and are totally engrossed in one another. As mentioned earlier in this book, this is the process of attunement that is so important to the baby's development. The intensity of their interaction rises between them as their responses create mutual amplification. The intensity then reaches a level that makes the baby uncomfortable and over-aroused. There is now just too much stress in the interaction for him. So suddenly he looks away, switches off and totally ignores his mother.

He looks at the ceiling or at his hands in his lap and his mother (being in tune with him) wanders off. The baby sits propped up in his chair, his shoulders tense, his eyes downcast. Then, over the next few minutes, he calms and relaxes and starts to throw glances at his mum.

His gazes last longer and longer in her direction as he relaxes more and more. Then the cycle starts again. He laughs and waves his hands to attract her and back she comes. And the dance continues like this, over and over again. Baby leading, mother following, attraction, rejection, attraction, rejection.

The baby has learned that when he gets over-aroused, stressed and uncomfortable, if he looks away and shuts it out, he can calm himself down. This is an invaluable lesson, the first element of a regulatory system that gives him control over the input from his environment. It is the start of the ability to concentrate undistracted on a task.

THE SIX-WEEK-OLD BABY

Now, back to the beginning. The colic syndrome starts at four to six weeks of age. Before this, the boundaries of his attention do not stray much beyond his mother's body, particularly breasts, and its warmth, taste and smell. But now his eyes can focus further and his horizons expand, and he starts to take in his surroundings. It is about a week before he smiles.

Once he starts smiling, so people around him respond. They gaze at him and he gazes back. He watches the curtains flapping by the window. Then Grandma visits and she can't take her eyes off him. With this new attention, his excitement rises to a level that makes him uncomfortable but, alas, he has not yet developed the ability to switch off the input and self-soothe. As the stimulation and stress levels rise he starts to get distressed.

He becomes tense and begins to strain and groan, especially late in the day. His parents become anxious: 'Is he constipated? Why does he writhe, double up and then arch his back?' Soon his distress level makes him cry and scream. He sounds like he's in pain. He is picked up and passed around the family who gaze at him, trying to fathom the cause of his discomfort. Then this wound-up, over-aroused baby is given to Grandma, who takes him around the back garden 'to show him the birds'. Or he is put into a baby carrier on his father's front, facing outwards, and taken to the shopping centre. And our overstimulated baby goes into orbit.

What can a baby do? Upset babies find sucking calms them down. Biochemists have found that babies secrete a calming opiate-like hormone into their circulation just by the act of sucking. So our baby starts to feed frequently, sucking, sucking, sucking in an effort to calm himself.

'Reflux'

Despite having a full stomach after a good feed, the sucking (and milk intake) continue. He's like a limpet; he won't leave the breast alone for hours at a time. This extra food, in combination with the straining, soon becomes a spectacular projectile vomit over the parent's shoulder. Panic ensues. He is driven urgently to the hospital, admitted and investigated with an ultrasound to exclude a condition called pyloric stenosis. Then he is given a barium meal, an oesophageal pH probe study, and treated with a number of medications that stop stomach acid production with the presumptive diagnosis of gastro-oesophageal reflux disease (GORD – more details on this and other related medical issues appear in the next chapter). And to add insult to injury he is also taken off the breast because 'the flow is too fast'. Then his mum gets mastitis. Poor Mum, poor baby.

Unfortunately, even if he's just unsettled and isn't vomiting, he's still diagnosed with 'silent' reflux. And given all the same medications.

Lactose intolerance

In addition, with his increased feeds he gets an increased intake of lactose (the sugar in milk). Lactose is absorbed in the baby's small bowel, but this has a limit to the amount it can cope with. With the vastly increased intake the absorptive ability of the small intestine is overloaded. The unabsorbed lactose then moves on and spills into the large intestine, which cannot absorb sugar. There bacteria ferment the sugar to form lactic and butyric acid and lots of hydrogen gas. So our baby develops a swollen tummy and 20 gassy explosive stools a day, and farts like a trooper. Medical professionals decide he has 'lactose intolerance' and consequently advise the breastfeeding is to be stopped and lactose-free formula started.

What a tragedy! He doesn't have 'lactose intolerance'; he has 'lactose spillage' from excessive feeding in an effort to calm himself down. Young babies can get lactose intolerance but it is excessively rare for them to be born with it. The usual cause is for the baby to catch an infection in their bowel from a gastro virus, such as rota-virus. This gastroenteritis infection can temporarily interfere with the bowel's ability to absorb lactose, so these babies can develop gassy diarrhoea. In the case of a breastfed baby, healthcare professionals generally allow them to continue to breastfeed (and the parents change their nappies a lot) until they recover. Only rarely is it necessary to stop the breastfeeding and put them on a lactose-free formula until the bowel lining recovers. Such recovery usually takes from a week to a month.

Burping and wind

As the unsettled baby lies in his cot he sucks his tongue or his fingers to comfort himself. And so he swallows air. Hence when the distressed baby is picked up, he burps . . .

'Ah, that's why he's crying – he needed to be burped!' cries his father.

Alas no! He's burping because he's crying, he's not crying because he needs burping.

The 'burping babies' story is a bit of a myth. The valve between the oesophagus (gullet) and the stomach is not very efficient. At times it can barely trap a feed, let alone trap an air bubble. We know from studies (see the one from Vandenplas and others) that this valve frequently relaxes and allows stomach contents to flow up into the oesophagus. That's why babies regurgitate frequently following a feed.

Can you imagine how you would feel if after a wonderful soothing meal, you're just dropping off to sleep and somebody comes up and starts pounding you between the shoulder blades?

So burping the baby after a nice feed . . . Don't bother: let him sleep.

That is not to say that babies don't like to lie on your chest and have their back gently patted at maternal heart rate after a feed. That's because the experience has a womblike feel, not because they need to bring up the 'magic bubble'.

Over-aroused baby

So now our 'colicky' baby is in full flight with episodes of screaming and unsettledness interspersed with a brittle calm. He reacts to anything in his life that changes. Recently I had a mother bring to me her baby who she swore had a urinary tract infection. 'He screams every time he wees,' she said. What became obvious during the consultation was he screamed any time *anything* happened to him. He was a cat on a hot tin roof. He passed urine, he screamed. He pooed, he screamed. Different action, same response.

It is for this reason that 'reflux' has been so fashionable over the last few years. Even the tiniest bit of gastric juice in a baby's throat will upset him if he is tense and brittle; the tiniest amount of stomach distension will cause wails of anguish, and naturally most parents think this is the cause of the problem, not realising that this issue is downstream from the main event.

And, of course, an upset baby is going to be more windy and refluxy than a calm baby. As mentioned, when babies are upset they suck to calm themselves and swallow air. If there is a breast available, they will suck and take another feed, even though they are already full. Also, when they get tense and scream, they tighten up their abdominal muscles, creating increased pressure inside the stomach, which jets the contents up into the throat and produces either projectile vomiting or 'just reflux'.

So in this way it is true: unsettled babies are often reflux babies but the reflux is the effect of the screaming, not the cause.

MEDICALISING NORMALITY

The phrase 'medicalising normality' has been used in medical literature to aptly describe what is happening here.

All the medical diagnoses inevitably flow from a series of vicious cycles, all downstream from the true cause of the baby's distress.

THE VICIOUS CYCLES OF COLIC

The colicky baby behaves as he does because he's caught in a set of vicious cycles.

1. He is tense and overstimulated and, reasonably, because he is upset gets over-handled.

2. The tension causes him to draw his knees up and scream, looking like he is in pain.

3. This increased handling and contact makes him even more overstimulated and aroused.

4. This makes him over-fatigued and irritable, which keeps the cycle going.

5. In an effort to help himself, he initiates cycles of overfeeding.

6. This causes more handling and stimulation.

7. The overfeeding also causes reflux vomiting.

8. The increased intake of milk presents more undigested lactose to his large bowel, which causes lactose spillage into his stool.

It is these downstream, secondary physical symptoms that occupy the attention of his carers, and it is often hard to see the primary cause of them all.

The upper part of this chart shows the vicious cycles your baby can get into when the 'colic syndrome' starts. The lower part with dotted lines shows the results and wrong diagnoses made. The over-aroused and stressed baby cries excessively so handling increases, which stimulates the baby even more, and around we go!

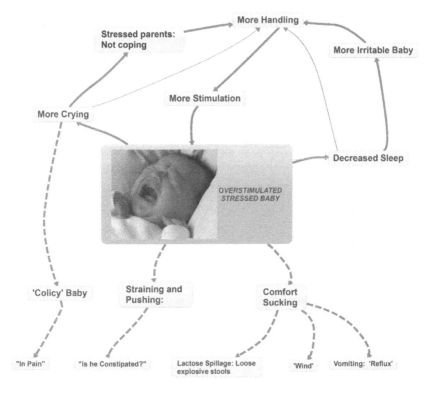

Colic's vicious cycles

Christmas colic

There is a condition I call 'Christmas colic' when babies demonstrate the above symptoms in spades. Too many relatives, too many parties and too much excitement lead to lots of screaming babies in emergency departments of children's hospitals in late December.

Fixing the problem

So how do we fix the problem? It is simple in principle and tough in practice. We have to reduce the stimulation in the baby's environment to a level he can cope with, and do it for long enough to reduce his active stress response. We can't just switch this off like a tap. We have to do it slowly by calming him a little; then he will sleep, and the more he sleeps the less stressed he becomes and the *more* he sleeps. Day by day the baby will improve, as long as he has nothing to arouse him and stop him reducing his level of stress. After a few days he will be more sleepy, with a low level of stress hormone in his circulation and an increased ability to deal with his day-to-day life.

But to achieve this we have to 'bore him to sleep'.

Calming the Baby regime

- Send overly attentive grandparents home (unless they can help you handle the baby calmly). If you have a toddler, send him with them.
- Stick a note on the front door saying that you are out.
- Go into the baby's room, draw the blinds and dim the light in the room. Put on some quiet, restful music; that's for you, but babies do like a background of 'family sounds' and gentle rhythms rather than silence.
- Get the baby and take him into the room with you. Do NOT leave him on his own when he is distressed.
- Feed him on demand in the dim light, *avoiding long periods of eye contact with him.* (But of course you can look at him!)
- Put him on your chest with his ear against your heartbeat and cuddle him until he settles. This reminds him of the sounds and feel of the womb. It may take some time. Be patient. Calm him.
- Then wrap him firmly in a sheet or swaddler, with his back rounded and his limbs contained – this will also remind him of the containment of the womb and help him feel secure. He may want to have his arms free, but it is preferable to flex them over his chest, just like in the womb.
- Place him in his cot. Pat him gently on the bottom at about 70 pats to the minute (mother's heart rate) and just . . .

- BORE HIM TO SLEEP.
- If it helps, give him a dummy.
- If he gets upset (and he will), rewrap him and continue cuddling, patting or feeding. If you're both going crazy, pick him up and get someone else to cuddle him, while you take a break. Cuddle him, then put him in the cot and pat him again.
- Continue this (hour after hour) until he settles. Do not leave the baby to cry, but you can leave the room when he finally sleeps.

Generally the first 24 hours can be hell on wheels, but if you persevere, things will improve. He will eventually start to, as the psychologists say, 'return to base'.

By the second day he will be calmer but do not take him out of the room, even though he appears improved. Give it another day to be sure he loses some of his fatigue and stress.

The more he sleeps, the less opportunity there is for him to be stimulated, and the more he will sleep and the calmer he will become. This is a good cycle, not a vicious one. When he's calm and sleepy, you can return him to the living room.

You then need to keep the activity and stimulation in his environment down to a level that he can handle.

But now watch him very carefully. It is time to attune to him all over again – particularly working out what his signs of over-arousal are. If his movements start to become jerky, his eyes start to dart around or he starts to frown, it may be time to put him back into his darkened room and allow him to become calm again.

Don't worry about 'sensory deprivation'. We only have to continue this regime on and off until he is about three months of age. At that age he will develop his own ability to regulate the input from his environment and cope with people around him. The most important lesson for a baby at this age is to learn how to calm themselves. Later that will stand him in good stead when he needs to learn to concentrate on the job at hand.

How much stimulation your baby can cope with, how quickly he responds to the treatment and whether the problem recurs depends on his basic temperament and the activity in your environment. All families are different, as are babies. Most babies have a threshold or limit and you need to find out where it is for your baby, and keep the level of stimulation under that. Some babies can barely leave the confines of their darkened room for the first three months of their life.

It is also important to remember that even when the overstimulated crying has diminished, the 'inconsolable' crying may still occur. If it does, just be there for your baby, cuddling and soothing, but don't take the crying personally. That's just what babies do. And remember, time cures all things – but especially this.

EMMA'S STORY

My name is Emma, I'm from England and have a nine-week-old little boy. He was born two weeks early. I was completely paranoid that I had caused him to be a 'stressed baby' as within a couple of weeks of being born, he was screaming . . . a lot!

Christmas came, with a trip to the in-laws'. To put it gently, it was intense . . . lots of noise, lots of people, and quite noisy people at that. The poor lad was beside himself and I was stressed out too as people thought they could comfort him when all he wanted was feeding or to be with the two people he recognised. So within another week he was in full-on meltdown (what I now understand to be a good case of what you call 'Christmas colic'). The health visitor told us it was colic, as did most people we knew and we even succumbed and bought Infacol [medication for wind].

We then used your technique of 'boring our baby to sleep' and it worked . . . on day one! To be honest I think we both needed it, as I have felt much more relaxed since then too. We patted his bottom when he was crying, kept everything quiet, and he was a different baby on the Monday (we did it over a weekend).

We have since made sure he is not overstimulated. It turns out he is one of life's more sensitive babies, although he is toughening up a bit and likes being held by other people. (He's still not keen on the in-laws, though.)

CHAPTER 13

The unsettled baby, Part II: the medicine

AS UNSETTLEDNESS IN BABIES IS SO common – it is indeed an unusual baby who goes through his early life without having a crying jag at some point – it is very hard to estimate how often the unsettledness is caused by organic disease. The published level of approximately 10 per cent is about right.

The difficulty is knowing which 10 per cent, especially as babies who are screaming, arching and drawing up their knees give a very good imitation of being in excruciating abdominal pain. Health-care staff can be as susceptible as the parents to such misleading signs and overdiagnosis of diseases happens frequently.

Let us examine the common ones and try to shine the light of evidence-based medicine on them.

> Danielle bustled into my office and was talking to me even before she sat down.
>
> 'Hi, Doctor, I'm afraid Sebastian has got the acid reflux!'
>
> I greeted her before consulting my notes. 'Ah, little Sebastian, how old is he now?' I wondered.

'He'll be six weeks on Thursday,' said his mother.

'So how do you know he has reflux?' I replied.

'Well,' she took a deep breath, 'it started about a week ago. After a few minutes on the breast he started pulling off and arching his back like there was something the matter with the milk. You can hear his stomach churning. He keeps swallowing and swallowing as it refluxes back into his throat and he has also been really irritable and unsettled since then. We can't lie him down, we can't change his nappy; he seems to be only comfortable when he's sitting up.'

'Does he vomit?' I asked.

'He doesn't vomit a lot but he usually does a little bit after each feed, just a dribble from the corner of his mouth. When he does you can see he doesn't like the taste and he screams and screams!'

'How is his weight doing? I asked. 'He looks pretty chubby!'

'Oh, that's doing well,' she said. 'He put on 320 g last week.'

GASTRO-OESOPHAGEAL REFLUX DISEASE (GORD)

With a conversation starter like that it's going to be a hard job to challenge the diagnosis. This boy has been decisively diagnosed by the friends in Danielle's mothers' group. Now, it is certainly possible that the baby may have gastro-oesophageal reflux disease (GORD), but it is certainly not self-evident based on Sebastian's group of symptoms.

GORD was an unusual diagnosis in babies before the early 1980s. If you were irritable and crying before that, you had 'colic' and if you vomited a lot, you were labelled as 'refluxy' – even if you did both, nobody got too excited. Then, a couple of events conspired to change the landscape. First, influenced by a local gastroenterologist, a group of mothers in Queensland who had irritable, vomiting babies formed the 'Vomiting Infant Support Association' or VISA and put out a regular newsletter for similarly affected families. Paediatric gastroenterologists also fanned the flames. A paper was published by such a group in 1983, which linked oesophagitis (when acid refluxes up from the stomach and burns the bottom of the gullet, causing inflammation) and persistent crying. The reported study noted that most of the babies who had oesophagitis visible when examined with an endoscope also had excessive crying and sleep disturbance. It also noted that they tended towards failure to thrive (that is, didn't put on enough weight) and frequently vomited blood.

From then on everyone with an irritable baby who puked came to the party. It was reasoned that if your baby had persistent crying even without vomiting, they probably also had oesophagitis. Unfortunately that was reverse logic.

There are many reasons to have persistent crying and unsettledness, and between 40 and 70 per cent of babies posset their feeds normally; that is, have a daily small (or large) vomit. In fact if you study babies by putting a soft probe down into their oesophagus just above the entrance to the stomach, you find that nearly all babies reflux acid up into the oesophagus, and most of them are doing it nearly once an hour! But only a tiny percentage of such babies would have an inflamed oesophagus. This was frequently pointed out at the time, but by then it was too late.

From then on, if your baby was unsettled, even if he didn't vomit, there was a good chance he would be diagnosed with reflux and be given the medicines to treat it, usually antacids or drugs to prevent the production of stomach acid.

For the next two decades the frequency of the diagnosis grew in epidemic proportions. By 2005 in the United States, prescriptions worth over $13 billion were written for such drugs. This was despite a number of careful studies and commentaries from experts like Heine and Orenstein that showed that the treatment made no difference to the babies, and the amount of reflux (that is, the measured amount of acid in the oesophagus) bore no relationship to either crying duration or general irritability in babies. Not only that, it was found that in babies under three months of age, so-called silent reflux causing crying and irritability without vomiting did not occur in normal full-term babies, and occurred only occasionally in the ex-premature or babies with neurological problems.

In addition, information has started to accumulate that the drugs that stop the production of acid in the stomach (so-called H_2 antagonists and Proton Pump inhibitors – PPI) may not be completely harmless. It may be helpful to have acid in the stomach to prevent infections in the gut and decrease the incidence of food allergies.

So where does that leave us?

The truth is that most babies vomit and all babies reflux. This is a normal physiological phenomenon and should be treated as such. That is, not with medications.

GORD does occur in babies, but these babies are often ex-premature or have other medical issues. Of the full-term babies who have it, they are not just irritable and vomiting – they also tend to:

- have poor weight gain and are failing to thrive
- vomit persistently (as in, all the time)
- have feeding difficulty or refuse to eat and
- have blood in the vomit.

So this is not a healthy, chubby baby who doesn't sleep, who cries a lot, especially in the evening, and who pulls occasionally off the breast during a feed. Babies with reflux disease are quite unwell.

Many mothers will attest that their healthy but unsettled baby improved after medical treatment (ranitidine or omeprazole, or other PPI) was started. It is worth noting, however, that with crying babies the placebo effect for any medicine is around 28–50 per cent, no matter what.

So look for other diagnoses for the symptoms before jumping to the assumption that he's got reflux disease!

The infant who vomits

The 'reflux' that most commonly causes mothers to bring a baby to a doctor is not irritability or crying, it's just vomiting.

As mentioned, the valve between the oesophagus (gullet) and the stomach is not very efficient in most babies. Many will posset or regurgitate a little after a feed. These minor spillages are a daily issue for most mothers, which is why they tend not to wear their favourite shirt when they feed their infant.

If the volume of vomit starts to get excessive and it's not just the mess but concern that the baby is not putting on enough weight, then medical help is usually sought. There are several things that can help:

1. It may be that the mother has excessive milk volume from her breasts. A visit with a lactation consultant can help by gradually bringing down her milk supply to meet her baby's needs. Breasts produce a factor whose function it is to suppress milk supply. They're designed that way so that if there is excessive production, the baby will leave some in the breasts at each feed and this residual milk factor will reduce the production. Also, for mothers with a vigorous, high-volume letdown response at the start of the feed, expressing a small amount at that time can reduce this.

2. Sitting the baby in a more upright position will help the stomach retain the milk. Even tilting their cot up as much as 30 degrees can help to some extent, but be careful the baby doesn't end up in a heap at the bottom of the cot. He might even need to be in a body sling suspended from the top of the cot to maintain this posture.

3. Trying smaller feeds, more often, is a suggestion, but babies feed when they want to and a demand schedule is probably the easiest and most efficient. Trying to put a schedule in place sounds great in theory, but it's hard for the mother and baby to maintain.

4. It is reasonable to try a short trial of treatment (ranitidine or omeprazole) for a week or so. But this should be stopped if there's no visible improvement in that time.

5. The mother could try a short period of giving up dairy in all its forms (see the following section). It might actually make them feel better too, as an added bonus.

6. If the baby is formula fed, a thickener can be added to the feed or an anti-reflux formula tried.

7. If the baby is older and wants to sit up all the time, he tends to do little abdominal crunches (contracting his stomach muscles to try to sit). This tends to induce vomiting too, by squeezing the stomach. Try some 'tummy time' by putting him on his front. This puts the oesophagus at a higher level than the rest of the stomach (which makes it harder to vomit the contents) and also may decrease the contractions of his stomach muscles.

But time will sort it out eventually! If you get sick of smelling like sour milk and having all your clothes ruined, take heart. Many babies improve at about four months of age when the valve appears to improve its function. And if they miss this bus, there is another one along at eight months, perhaps because they also spend more time sitting up by then. And there are only a few babies still puking at 12 months.

Cow's milk protein allergy (CMPA)

There is no doubt that of late, with all the studies and science now being understood, the frequency of the diagnosis of 'acid reflux' in babies is on the wane. What a pity it's just being replaced with a cow's milk protein allergy diagnosis instead.

It is true that somewhere between 3 and 7 per cent of babies are sensitive to the protein in cow's milk. Whether a baby reacts to this protein or not depends on two factors:

*   whether she is genetically 'atopic'; that is, she has a tendency towards allergy because there are a lot of allergies in the family.
*   the dose of cow's milk protein presented to her. Some babies react to a few molecules, and others need over 100 ml.

There is no doubt that some babies react to this protein and when they do, it can make them irritable, vomity and generally upset, and even give them a livid rash on their face. If they are affected severely they may not put on weight, and can develop severe diarrhoea and even have respiratory difficulties, such as wheezing. Rarely, older children may even develop anaphylactic shock and need to be admitted to hospital.

However, the number of babies who are affected severely is really very small. As mentioned, they tend to come from families that are very atopic, and these babies are usually not breastfed but are on formula, which of course is usually based on cow's milk.

It's unfortunate that often breastmilk contains some cow's milk protein, albeit at a very low concentration (actually about 100,000 times less than in cow's milk itself). Breastfed babies tend not to develop CMPA because of this minuscule amount in their milk. Their incidence is around half a per cent of babies, and when they are affected it is usually only mildly.

Symptoms of CMPA

Mild to moderate:

- Vomiting and regurgitation
- Diarrhoea
- Blood in stool
- Rash around anus
- Eczema rash.

Severe:

- Vomiting and diarrhoea, causing:
  - no weight gain and failure to thrive
- Blood from bowel in stool in amounts causing:
  - iron deficiency anaemia
  - severe eczema rash on face and body.

As mentioned, the latter group are almost invariably formula fed. So for this severe group it is essential to stop giving any form of cow's milk to the baby by using an amino-acid-based formula and get specialist help from a gastroenterologist.

For the milder group it is a little awkward, in that there is no specific diagnostic test to firm up the diagnosis in these babies. Skin tests looking for CMPA may or may not be positive and either way, there is still uncertainty. Also there is no exclusive symptom. All of the above mild symptoms can occur in babies with GORD, 'colic' for other reasons, or those who are completely normal.

The only way to check it (and treat it at the same time) is with an elimination diet; that is, eat nothing containing cow's milk protein (dairy products). As mentioned, it is likely when you do that your body will thank you for it and you will feel better day by day, so give it a go anyway!

Breastfed babies: The mother should cease all dairy products for at least two weeks. This means checking the packets of all foods, as milk proteins are often added surreptitiously to otherwise harmless foods. If this helps the baby, the mother should then reintroduce dairy to her diet and see whether the baby reacts. If he does, he is likely to have CMPA.

Formula-fed babies: Normal cow's milk formulas should be stopped and a 'partially hydrolysed' formula started instead. These formulas have had the cow's milk protein denatured (the molecules broken down) so the dosage to the baby is much less. If the baby still reacts to the tiny bit left, then an amino acid formula should be tried. Trying soy-based formulas on these babies can be unhelpful as a fairly high proportion of babies (over one-quarter) who react to cow's milk also react to soy protein.

Down the track, happily most of the babies who react to cow's milk protein grow out of it, often in their second year. Some of them, unfortunately, also have other allergies, such as eggs or peanuts, and these allergies take much longer to shake off.

Lactose intolerance

Another diagnosis thrown at babies who are crying, irritable, and have rumbly tummies and loose stools is lactose intolerance.

Lactose is the main sugar in mammalian milks and forms nearly 100 per cent of the carbohydrate in it. Consequently the chance of your baby being born with lactose intolerance is incredibly rare as, in the wild, he would surely die. The very rare babies who have this genetic anomaly are usually from either Russia or Finland.

Babies can develop lactose intolerance and this is usually as a consequence of a viral infection of their bowel (gastroenteritis), normally caused by rotavirus. When this occurs you will know your baby is unwell. His stools will start to become 'urine-like' (clear water, different from the milky, opaque stools of the exclusively breastfed baby). He will also be unwell and upset and generally 'not himself'. Following such a bout, the baby's bowel may be affected and it cannot absorb as much lactose as before. So his watery and copious stools continue.

If such a baby is formula fed it is logical to withdraw the lactose, and appropriate lactose-free formulas are easily available.

If he is breastfed, however, generally it is advisable that the breastfeeding continues (even though it contains lactose). Interrupting the process is often difficult for a mother, as in order to maintain her milk supply, she needs to express her breastmilk and freeze it for later, while her baby is given lactose-free formula. It is worth trying to continue while the parents battle through, changing lots of nappies until the baby recovers spontaneously, usually within a couple of weeks. Only occasionally does the baby need to stop having lactose completely.

Most babies who are accused of lactose intolerance have, of course, no such thing.

The lactose in the milk is absorbed in the small bowel by a special mechanism utilising the enzyme lactase, and there is a limit to this mechanism. Some mothers with excellent milk supply can feed their babies with more lactose than they can absorb. This excess lactose then passes through the small bowel (which has no germs in it) and enters the large bowel (which does). There it is fermented by these bowel germs to produce hydrogen gas, acid stools and lots of fluid. Some babies, who are completely normal, may pass 20 liquid stools a day when breastfed but they have lactose 'spillage', not intolerance.

The confusion starts especially for a baby who is feeding moderately, absorbing all the lactose, and producing 'peanut butter' or 'pesto'-like stools for a few weeks. Then if he begins to get upset (for whatever reason) often he will start to feed more vigorously and more frequently because the act of sucking calms the baby as it helps him secrete calming neurohormones.

As mentioned earlier in the colic section, as his milk intake increases, he starts to reach his maximum lactose capacity. Suddenly this upset baby's stools become loose, gassy and copious. Alas, the loose stools are thought to be the *cause* of his upset. He is then accused of lactose intolerance and taken off the breast and put on a lactose-free formula . . . What a disaster!

It is most unusual for an otherwise healthy baby to develop lactose intolerance. Such a baby needs calming, so he feeds less often. Then his stools will become normal again.

Wind

While we're on the subject of gassy, explosive stools we should probably talk briefly about 'wind'.

It's a rare mother who gets through her first week of postnatal life without having her baby accused of having wind whenever he gets upset. It has been the default diagnosis for all miserable babies for decades, and despite science and common sense, it is likely to continue into the future.

All babies are windy. They are swallowing air all the time, especially when they are upset. At the bottom end, babies, it has to be said, fart like troopers. As mentioned above, their diet is full of lactose, which produces litres of hydrogen gas when it enters the large bowel. In addition the bowel is filled with swallowed air.

Over the page is an X-ray of a normal baby's abdomen. The darker loops show all the gas in the bowel.

As you can see, the intestine is full of gas, both swallowed air and hydrogen from the feeds. The contented baby that chortles, burps and farts in his cot is generally a source of amusement for the family. However, let that baby get upset and suddenly it is a potent source of anxiety. It is true that upset babies are actually more windy than the calm ones. As mentioned above, that is because they try to calm themselves by sucking – on fingers, dummies or

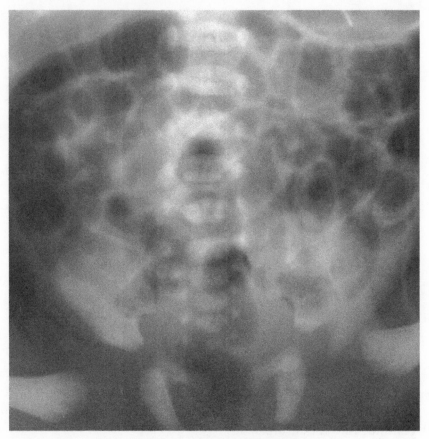

X-ray of normal baby's abdomen
(Note: bone is white, air/gas is dark)

mothers, and swallow more air and feed more. But I repeat, the wind is caused by, not the cause of, being upset.

Following a blissful, soothing feed, the act of 'burping' the baby – that is, 20 minutes of ritualised back-pounding – is more likely to produce crying than burping.

You might even be recommended medicines to 'bring up the wind'. These, like 'gripe water' or ones containing simethicone, have been extensively tested and not surprisingly they have been shown to be no better than placebo (i.e. water with nothing in it). Sad but true. Don't waste your money.

CHAPTER 14

Quiet nights

BEFORE BABIES ENTER OUR LIVES, MOST of us take a good night's sleep for granted. But, like with oxygen, it is only when we're short of sleep that we realise how precious it is.

With it, parents can think straight. They're able to relax, enjoy and observe their baby enough to learn his cues in order to anticipate and meet his needs. They can develop confidence in their caring ability, and an easy attachment to their baby.

With a baby who sleeps poorly, however, life gets tough. With fatigue overwhelming their confidence, the parents start to question their caring skills, or whether their baby is normal or is exploiting them. They question whether their own needs are unreasonable. Small issues become big problems. Often the relationship between partners starts to suffer and the potential for depression, especially in the mother, grows.

And with a sleepless baby, an avalanche of intrusive advice can engulf the mother. They are told to fix it now or the child will never learn to sleep; that they are spoiling him and he will end up a brat; or if he doesn't sleep, he won't grow properly. But the harder they try, and the more intense their need for a solution, the worse it gets.

Read on and don't weep. There is always a solution. But first, some facts.

SLEEP FACTS

For babies, sleep is the brain's main activity and they spend an average of 15 hours a day (with a range of nine to 19 hours) asleep. Even beyond toddlerhood children sleep about half of the time.

Sleep appears to be an essential function of the brain, which needs time out to process the events of the day and recover from the intense input it receives during our waking hours. Sleep is actually quite a complex neurological function involving many areas of the brain.

Let us look at its basic structure to give us an understanding of what we should expect from our baby.

LEVELS OF SLEEP

When sleeping, babies cycle through different levels of the sleep state about every 50 minutes. As we get older, the cycles become longer until by adulthood they are about 100 minutes long.

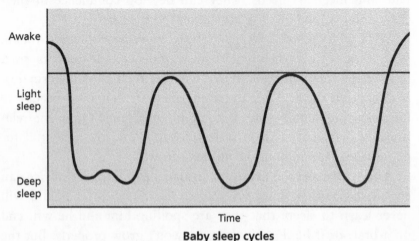

Baby sleep cycles

As you can see we are not 'fast asleep' most of the time, but have brief arousals followed by a rapid return to quieter levels.

Light sleep

Babies really have just two types of sleep state, active and quiet. Fifty per cent of the time babies are in active or light sleep. Babies drop into this level when first falling asleep (as they get a little older they will drop into deeper sleep right from the start). It is because this first sleep for them is so shallow that they may need help to maintain it by being held or rocked until their sleep is deeper. If you put a young baby down straightaway after they fall asleep, it is likely they will arouse from this shallow state and need more settling. It might take 30 minutes before they settle into a deep, more reliable, sleep state.

In this light state they move, grimace, have rapid eye movements from side to side that you can see under the lids, have irregular respiration, and may make little sounds, such as grunts and whimpers. During this type of sleep the brain is busy making connections between its millions of neurons, wiring it up and preparing it for future functioning. As babies mature, this becomes true rapid eye movement (REM) sleep that you and I associate with dreaming. Later on, it is during REM sleep that the experiences of the day are processed and memories are consolidated.

Deep sleep

Babies spend the rest of the time in quiet or deep sleep (slow wave sleep) and sometimes in shallower (but still non-REM) states. In quiet sleep they lie very still, their breathing is slow and regular and they have no eye movements. As they are in deep sleep they are hard to wake. It is deep sleep that is restorative and it is during this phase the hormone that regulates our growth is released from our brain. Hence the idea that 'if you don't sleep, you don't grow', which is not strictly true unless it is extreme.

DEVELOPMENT OF SLEEP STATES

As babies get older, their sleep states mature. From late infancy, they fall asleep into a non-REM sleep (that is, they sleep soundly right from the switch-off). This state can last for a few hours before cycling into the lighter levels. Also, the percentage of REM sleep increases and the amount of deep sleep decreases. It is for this reason that often infants will sleep well for a few hours early on in the night, before waking frequently later on.

Over the first six months, the non-REM sleep divides into three distinct stages.

Level 1: On falling asleep a state of drowsiness is entered, where awareness diminishes, and brief muscle jerks (hypnagogic startles) may also develop. (This is the equivalent of the feeling of falling, or the 'jump' that can accompany the process of falling asleep when you are older.)

Level 2: Going deeper, true sleep is entered and the brain's electrical waves show a distinct and characteristic pattern of alternating fast and slow waves.

Level 3: The sleep level bottoms out in deep sleep, shown by long, slow waves.

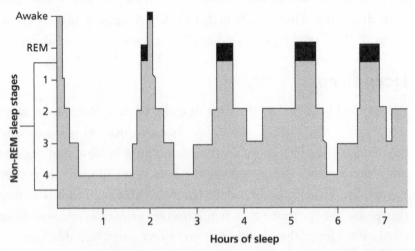

A typical child's sleep pattern as shown on 'hypnogram'

MATURING SLEEP PATTERNS

In the first few weeks very young babies tend to sleep and wake regularly throughout the day and night. As the weeks roll on, however, they do establish a day/night or diurnal pattern (some within two weeks – lucky parents!), and this can be encouraged by having the early morning feed in a bright, sunny room. The light on the retina of the eye communicates to the brain, telling it, 'Hi! This is morning,' and resets the body clock (and this drives the diurnal hormone rhythms).

After three months the baby starts to consolidate sleeping into longer periods at night and more wakefulness during the day and their brain starts to produce melatonin (the hormone of sleeping). Interestingly, breastfeeding mothers produce a higher level of the amino acid tryptophan, which is a building block for melatonin, in their breastmilk towards the evening, so breast-feeding babies ought to have a sleep advantage over formula fed. This effect is somewhat offset by the fact that breastmilk tends to leave the stomach faster than the chunky curds of formula, so breastfed babies often need feeding more frequently. However, they tend not to be so constantly hungry at this age anyway and most of the feeding tends to take place during the day, with the first feed of the day being the largest, to catch up after fewer night feeds.

Video observation of babies and infants at night shows that during their episodes of light sleep (as mentioned, every 50 minutes or so in the newborn), they arouse, whinge, move their limbs, and even open their eyes and scan the room, before slipping back into deeper sleep. These arousals continue (but less frequently) as they get older. It is important that these episodes are not misinterpreted as awakening, and the infant is not disturbed.

DO NOT DISTURB
Don't mistake brief whinging arousals from sleep for true awakening.

As you can see from the sleep cycle illustration, every 40–50 minutes the baby arouses to a light level of sleep. He may even wake at that time. It is a mistake to jump in and help him settle every time he stirs. First see if he will sooth himself for a few minutes before helping him with patting, soothing words or even a feed.

As they mature in these early months, so the ability of the infant to self-soothe and resettle herself after arousing improves. Although this settling ability is in-born, there is no doubt that there is also a learned element to it and babies can get into a good pattern with gentle help from their parents.

LENGTH OF SLEEP/NAP TIMES WITH AGE

As you can see, as the infant grows, the total hours of sleep diminish, as do the number and length of nap times.

Age	Daytime sleep		Night-time sleep	Total sleep
Newborn		(5 naps)	Too variable	16 hrs
One month		(4 naps)	Too variable	14 hrs +/– 1½
Three months	4½ hrs	(3–4 naps)	8 hrs +	13hrs +/– 1
Six months	3 hrs	(2 naps)	9½	12½ hrs +/– 1
Nine months	2¾ hrs	(2 naps)	9½	12¼ hrs +/– 1
12 months	1½–2½ hrs	(1–2 naps)	9½	11½ hrs +/– ¾
18 months	2 hrs	(1 nap)	9½	11½ hrs +/– ¾
2 years	1¾ hrs	(1 nap)	9½	11½ hrs +/– ½

INFANT SLEEP DISTURBANCE

In the early 1990s, 14,000 families in the United Kingdom were interviewed and studied in the Avon Longitudinal Study of Parents and Children. The results were as follows:

- Six to 12 months – 25–60 per cent had 'sleep disturbance'
- One year – 50 per cent had 'trouble settling' or 'night waking'
- Toddlers – 25–30 per cent had 'stalling and resistance' at bedtime.

A national survey in the United States found that 74 per cent of parents of four to nine-month-old infants reported discussing night waking and fussing with paediatricians.

Things are not much different in Australia. A recent large internet survey of parents done by Arthur Teng and others showed that about 30 per cent of them thought their child had a sleep problem.

You are not alone!

The cost of these disrupted nights in the older children was noteworthy. These children tended to have poor daytime behaviour with disruption of their attention span and their ability to learn. It has even been found that the sleepless babies tend towards obesity later on. There was family stress, with the mother's well-being in particular being affected – as she was characteristically the one who had to deal with the long, noisy nights.

DEALING WITH SLEEP/ UNSETTLEDNESS ISSUES

How these problems are dealt with varies with the age of the infant. Not only that, even within each group one size does not, and will not, fit all. What will work for one baby will make another baby worse. What one parent can cope with would drive another parent mad.

Different parents – different abilities to cope

One size does not fit all.

Many studies have shown the wide range of tolerance parents have for the wakeful, crying baby. Some parents have just been misled into thinking that babies sleep rather like they do, and become concerned when they find that their baby wakes frequently during the night. It's tough but true that babies are just not designed to sleep for long periods and they also need to be close to their parents for much of the time. As has been discussed elsewhere in this book, human babies are relatively immature and need frequent feeds and constant security. It is an unusual baby who sleeps 'well' and expecting it leads only to disappointment. Margot Sunderland, a prominent infant psychologist, put it succinctly when she said, 'Babies are awful sleepers.'

Unfortunately, the parents who are lucky enough to have the unusual good sleeper often cannot resist the temptation to brag about it. 'My baby's sleeping through the night, isn't yours?' has to be one of the more useless remarks in parenthood. The listeners then assume that it is their inability to deal properly with their babies that have led to sleep becoming an issue in their home. Keep firmly in mind that the sleepy, quiet babies are not average – their parents are merely lucky.

Don't forget also that we are natural bed-sharers. Babies were designed to have a protective body close to them in bed, and this is the strong preference for most babies. (See Chapter 15 for information about co-bedding and bed-sharing.)

Our ability as parents to cope with a wakeful baby depends on many factors, and they feed into whether or not we have a shorter or longer fuse when dealing with the noisy nights.

Tiredness can get us into a vicious cycle that decreases our ability to deal with anything stressful. One thing I learned as a junior doctor was that you absolutely cannot think straight, especially about emotional issues, when you are tired. There is no solution other than to sleep, so one of the most useful tools for dealing with a poorly sleeping baby is getting someone, a friend, relation or (if you can afford it) paid help, to regularly mind the baby to allow you to get some catch-up shut-eye. This is not a luxury. This is essential.

Our own childhoods leave us with a legacy of lessons, instilling beliefs about what is 'normal' for a baby, and giving us the tools we use to deal with variations of this. Remember also that even in the recent past leaving a baby to cry so they could 'learn to sleep' was very prevalent. Not to do so was considered to produce a baby who was clingy and overly dependent. Later experience and research showed that that was completely the opposite. Such babies tended to have had more 'hands off' and distant, routine-based parenting. The technique of leaving them to cry created a situation where they learned that life was uncertain and insecure (which made them clingy and dependent), and these beliefs were often carried into adulthood.

In addition memories of past hurts and disappointments fuel their unconscious (and conscious) feelings about themselves and reflect on their abilities to cope when things go wrong. These often negative feelings can emerge especially when people get stressed and tired.

Some people have a rather rigid view about their personal performance in life. They have to-do lists and feel uncomfortable if the house isn't spotless and the baby clean, fed and asleep. This attitude can be seriously unhelpful if the baby is needy and erratic. It reminds me of the bus conductor who worked hard his whole life, hoping that one day everybody would be where they wanted to be, and his bus would be empty. Needless to say, he retired disappointed!

The people who survive a wakeful baby are those who tend to go with the flow and accept that life can get a little chaotic temporarily. They recognise that babies are not young for very long and tomorrow is not necessarily going to be the same or worse than today. It might even be better. They deal with the situation as it is, and don't fantasise about the way they would prefer it to be.

So, sure, not everybody can sleep when the baby sleeps, but parents should aim for that level of pragmatism in their lives with the new baby. It's worth a try.

BABY TEMPERAMENT

As mentioned earlier, right from the start babies are born with differing temperaments. Whether the variations are due to the intrauterine environment or are just genetic is debatable. It's probably a combination of both.

At one end of the spectrum is the 'self-soother' who is relatively easy to manage and can move smoothly from one state of consciousness to another, giving the parents time to anticipate his needs before his demands become too intense.

At the other end is the 'supersensitive' or so-called high-needs baby. He always seems to be on an emotional knife edge. These babies need very intensive and specific handling. They are often very aware of the emotional tone of their environment. Parents need to always be as calm and supportive as possible by giving lots of both physical and emotional reassurance with copious cuddles and close secure contact. These babies are also very sensitive to overstimulation and become over-aroused in the presence of too many people, too much activity or emotions that are too intense.

Most babies lie somewhere between these two extremes; however, on occasion, and through development, they can move from one end of the spectrum to the other.

Clearly your baby's temperament will determine how well they sleep in the early days and the ways you can negotiate with them for a different pattern.

As the months roll on, so many other factors, aside from their inherent personality, can impinge on their sleep pattern.

Minor illnesses, the presence of visitors, a change in environment, over-tiredness or even a developmental step can totally change what was a tolerable sleep pattern. Such changes occur frequently and are as variable as the weather.

It is an important lesson for all parents. When a change in the sleep pattern occurs in your infant, don't panic. Do not assume that the change is permanent, or that the sleep pattern will deteriorate still further. It is just as likely to return to its previous stability in a few nights.

A really powerful way to prolong it, however, is to react and try to 'fix' it. A better strategy is to wait and see and make no changes. I can't tell you how often I am messaged or phoned by a frantic parent whose baby has gone from sleeping through to waking every hour, and by the time I reply (and I sometimes give such messages 48 hours or so before replying), the problem has resolved itself.

BIRTH TO THREE MONTHS

There is, however, a world of difference between the newborn (under three months) and older infants. At this age the problems are not so much 'sleep' problems but that of general crying and fussiness.

In the first weeks babies' sleep patterns are mostly dictated by their stomachs. When they're hungry they wake; when they are satisfied, they sleep.

They can fall asleep in fairly noisy environments but they also have frequent arousals and can wake often. That's just the way they are. Babies were never designed to sleep for extended periods of time, especially on their own. As a species we are of the continuous-contact variety, with our immature babies designed to be in close contact with their mother, their source of warmth, love, security and food, for much of the time. Settling problems with babies at this stage (and older infants to a smaller degree) are a product of our culture. We no longer tend to bed-share and we encourage independence in our babies, even at an age when it is biologically inappropriate. There is good scientific evidence to suggest that in the early months, prompt attention to distress leads to less frequent waking and disruptive crying patterns later on.

So, always check that your baby is not hungry. Remember that some babies require another feed within an hour of the last one. Studies have shown that the stomach may empty within 30 to 40 minutes following a breastfeed. Don't worry if he falls asleep on the breast. This is not an important issue until he gets nearer to six months of age.

If he does not fall asleep spontaneously following his feed, all you should do is keep him calm and keep him close. Babies cannot be taught how to sleep. They have virtually no working memory and little ability to retain information, habits or instruction. The newborn baby emerges in a relatively immature state, so he will respond to an environment that reminds him of the womb. That is:

- He's snugly contained (but not so tight it interferes with his breathing), with rounded back and flexed limbs. In the womb all the limbs – elbows, hips and knees – are flexed, and that posture is comforting. That's why swaddling babies for settling has worked for thousands of years. Remember the swaddling is mostly the arms, flexed and across the chest. Not so much the legs, which should be flexed up at the hips and if possible slightly splayed at the knees. (See over the page for more detail.)

- He is surrounded by rhythmic noise (the primary noise within the womb is that of the mother's heartbeat, hence that is the tempo of lullabies and the rate we pat babies, and gives us our instinct to hold babies over our hearts).

- Within the amniotic fluid, he was immersed in the taste and smell of his mother and her diet, absorbed from her body. He loves lying skin to skin with his mother, smelling, tasting and feeling her.

- It is also very low key and boring within the womb. The inside of the uterus is like a floatation chamber, visually very unexciting. On a particularly fascinating day he'll see the umbilical cord drift by; the rest of the time it's just the inside wall of the womb. The environment is quiet, meditative and calm.

If you can reproduce this environment, it is likely your baby will sleep.

If, despite your best endeavours, the baby is still unsettled and disrupted, then it may be appropriate to use the 'calming the baby' regime in Chapter 12 of this book.

David is seven weeks and five days old, he is breastfed and weighs 5.7 kg. He was born by emergency caesarean. I don't feel like he is in pain, he just likes to be awake; I don't feel like I have a low milk supply as he seems satisfied after a feed. I try to feed him on a three-hour cycle but usually it's every two or two and a half hours. Feeding always calms him; he also calms in the shower. He takes quite a while to settle and wakes after 30 minutes, on the dot. I try to resettle him, but normally that's when he starts to scream. He slept well up to about four weeks. I only take him out when I really have to and feel like I've created a fairly calming environment for him at home. He sleeps in our bedroom, sometimes in his bassinette, sometimes in the bed if he falls asleep feeding, and he likes to sleep either on me or my husband. He smiles a lot and seems to be developing well. Everybody keeps telling me it's my milk that's the problem . . . I don't drink or smoke, I don't have caffeine, chocolate, or any junk food. I really want to keep breastfeeding him. If you have any tips I'd be so grateful.

Swaddling

Swaddling is such a good way to settle a baby. Some of the professional swaddlers available nowadays are very efficient, easy to use and are very safe, if used correctly. They are mostly useful in the first eight weeks of a baby's life, but can be used safely afterwards as long as you keep in mind that once babies can roll over, if they are in a swaddle it can increase the risk of Sudden Unexpected Death in Infancy (SUDI, or what used to be known as SIDS). They can be pinned down and unable to move, so be extra vigilant with the older baby.

Everyone knows that as a baby, Jesus was wrapped in a swaddling band, and until the 18th century most cultures practised it. Those swaddling practices of yore, however, judging by the contemporary illustrations, were usually tight and restrictive, and

> A question about swaddling. My baby really likes to be swaddled; it seems to put him to sleep almost immediately. But now my childcare centre says that it's bad for their hips and can cause SIDS so I don't know what to believe. He will be one month old tomorrow. Is it safe and for how long can we continue to swaddle him? My mother also said she had read about some concerns with mobility and development.

tended to stretch the baby out into an extended posture, with legs straight out. Often the binding was so tight that it also interfered with breathing and even caused limb deformities in some.

Then opinion changed and swaddling became associated with 'bad mothering' – it was often used by 'wet nurses' because swaddled babies needed less care as they were quieter and could be left unattended. Physicians became worried about the limb deformities and respiratory ailments, and philosophers worried about the possibility that it made a baby grow up to be quiet and passive. So except in some Middle Eastern and rural cultures, the practice decreased.

New interest in the West was sparked by research groups who used the technique when investigating breathing patterns in the newborn. They found that swaddling had a marked effect on the ability of babies to settle themselves and enter sleep. Since then other studies have shown that as long as one used modern techniques and was careful to adhere to standard guidelines, it was remarkably successful as a settling technique in young babies.

These well-conducted studies, summarised by B.E. van Sleuwen and others, showed that swaddled babies slept longer, aroused less and had fewer startles. The babies found it easier to settle themselves after brief wakening. Premmies who were swaddled were more settled, had better motor coordination and regulated themselves more effectively. When they had heel prick blood tests they also had less distress and were quicker to soothe when swaddled.

Parents have now begun to see the advantages and the practice has become more common, especially in Europe, the United States, Australia and New Zealand. In some countries, though, it has never caught on; Sweden, for instance, does not believe it is necessary or healthy.

Yet there is a world of difference between the swaddling of the past and the practice of today. Done properly, it is a useful and safe practice that quite definitely helps to calm babies and improves their sleeping pattern for a couple of reasons:

- The swaddled position reminds them of the comforting familiarity and security of the womb. The arms are across the chest, bent at the elbow; the legs are flexed at the hips and knee, with the knees slightly splayed.

- As mentioned, all babies have a startle reflex during the first three months. If the baby's head drops backwards, extending the neck, their body thinks that they may be falling, so the arms involuntarily fling out and make grasping movements in the air. It really upsets them. Swaddling and containing the arms suppresses this reflex. Unfortunately, stomach sleeping also suppresses this reflex but, as we now know, this posture is dangerous as it predisposes the baby to SIDS/SUDI. Swaddling allowed the baby to sleep as well on his back (the safe sleeping position) as on his front and decreased the temptation of tired parents to put their unsettled babies face downwards in the cot.

There are, however, a few precautions that should be taken when swaddling your baby:

- It is very important that the baby should sleep on his back. We know that all babies should be put down 'back to sleep' anyway, but when swaddled it is even *more* important as the wrap restricts their limb movement and their ability to wriggle around and keep their airway clear.

- For the same reason it is important to make sure your baby cannot wriggle free of the swaddling cloth and get it over his face, which might restrict his breathing. Also make sure that there are no other sheets, wraps or bumpers in the cot that might do the same thing.

- Still on the subject of breathing, it is crucial to make sure that the swaddle is not too tight around the baby's chest. It should be snug but you should be easily able to get a couple of fingers between the baby's chest and the wrap.

- It is equally important to make sure that your snuggled-up baby doesn't get too hot, so keep the room at a moderate temperature and do not use too heavy a wrap in warmer weather. Make sure also that you do not wrap or cover his head. Bonnets are not necessary in any but the coldest temperature and a bare head helps the baby control his body temperature.

- There is a significant worry about hips and swaddling – it is critically important that the legs have freedom of movement, with the hips flexed and the knees slightly splayed. This position helps in the development of the hip joints. Strapping the legs straight out over months can cause hip dysplasia in which the socket is too shallow – a serious orthopaedic problem – and this was addressed in detail in Chapter 3.

- After the age of two months babies get more mobile and are a little more able to free themselves from their wrap (which might possibly cover their face). Some can also roll over into the prone position. As mentioned, sleeping in the prone position increases the baby's likelihood of SIDS/SUDI and even more so if the baby is also swaddled. So after this age, review whether swaddling is necessary for your baby and, if it is, increase your vigilance and attention to your technique.

There has been a recent further controversy in the literature regarding the safety of swaddling, mostly coming from the United States. A number of deaths of swaddled infants occurred there, which naturally created a firestorm of concern about it. After careful investigation, the danger was found to be predominantly in childcare centres where babies were cared for in large groups, with therefore less intense supervision than there would be with the parents. Not only that, the babies tended to be old enough to roll themselves over. Some of these babies were sometimes put on their fronts to sleep (which is always a no-no), and they had busy carers who may have swaddled them too tightly and who had not necessarily been trained well. Also, swaddling a larger, mobile baby who had never been swaddled before was found to increase their risk, for the reasons outlined above.

Swaddling in the home, especially using the professional swaddlers, is a safe and very useful technique that can give you a baby who is calmer, and sleeps longer.

THREE TO SIX MONTHS

At three months most babies cross a threshold. Their ability to spontaneously calm themselves becomes much more pronounced. This is basically a developmental step and is why the unsettledness from 'colic' miraculously disappears (and, as mentioned, why it is called three-month colic). The baby is no longer at the mercy of surrounding stimuli, and if she is overwhelmed, she has the ability to look away and switch off the input, and calm herself.

Generally by this age, most babies can sleep independently at least some of the time; however, they still have two to six arousals during the night as they transition from deep into shallower REM sleep. Most babies can spontaneously settle themselves when this occurs, but around 25 per cent of babies tend to wake and require a parent to resettle them.

Babies at this age continue to have 'object impermanence'; that is, they have no concept of the existence of things they cannot see. So if they wake and they are alone, they assume that they have been abandoned by their carers. This makes so-called sleep training inadvisable (and usually unsuccessful anyway) at this age. However, it does not mean that the parents are at the baby's mercy. It is during this time that the parents' experience of their particular baby starts to really make a difference. Their attunement to their baby's needs and their knowledge of the baby's cues allows them to determine when intervention is necessary.

There is no doubt that babies can develop into 'trained criers' from those parents who intervene too frequently and at inappropriate times, perhaps when the baby is just whinging gently as she settles herself down after an arousal period. We need to gently allow babies to exercise their ability to settle themselves. Not every whinge and cry during sleep needs parental attention, only those that indicate distress, or an emotional or physical need. That is a world away from controlled crying and leaving babies to howl. Most parents by this stage have an inner knowledge when their baby is just settling herself, and when she needs outside help to do so. If the outside help is needed it should be as low key and as gentle as possible. Perhaps just a gentle rhythmic pat on the bottom may be all that is needed.

The importance of naps

During this period she will consolidate her sleep into longer periods of time and is able to cope with longer wake-time during the day without getting ratty. In the first few weeks, babies catnap regularly throughout the day and night seemingly without much pattern. After three months, however, it becomes increasingly important to enforce a good nap program.

In various cultures across the world there seems to be very little variation in the need and timing of daytime naps, but much greater variation in night-time sleeping habits. It is possible that napping is genetically determined, whereas night sleeping habits are more cultural.

From three months onwards babies need about three naps a day, although some will decrease to two as they near six months. If possible, these nap times must be at least one hour long. Shorter naps of 20 to 30 minutes are of much less value in terms of recuperation. If your baby starts to wake after half an hour, it is worthwhile going to her, keeping her quiet, patting and singing to her, and indeed doing whatever you can to try to return her to sleep. Do not give up too easily. Try to get a regular nap routine going and do your best to stick to it. Your baby's specific nap times and routine should be determined by your baby's body. When you see her tired signs, put her down to sleep as soon as possible and usually the timing will recur day by day. If, however, she looks tired and it is not her nap time, put her down anyway. Missing the 'sleepy window' can result in a wakeful whinger who has little prospect of getting to sleep.

The cot

As they head towards six months, infants become increasingly aware of their surroundings and such familiarity breeds contentment. It is important therefore that their cot becomes a happy and secure place. It is worthwhile them spending some playtime in their cot in these early months to emphasise this. But in general, it is also a good idea to keep active toys and objects that excite the baby away from the sleeping area so it becomes associated mostly with sleepiness.

Drowsy but awake

Breastfeeding is a beautifully sedating activity for babies (and mothers), so in the early weeks it is normal, even appropriate, for a baby to fall asleep on the breast. However, once she heads towards and beyond three months, it is a good idea increasingly to persuade her to leave your breast before she is asleep and put her down in her cot, drowsy but awake. Some babies will resist this, as the act of breastfeeding fills them with comforting, sedating hormones. The problem is that if this becomes a firm 'sleep association', whenever she wakes she will feel she needs the breast in order to fall back to sleep. Unless she is told, and has it demonstrated to her, she will be unaware that falling asleep and breastfeeding are two separate activities! It is a good idea to gently dissociate them from about three months onwards. Like everything else we do to negotiate with our babies, it should be done tiny step by tiny step.

1. Just as she's falling asleep at the end of the feed, gently detach her from the breast while she is only just awake, and put her down into the cot.
2. If she awakens and complains, put her back on the breast.
3. As she is falling asleep, gently detach her again, and put her back in the cot.

You can do this over and over again. You don't have to win every round and she can still fall asleep on the breast occasionally but persevere day after day. After a few days of trying, she will accept it.

Routines

She still needs a calm environment but recognises routines more and more, so sleep times should become more ritualistic, at a set time with a predictable pattern of events. If you aren't already doing it, now is a good time to make sure that the first morning feed is in a bright room to get the diurnal rhythms right. If so, most babies need to go to bed between about 6.30 and 7.30 pm. If she is napping too late or too long in the afternoon, it might be necessary to wake her to give her enough activity to be sleepy by this bedtime.

You might need to set aside a week or so at about this age to establish a good nap and sleep rhythm. If you have other young children or a busy schedule that tends to disrupt your baby's routine, this 'time-out' week may help your baby to consolidate her sleep patterns rather than continue in a chaotic manner.

Trigger words

When sleep time is due, teach her 'trigger' words or songs associated with sleep (for instance, 'Sleepy Eyes' or 'Twinkle, Twinkle, Little Star'). These sounds set her up for sleeping. You can also use recordings of womb sounds or other calming background noise, like that of the seashore. The familiarity of these sounds becomes of increasing importance as the infant gets towards (and beyond) six months. They remind her of the security and familiarity of the home and induce contentment and relaxation, creating a good 'sleep association'.

Don't use these sounds when she is unhappy or crying, only when she is drowsy and falling asleep. The sounds should always be associated with calming and falling asleep, not with desperate, sleepless times.

Changing the infant's patterns

During this three to six-month era most babies will settle on a pattern acceptable to most parents. There will now be two to three nap times a day with at least two of them being more than one hour long. They will also sleep for longer periods of time at night, most managing five hours at a stretch and some much longer.

If this so-called sleep consolidation does not appear to be happening in your family, it is reasonable to exert a little pressure to head it in that direction. However, if your baby's pattern is not as mature as this but the family is getting enough sleep all-round, there is no need to do anything other than wait for time alone to mature the pattern appropriately.

Equally, if you are bed-sharing there is every likelihood that such sleep consolidation will come more slowly, as more intensive night feeds will still occur while it remains so available.

It is incorrect to say that these issues need to be addressed sooner rather than later. They should be addressed when the family thinks it is right to do so, and no sooner.

As mentioned above, having determined the need for a change, the main principle of changing babies' sleeping or settling patterns is to do things slowly, step by step.

This method isn't as immediately attractive as the 'crash through' techniques, which offer quick-fix solutions that promise a baby sleeping through the night by the end of the week. They were very popular in the era that thought babies needed discipline and an inflexible lifestyle to develop properly. There was also a view that babies were fairly similar and what was good for one was good for all. These are all thoroughly discredited notions.

The more gradual techniques are psychologically sound and are much more humane. They are based on the need to support our babies emotionally as they grow both mentally and physically. They also happen to fit in with what attuned and aware parents instinctively want to do anyway.

No-cry techniques

Suppose your baby is four months of age and continues to insist upon falling asleep in your arms. There is no doubt that by putting him into his cot, walking away, closing the door and putting in your earplugs he will be sleeping soundly in his cot within a few days or weeks. However, the transition for him and you could be disruptive and potentially damaging to his future mental health. I'll discuss this in the 'Sleep training' section to follow.

A better way for you both is to transition him step by step. So first he lies in your arms as you sit next to his cot until he is nearly asleep. Then you quietly bend over and lay him in his cot, still in contact with your body with your arms still under him as he falls asleep. Slowly remove your arms and if he stirs, put a hand on his body and gently move it at your breathing rate. That is the movement of your body that he senses and for which he looks for security.

If he fully wakes, pick him up, calm him and sing softly to him. And as he is falling asleep, place him back down again in the same way. Repeat this exercise, over and over again.

If he strongly objects, back off and try again later. Eventually he will accept the new situation and you can move on. Soon you will be able to put him down and remove your hands earlier. After that you will be able to put him down when he is not as sleepy as before. It goes step by step, recognising that sometimes we have to beat a retreat and advance again after a few more days. All the while we are exerting gentle pressure to get him to fit into the new pattern.

Within a short time you will have a baby you can put into his cot and who gently falls asleep on his own. You can then pat yourself on the back and celebrate . . . and the following week he catches a cold and you're back where you started!

Unfortunately that is the nature of the beast. Babies do not progress in a straight line. Do not despair if weeks of hard work appear to evaporate with the first virus that your baby catches. You now know his rhythms and his capacity to settle and he knows you and the direction you want him to go, and it will be easier to gently negotiate him into an acceptable sleep pattern in the future.

It is a good idea to have your objectives clear in your mind before you start and it may be necessary to take notes so that you can monitor increments of progress. Some people (usually the more obsessive) use sleep charts so they can get a visual record that helps them see progress (or lack of it). That depends on you. Most mums are busy enough without forensic record keeping. There are even apps on your phone nowadays that allow you to monitor and record every sleep, nap, feed, poo and burp (and later draw graphs and pie charts about them to show your paediatrician). Life is too short for this!

'Sleep training'

There is a school of thought that suggests you can teach babies of this age to sleep by walking away and allowing them to cry. Though as a technique this can work (that is, silence your baby), it is for most babies distressing and potentially harmful. Babies evolved to cry for help if they were needy. If there is no response, sensing that they have been abandoned, they would then 'extinguish' their cry and become silent to avoid attracting predators. We now have a mass of reliable scientific evidence that suggests this process of extinction can teach the baby that his parents are unreliable, their love is conditional and he is not valuable to them. Think about it – what kind of message is 'My parents love me during the day, but at night, when it's dark and scary, they don't seem to. I'm on my own!'

Apart from the lack of self-worth that this encourages, it also sets him up for a poorer ability to deal with stress later in life. It is entirely possible that the present epidemic of depression in our society today may well be a legacy of the extinction sleep programs so popular a generation ago.

Brain scientists, using scanning techniques, have discovered that during a baby's first year his brain wires up the ability to deal with stress. How that stress response is programmed into the brain depends on the baby's experiences and his environment. If he is responded to lovingly and calmly when he is distressed, he learns how to deal with his stress response in an appropriate and calm way. He learns to trust his carers and the world. If he is ignored during times of distress so that he is forced to extinguish these cries, he then programs his brain not to be too trusting, to accept insecurity as his lot in life and, later, be less capable of dealing with stressful situations.

In times past it was the general view of childcare advisers that to answer these cries of distress would lead to babies and children who were overindulged and spoilt. We now know how wrong-headed this information was. Responding promptly and sensitively to children's needs early on gives them inner strength and self-confidence, leading them to be more self-sufficient and independent as they grow up.

It is for this reason that 'crying it out' or 'controlled crying' techniques are potentially harmful in the first months of a baby's life. Indeed most of the studies done on these techniques were performed on babies aged over one year, and the results inappropriately transposed to the younger age group. The central issue is that in the first months of life babies have object impermanence; as mentioned, this is when a person or object can no longer be seen by the baby, and it no longer exists. They have no memory for things they cannot see. So if Mum isn't here, and I need her, she has abandoned me forever!

I'll say again that during this period it is a very good thing to remember that babies change week by week. If he's waking hourly and you're going crazy, remember the chances are that this will change very soon. If, at this time, you go in heavy-handed to force a change, there is every chance that you will prolong the situation or make it worse.

If you are breastfeeding, it is good to check that your milk supply is keeping up with his needs. Babies will often start to feed frequently at night to boost milk supply. As mentioned earlier, night feeds boost the milk-stimulating hormone prolactin more than day feeds and babies know this. So check his weight and perhaps consult with a midwife or lactation consultant if low supply is a possibility.

And apart from this (at this and any other age) have him checked by his family doctor or paediatrician to make sure that there are no medical issues causing him to be more wakeful. For apparently healthy babies, these conditions are actually quite unusual, but certainly it is good to be reassured during the day so you can be confident about this during the (long) nights.

Prevention of later sleep problems: six weeks to six months

By the quiet observation of your baby you will soon see those signs she exhibits when she is tired and requires sleep. Signs such

Our son is now four and a half months old. My issue is that he loves falling asleep on the boob (i.e. he wants it each time he is tired, wherever he is). Therefore he won't fall asleep in the pram or car seat (he screams until he gets it), which makes things rather complicated . . .

I've tried to establish a bedtime routine and tried not to give in, but we both felt really miserable, so I gave it up after two weeks. I still try to follow the same bedtime routine (bath, feed, story, singing and then carrying him until dozy before putting him into bed), but now if he screams I end up letting him fall asleep on the boob again (which is 90 per cent of the time).

He seems to have figured this out, as now he refuses to feed, fusses during storytime and singing, and just wants to go straight to the part when I lie next to him and let him fall asleep on me.

The truth is that I enjoy it when he falls asleep lying attached to me and I wouldn't mind it if there was a way to teach him to self-settle and fall asleep alone when we are out.

as yawning, grizzling, grimacing, frowning, flailing limbs and a distracted gaze are all examples, but each baby is subtly different, with their specific signs becoming clearer to you over the early weeks.

Babies can detect how you are feeling by the tone of your voice and the way you handle them. If you are irritated, they know; if you really need them to sleep, they won't. If your body is tense and your mind in turmoil, your baby perceives, 'maybe there's danger, better stay awake to check . . .'

About three-quarters of babies start to sleep more during the night than the day as they head towards three months of age. On average between three and five months infants are sleeping for about ten hours at night, with the longest sleep being between six and seven hours and 75 per cent of babies at this age have at least a five-hour stretch.

If you have a baby who can't manage this, as she heads beyond three months (depending on the individual) there is good evidence to suggest that a gentle program to encourage her to prolong her sleep will pay dividends. I emphasise that this is a 'no-cry' preventive program. It is not designed to teach the baby to sleep, as she is still too young to learn, but it will help her establish for herself the 'normal' structure of sleep that most babies exhibit at this age.

The concept is to gently disassociate the act of waking with the reward of feeding, which becomes a conditioned reflex. If, whenever we wake, we are fed, we will tend to wake more often. By avoiding reinforcing this wake–feed behaviour, and by reinforcing and rewarding quietness, we will decrease the tendency to wake.

Thus:

1. Make the first feed of the day in a brightly lit room to switch on the day/night hormone rhythm in the baby's body.

2. Make the difference between day feeds and night feeds as obvious as possible. Also cluster activities such as playing, changing and feeding into discrete episodes during the day, interspersed with periods of calm and hopefully naps. During the night, however, the environment should remain dark, quiet and unstimulating.

3. If she lets you, introduce placing the baby into the cot before she falls asleep. But if she insists on falling asleep on the breast, let her do it at least for the first few months. The cot should be in the same place every night. Bedtime should be at approximately the same time, with the use of the same routines, songs and words.

4. When the baby re-awakens in the night, don't delay going to her but *delay the start of the feed* for a short while. So change her nappy, give her a cuddle and walk with her, all in a calm, dark environment. Then feed her.

This program should be introduced gradually, with stops and starts over a number of weeks. I emphasise: it does not involve leaving the baby to cry. It is merely to allow her to practise her own settling abilities and to make sure you don't reinforce a cry–reward reflex.

As mentioned above, by the age of three months about 75 per cent of babies have spontaneously initiated a good day/night sleep difference. A nice study from Nikolopoulou and others in 2003 showed that utilising the above four-step regime will improve most of the other 25 per cent. It is not that they are learning something (because they are still too young to learn very much at all). What the program does is establish the innate structure of behaviour that is present in every baby at this age, which helps them to regulate their sleep patterns.

SIX TO TWELVE MONTHS

At six months most babies have got their act together and are sleeping for reasonable stretches at night. They still require at least two naps, though, as the months turn, so interested do they become in things around them they can develop resistance to staying down during the day.

Infants at this age and beyond also develop increasing object permanence, and start to recognise patterns and routines in their daily lives. They still require the presence of carers to calm and reassure them. This need continues throughout infancy and it is actually not until four years of age that children become increasingly comfortable being apart from their carers and have an inherent sense of personal security.

We know that physiologically most babies do not require food at night after six months. However, this is not written in stone. If you're breastfeeding, it is a personal decision between you and your baby whether you wish to curtail these feeds after dark. There is no right or wrong way, so don't take your friend's advice on this one. There is more to breastfeeding than food; there is also love and reassurance. Don't be pressured to stop if you're both enjoying it. And certainly if you are bed-sharing, you have fewer grounds for negotiation!

Transitional objects (such as teddies, comforters or a worn mother's T-shirt) play an increasing role from this age onwards. These familiar things feel and smell right to the infant and offer security and comfort in the absence of the parent. They continue to play a big part in the infant's life for years to come.

However, by this time, babies have usually consolidated their sleep patterns into a reasonable routine and many babies will be sleeping more than eight hours a night, with two daytime naps. But some will not, and this can still be a difficult time, with sleep problems emerging even in those babies who that have not had them before. Keep in mind that the sleep pattern at this age is not stable and babies frequently have short-lived sleep disruptions, which, when dealt with lovingly but pragmatically, right themselves soon enough. Also the younger the baby, the more likely it is that any gains made from any sleep training will be only temporary.

Sleep associations

As explained earlier, it is at this age that babies develop sleep associations; that is, objects, sounds, smells or events that have always been present on falling asleep and hence can trigger it. The most common association for the breastfed baby is the breast itself. Breastfeeding induces comforting and sedating hormones in the baby's body that tend to induce sleep, so in the early months this is not an issue. That is the way the system is designed. It can, however, become an issue as a baby gets older. They may believe that feeding and sleeping are one activity and just do not recognise that one can actually fall asleep without having a breast present. This would be similar to you waking in the night and finding your pillow on the floor. You cannot envisage falling asleep without picking it up and putting it back on the bed. To the baby, your breast is their pillow.

Of course, many sleep associations are helpful. Teddy bears, the favourite blanket or the thumb in the mouth can be very comforting and should not be interfered with. It is only when they are disruptive or require the parents' intervention that the situation needs to be addressed.

Dummies and thumb-sucking

The dummy or pacifier is one case in point. Dummies of themselves are not bad for babies. Indeed the American Academy of Pediatrics has recognised that many babies benefit from their presence. In a large population studied, there was a lower incidence of SUDI/SIDS in those babies with dummies.

A problem emerges when a baby requires a dummy to fall asleep but is not very good at retaining it in her mouth. So when she goes from deep to light sleep and briefly awakens (every hour or so), she requires the dummy in her mouth to return to sleep, and calls for her parent to find it for her.

Straight removal of the pacifier is hardly fair or caring, and will probably lead to tears. It is a better idea to observe the baby as she falls asleep and as her suck pattern on the dummy slows, gently remove it. This should be repeated whenever she falls asleep and slowly the baby's requirement for the dummy's presence should diminish over a number of days. As always in changing babies' behaviour, it's tiny steps, gradually.

Thumb (or finger) sucking in young children, however, rarely has any downside. Many children suck their thumbs especially when they are falling asleep for years without detriment to themselves or their teeth. The practice has a reputation of creati malaligned teeth but this only occurs after the permanent teeth have erupted and if the thumb is constantly in the mouth, day and night, after the age of four years. The more common situation is when it is used only for falling asleep, in which case the practice should be ignored and no effort put into changing it.

Most children give it up spontaneously as they get towards school age (and the peer pressure that then incurs). But even then there remains a proportion of children that will do it into their teens.

The 'coercion trap'

As the infant is now starting to retain memories of events, it is at this stage that the common 'coercion trap' emerges. They discover that by night waking and crying they are met with a reliable, and rewarding, parental response. This response reinforces the behaviour and perpetuates it. An inconsistent parental response will also feed into it, as the infant finds that persistence pays off. When the parents try to control it by modifying or withdrawing their response, it creates a more intense response from the infant (called a 'post-extinction response burst' or PERB – see 'Sleep training techniques' on p. 177), which further coerces the parents to abandon the attempt at control and respond as before, and so perpetuate the cycle.

Towards nine months most babies, even the ones who were previously good sleepers, start waking at night and demanding attention or a feed. Many of these babies are developing the separation anxiety that happens at this age. The baby starts to feel the world changing as they recognise that they are in a different body from their parents, an intoxicating but terrifying concept. These babies need reassurance and lots of it to let them know that you are still reliable and close. Soon they will relax and start to sleep again.

There are some babies, however, who are clearly coercing their parents. These are the babies that cry to get you into their room, then when you arrive, switch on a beatific smile and decide it's playtime. With them, it is often necessary to change their pattern with a little coercion yourself. Make the interaction loving, but brief, business-like and relatively unrewarding. Explain the issue: 'Sorry darling, we sleep in this house at 3 am. Goodnight.' Pat, pat.

Be more careful of the baby who is obviously anxious when he is calling you and who clings when you arrive. This one needs gentle soothing and more time before you try to pressure him to sleep longer.

New developmental steps

Just when you think you've got control, and your little one is sleeping for longer, she suddenly realises that with a little help from the bars of the cot she can stand up. What a thrill! The problem is she hasn't learned to sit down again. Babies love to practise their new tricks and often won't be deterred by mere darkness. So you get squeals every hour from the baby's bedroom as she needs help to put herself down again. Similarly with rolling over and sitting up. The day isn't long enough to get in sufficient practice.

This is a really common issue as the baby moves through each developmental stage and then teeters on the edge of toddlerhood. These phases are usually quite short-lived and disappear quickly, as long as you deal with them in a calm and neutral manner. Very quickly she will learn to drop herself down onto her bottom and will no longer need help.

Separation anxiety

Towards 12 months, infants start to realise that their body is separate from their mother and they are independent people. This is exhilarating and terrifying at the same time and infants will become more clingy and wary of strangers for the first time. This is absolutely the worst time to start sleep training your little one. I know it's a pain to not even be able to go to the loo alone, but it is a relatively brief period as long as it is not made worse by too much pressure from you. As months go by, so they become increasingly confident and exploratory and they start increasing the distance between you and them. This is a critical transitional period that needs patience and understanding. The more you impose separation, the worse it will get and the longer it will remain.

Have you got any suggestions regarding my 12-month-old practising sitting and standing in his cot before bed and while he's supposed to be asleep? The problem is that he becomes extremely distressed when we lay him back down; he's not just unhappy, but really distressed, screaming and gagging for sometimes an hour. It goes like this – we put him to bed drowsy, he wakes, sits up, stands up. We tell him it's time for sleep and put him back down. Sits, stands, cries, we put him back down, pick him up for a cuddle when he's losing the plot, put him back down. On and on and on. We have tried letting him sort it out himself; I mean that we have tried saying goodnight and leaving the room before he becomes upset, while he's having a play in the cot. We never leave him to cry alone but he becomes equally distressed. Any ideas? This has been going on for weeks, four to six times a night.

HC: What you have here is a one-year-old who has discovered new motor skills and is so excited he wants to explore them day and night. This is just a temporary period until he moves on to the next stage. Once he gets up in his cot he probably doesn't have the skill to get back down again so teaching him to bend at the waist and drop on his bottom would be a good move. Persistently laying him down after he stands up would be intensely frustrating for him.

Prevention of later sleep problems: six months to twelve months

1. Get to know the tiredness signs. By now these should be clear to you and very distinct. Irritability, distraction, yawning and eye rubbing are among the most common.

2. Arrange regular naps. Between six and twelve months, most babies need at least two nap times of an hour each and should be offered them whether they are demanded or not. If the infant does not wish to sleep, the time should be a quiet, calm time-out. At this age good naps equal good nights.

3. Too much daytime excitement can lead to night-time waking. So a busy schedule from the carer tends to lead to a wakeful baby later. Alternatively, a busy schedule of activity for the baby may make her sleepier at night. Only trial and error will tell you what works for your particular baby's personality.

4. It is even more important from this age onward to adhere to a bedtime schedule. This should be an enjoyable routine, looked forward to by the parent and child, and includes feeding, bath time, perhaps a gentle massage, then reading or gentle conversation. For a full hour or more before sleep time, there should be no excitement at all.

5. The child should be put into a cot that is now exclusively associated with sleeping. She should always fall asleep in the same location because she will wake up, except on special occasions.

6. Ideally, she should be put down drowsy but awake. If possible there should be minimal fussing after tucking in. Unless it is your choice and the baby's habit, once down, avoid rocking, cuddling or patting to sleep. And if it is, you have a choice to gradually wean the baby off such input or continue it.

7. There should never be TVs, computers or other screens in the bedroom.

8. After putting her down, allow time for the infant to self-soothe. If not settling, administer low stimulus soothing or lie with her for the minimum necessary time.

9. Any activities later, such as nappy changing, should be done quietly, with dim lighting and minimal conversation.

If transient problems occur, such as if the child becomes ill, or holidays intervene, don't stress too much. Almost all children have short periods of sleep difficulties and as long as the parent does not reinforce the problem, they will soon disappear. So keep all interventions at a low level with minimum stimulation and minimum reward.

Abandonment

The most important principle at this age is not to let any baby or child cry from abandonment. This creates a belief in the baby that that they are not valued, or even safe, and can lead to a stressed baby not only at the time, but down the track as well.

With frequent night crying, it is also worth asking yourself: is she crying from anger or anxiety? The angry babies are wondering why you aren't doing as you are told, and these can be offered a little gentle pressure to sleep longer. Anxious babies may be suffering from separation anxiety and pressuring them may make them worse – this group tends not to respond to sleep training anyway.

TWELVE MONTHS AND OLDER

As they grow beyond one year, the principles as described for the earlier phases do not change. What does change is the child. They develop into a much more sophisticated toddler and the developmental changes they go through can really impact on their sleep patterns.

These little dynamos are relentlessly busy as they find out new things and learn new skills and they see little reason why their activity shouldn't extend into the night. They also start to understand cause and effect and recognise even more keenly that night waking can give them some Alone with Mummy Time, when she is not distracted by others and is only concentrating on them and getting them back to sleep. Their acting ability also improves greatly and it is hard to resist the portrayal of abject misery that they can generate when they see that you are trying to resist party time at 3 am.

But the basic principle of a non-existent reward for these limit-stretching activities remains sound, with a few provisos.

- Separation anxiety can increase after 12 months and if this is the reason for their night calling, then they do require your closeness, love and security at that time. Generally the phase does not last long – perhaps a few months at most. But unfortunately for your sleep, forcing them into solitude under these circumstances will only intensify and prolong this phase.
- If they are unwell, then of course all bets are off. You will need to ride it out until they have recovered and then start again.
- Equally if your home situation is unstable either physically (because of a recent move or change in circumstances) or emotionally (if there is an upsetting situation brewing in the household) then it is not appropriate to offer anything other than reassurance and love until the situation settles down.

For the others, who greet you with a beaming smile when you get up to them or who appear angry when you do not comply with their wishes, the application of gentle but firm and unambiguous limits is the only way forward. There should be no rewards, no feeds or bottles, no playtime, and the bare minimum of attention. Just enough to inform them of the fact that it's sleepy time for the whole family and perhaps, at the most, provide gentle patting. Even picking them up out of the cot is reward enough for some.

If it is too hard to withdraw your attention in one go, a few days of gradually decreasing it, night by night, should get the message across gently but firmly.

Nap and sleep time

The sleep time at this age drops slightly to a total of about 12 and a half hours, of which one to two hours are from naps. Somewhere between one year and 18 months, most toddlers will drop one of their two naps and they will maintain this single nap till at least three or four years of age.

Beware the toddler who decides he no longer wants to nap. It is an unusual child who can arise at 6 or 7 o'clock in the morning and make it through to the evening without becoming irritable and cranky. They need to have a nap sometime towards the middle of the day and if they resist it they should not be offered any other attractive activity. Putting them into a boring environment, usually in their cot, and resisting their pleas to be in the living room will usually do the trick if you are determined.

Beware also of the naps that are asked for too late in the afternoon. It is very difficult to persuade a child to go to bed between 7 and 7.30 when they have napped from 3 o'clock until 5 o'clock in the afternoon. Bring forward their nap time to earlier in the afternoon and if necessary, wake them at 3.30 at the latest so they can generate enough tiredness by bedtime.

If you are having problems with early-morning waking or resistance at bedtime, it is worthwhile looking at your baby's total sleep time – on a formal sleep chart if needed. Some parents unreasonably still want their toddlers to sleep like babies, with two long naps and a 12-hour sleep at night. By removing one nap or making the bedtime slightly later, you should be able to find a combination that suits you all.

The changes that impact on the sleep pattern

One-third to one-half of parents still think their babies have a sleep problem at this age and these problems are sometimes compounded by the developmental advances of their toddler.

- Increased mobility: this is of critical importance. Now he can climb out of the cot, walk across the room, open the door and present himself to his parents' bedroom. When this happens, it is clear to all that this is a game changer. It is now so much easier for the child to physically demonstrate his disagreement with the limits imposed by his parents, especially around sleep time and location.

- Increased comprehension: he is now rapidly acquiring new knowledge and skills and wishes to continue exploring both his environment and what his body can do, even after dark. The upside of this is he is now more amenable to simple behavioural interventions as he can remember and learn lessons demonstrated to him. So now he remembers that waking is unrewarding, and that his mother is not much fun at 1 am. He is therefore likely to cease testing the limits earlier under the gentle pressure of no reward.

- He has increased reliance on his transitional objects such as a teddy bear and the favourite blanket, as he now ascribes to them the feelings of security and affection. There is a problem waiting to happen if these objects are lost, so it is worthwhile having identical backups available in case of such a tragedy.

- His developing imagination can lead him into increased night-time fears and the possibility of nightmares. Many children require a dim nightlight with lots of reassurance about these issues. But be careful of shadows cast by the nightlight that can morph into frightening shapes on the wall. Never underestimate the power of such fantasies in the bedroom. Brushing off the possibility of there being monsters under the cot is totally unhelpful to the imaginative toddler. This matter needs careful attention with lucid and reassuring explanation, and sometimes imaginative solutions (to fill the space under the cot, for instance).

- Toddlers are driven towards independence, alternating with regressive clinginess. This can lead to vocal resistance to bedtime routines, interspersed with a desire to resume co-bedding as a response to minor stress. The solution is loving firmness and an appreciation of the feelings without necessarily acquiescing to their demands.

Their own room

By 12 to 18 months over 80 per cent of children in Australia and New Zealand are in their own room. It is generally recommended that babies and infants spend their sleeping hours in the same room as their parents for the early months when they are at most risk of SUDI/SIDS, but in the latter half of their first year the level or risk falls at the same time as both parents and infants look for a little independence at night. It is certainly easier to establish good-quality bedtime routines with the infant's cot in another room.

The brain of the one to two-year-old

By the time the child is into his second year the fundamentals of his emotional intelligence have been established within his brain. It is not a completed system and there is still much for him to acquire during his second year and beyond, but nevertheless he now has a solid grounding in his personal feelings of security. This allows him to develop some autonomy and start exploring as a toddler. He also has a good amount of working memory and can work out the logic of cause and effect. The effect of these attributes is to better understand why parents don't want to play with him in the night, and why they do what they do to dissuade him.

This means if the situation demands it – that is, if he chooses to challenge the boundaries set for him – his parents can take a more sophisticated approach to dealing with recalcitrant behaviour and night-time waking. That is not to say they now have free rein to walk away from his needs at night time but for some situations and child temperaments they can consider alternatives. Most parents will come across these sleep training techniques from many sources and it is appropriate for them to have an understanding of what they entail and what they offer. The techniques are never an ideal way to manage an infant with sleeping issues, but under some circumstances some parents may find them useful, if they and their child's situation are not improving with the no-cry methods.

Sleep training techniques

The basic principle of all sleep training techniques is the behaviourist theory that withdrawal of the reinforced reward (parental attention) will remove or reduce the waking behaviour. Let us look at the various techniques on offer and examine their advantages and disadvantages:

- pure extinction, otherwise known as 'systematic ignoring'
- controlled crying (or controlled comforting) but technically known as a graduated extinction
- parental presence program (better known as 'camping out')
- a few finer variations of these.

1. Pure Extinction

This is the tough one. The baby is put in the cot and the parents walk away and don't come back till morning, unless he's sick.

Neither this nor the graduated extinction should ever be used in babies less than six months old, or in infants and children with separation anxiety.

In terms of getting the babies quiet and eventually to sleep it can be simple to implement and effective; however, there are significant, serious disadvantages.

It utilises a basic survival mechanism (extinction of the cry) programmed into our brain as babies. In order to survive abandonment (that is, your mother or carer is not available) you had best be quiet, or you might be eaten by a predator. Still, such infants often cry for long periods and then finally give up, feeling lost and helpless.

- It totally goes against parental instinct and most find it very stressful to undertake and carry it through.

- It wrongly indicates to the parent that their innate caring response to their child is misplaced and is not to be relied on.
- There is potential for the babies to lose confidence in their parents' reliability and love. With repetitive episodes of abandonment, the baby learns and has reinforced that he has no control over his environment.
- Such stress in the first year of life, as it is explained more extensively elsewhere in this book, can have ramifications with the babies' long-term feelings of security, their worldview and self-esteem.
- If the babies learn in their early years that their parents are not to be trusted, and it depends on the time of day whether they are loved or not, then this is likely to have long-term effects on how they view their parents' love later, especially in their teenage years and even beyond.
- It tends to be used in older children, but even so, serious problems remain in completely removing the child from his comfort zone at a time when the need for a secure bond with the parent remains high.

2. Controlled crying or comforting

This is one of the most commonly used techniques. Like pure extinction the child is put in the cot and the parents walk away. However, they return periodically to check on the infant, but without soothing.

- This technique is certainly better tolerated by parents, as it reassures them about the child's wellbeing and reduces their anxiety.
- However, studies by K.G. France and others show that out of these three, this is the least successful technique. The constant interruptions by the parents tend to reinforce the baby's cry and prolong the crying time before extinction occurs.
- Generally there is a strict regime of increasing intervals for the checks; however, there is some debate about the

maximum interval for absence (from ten minutes to unlimited). But eventually most infants will succumb to silence and sleep.

- Unfortunately, there is usually an attempt by the child to summon their parents with an increasingly intense and desperate cry. This is called a 'post-extinction response burst' (PERB). In pure extinction this is ignored and the child settles. In graduated extinction the parent will often return and induce this phenomenon over and over again, significantly delaying the result.

3. Parental presence program or 'camping out'

If you feel that your situation justifies a sleep training technique, and prevention and no-cry techniques have failed, then this technique has major advantages over the previous two. It is also better suited for the children who have separation anxiety. In it, the child is put to bed in the cot. The parent then sleeps (or to start with, feigns sleep) in a bed or chair near the infant for the first several nights of the program. They give the child their presence, but only a minimal amount of their attention.

On the first night the parent's bed may be relatively close, with an arm occasionally patting the child's tummy, and a few murmuring words of love and reassurance. As the days go on, the parent's input gradually reduces and the bed is moved further away from that of the child, until progress is made. Then the parent goes back to their own room.

This technique has a number of advantages:

- The parent is with the child so there is no feeling of abandonment.
- The reinforcing responses can be gradually withdrawn, the rate depending on the child's response and acceptance.
- Comparative studies with this and the other techniques have shown camping out to be the most successful for the least stress to both parties.

However, to the biologist or infant mental health psychologist there is absolutely no contest or need for discussion on whether one should manipulate babies' sleep patterns abruptly by formal sleep training or by no-cry solutions.

The no-cry solutions win hands down. To suggest the use of abandonment by loving parents at a time when the baby's vulnerable brain is learning the rudiments of relationships, security and self-worth is breathtaking in its ignorance. That is not to say that one has to tolerate every disrupted sleep pattern or go to their baby every time he wakes at night. But it is important to give your baby a clear and unambiguous message that at night, when it's dark and they're lonely, they are still loved as much as during the day.

So, as mentioned earlier, all manipulations of baby sleep patterns should be done step by tiny step. There are books available that will tell you that you can change the baby's sleep pattern in a couple of days using their methodology and for some babies it may be true, but at what cost? By abruptly changing the conditions at night you may be able to shock the baby's system into silence by 'extinction', but as the baby incorporates the knowledge of that abandonment into the hardware of his brain, so that wiring has the potential to come back to haunt you, and him, later.

The risk is cumulative

Whether or not your baby will suffer long-term security issues as a response to these sleep training techniques depends on four factors:

- *The emotional background at home*
  If the baby is generally surrounded by love and acceptance from his parents, relatives and carers and an extinction technique is used, it is less likely to have an impact on him. If, however, he lives in a stressful home with distant authoritarian parents, then the risks become progressively greater. Human babies do have tremendous adaptability and can usually deal with stress as long as the episodes are brief and immersed in a generally loving world.

- *The intensity and longevity of the technique*
  Some babies, almost ready to sleep longer, just take a little push to persuade them to do so. This is the case

for those parents who say, 'It only took five minutes and Sebastian was sleeping through.' If, however, the extinction techniques have to go on hour after hour and then be repeated week after week, the risks build up over time.

- *The baby's temperament*
Some babies are born easygoing and adaptable, and other babies are more inflexible and overly anxious. What the first group can cope with, the latter group find harrowing, even agonising. Our babies are all little individuals with their own unique sets of fears and foibles. On this subject there is no general rule for everyone and every parent (who knows their child better than anyone) can make a decision about a technique's relevance and appropriateness for their individual child.

- *The baby's age*
As babies under six months of age have no object permanence they have no concept that their mother is still nearby. They are, in essence, abandoned and this is a deeply stressful situation for a young baby. As they get older and they become more aware that their mother is hovering outside the door, tears in her eyes as she tries to instigate a plan that she is only half enthusiastic about, it becomes less stressful for them.

Most of the studies of extinction techniques have been performed in children over one year of age. There are very few studies of infants between six and twelve months and almost none below that. Nevertheless the results from these older children have been extrapolated to the younger age groups without a clear view of their side effects and problems. In addition, many of the studies have large variations in ages, development and outcomes and it is hard to develop firm conclusions from the data. Suffice it to say that no-cry techniques are far more acceptable, both to babies and parents. They are more in keeping with what we know about the importance of the essential relationship between parents and child and the latter's need for security, reliability and love during their early years.

However, I accept that it is no help to a child to have a stressed and chronically fatigued household, with the child dog-tired all day because he's been up half the night playing with his parents.

So especially in children over 12 months of age, and maybe in some circumstances under that age, a short period of gentle camping out, to 'reset' the situation, can be a godsend.

MARIA'S STORY

We came to see you regarding 11-month-old Maria's sleep issues. You asked me to get in touch to let you know how we were going.

We had to delay the sleep stuff (waking three to four times a night) as since we saw you she got a bad virus and ear infection so she was rather sick and I still fed her on demand . . . This then started to become four times a night once she started to get better; I think she got back in a habit of comfort sucking in the night to get back to sleep, something I have always done with her.

So this weekend when she was better we tried camping out. On the first night my partner slept in the room with her, Maria woke up around 11.30 pm and cried for one hour; he comforted her now and then but I could tell the cry was angry or frustrated – the 'Where is the booby?' cry.

She then continued to wake three more times during the night, the second time crying for twenty minutes, then progressively only ten minutes the other two times . . . again my partner stayed in the room with her.

The second night she woke at 1.30 am, cried for five minutes, then went back to sleep, woke again twice and cried for a few minutes and went back to sleep. Dad was still in the room.

The third night, I slept in the room with her . . . it was harder for me as I am conditioned after one year to wake as well.

She woke twice, I just patted and shushed her, and she went straight back to sleep.

Last night we tried not to camp out, she woke twice, with me just going into her room and shushing; she cried again only for about a minute then went back to sleep.

So technically this approach has worked for us, given that she is sleeping for longer stretches and settling without the boob . . . we are going to camp in tonight to see if she will just settle again.

Maria is now sleeping through from 7 pm to 6 am (when she wakes she comes into our bed for an hour until 7 am, so it is a nice time for us), so camping out worked for us.

She woke last night around 4.30 am and cried for one minute then put herself back to sleep. What a relief after a year of interrupted sleep for me!

Other aspects

Sedatives

The use of sedatives for sleep training has been recommended in the past but has now almost completely disappeared from conventional use. The sedatives can indeed deliver a sleeping child; however, when the drugs are ceased, the sleep problem often remains. In addition, children have variable, and sometimes paradoxical, responses to the sedatives, with some becoming hyped up rather than sedated. This is why sedating children on long-haul flights is a hazardous business. Instead of a sleeping child in your lap all the way to Canada, you could have a whining, half-drunk, groggy child who won't stay in his seat. Not to be recommended.

Follow-up

Unfortunately many successes from these programs evaporate in weeks. The younger the child when the technique is attempted, the more likely the results will disappear as the infant moves to the next stage of her development. Also, with the first viral infection, the sleep pattern evaporates along with your determination. A holiday or a weekend with the grandparents and we're back to square one.

Reinforcement – then extinction

For the older child who has learned by experience that the longer he cries the more he is likely to succeed to get his way, it might be worthwhile considering a period of a week or more where his cries are immediately responded to. This technique may 'unlearn' that persistence pays, and allow for a more successful 'reset' when camping out is attempted.

Conclusion

Whoever invented the expression 'sleeping like a baby' clearly never had one. Disturbed nights and broken sleep are an integral part of the gift of a new baby, as essential to the physiology of a baby as frequent feeds and outbursts of crying. Trying to embrace these more tiresome aspects, even enjoying them, as the temporary phenomena they are, can increase your enjoyment of the whole package of parenting. Resisting, always trying to suppress them and working towards a fantasy of some idealised angel baby diminishes the whole experience and leaves both sides of the relationship poorer.

Nevertheless a little prevention is much better than a cure and I hope the pointers I have outlined in this chapter can help you towards quieter nights.

It has to be said, however, that the combination of extreme parental sleep deprivation and a hysterical howling baby can push one to the edge of human tolerance and it can be a recipe for disaster. If you think you can stand it no more and feel bursts of fierce anger and resentment towards your baby, then accept this as part of the human condition, and deal with it sensibly. It is not possible to think rationally when you're feeling like this. Accept that we all have a limit somewhere and do not explore yours. Equally, do not feel guilty about it. Just recognise that within all of us there is this potential, and make urgent arrangements to fix it:

- Get some help. You need respite and you need it now. You need a friend, relative or health worker to take over while you get some sleep and collect yourself.
- Distance yourself from your baby. It is better that he howls on his own than you have a meltdown and shake him or harm him.
- If, after you have recovered somewhat, things are no better, consider a 'quick fix' extinction program with the help of your doctor or healthcare worker. Sometimes emergency situations require emergency solutions.

CHAPTER 15

Sharing sleep: talking about the risks

NOBODY HAS A PROBLEM WITH 'CO-BEDDING'. That's because the expression encompasses all the different sleeping arrangements where babies and parents are close to each other. This therefore includes sleeping in the same room with the cot near to the parents so they can see and hear their baby. There is no doubt that of all the alternatives this is the safest arrangement and affords the greatest margin for error. It is certainly safer than having the baby in her own room, and also safer than bed-sharing.

Bed-sharing with a baby is not for everyone, but actually it used to be. Early in the dawn of humankind, that was the way babies were designed – to be in intimate and continual contact with a caring person to give them security, food and warmth.

Then society changed. With the Industrial Revolution people got jobs and occupations that meant they needed a good undisturbed night's sleep. So babies were relegated into their own beds and were encouraged, even forced, despite their inborn need for short sleeps and frequent feeds, to sleep for long periods on their own. In sleep terminology, to consolidate their sleep pattern.

In the last few years, however, there has been a movement back to our origins, with a body of research suggesting that bed-sharing was natural and beneficial for both mother and baby. Lying warm and close together is an intimate and integral part of the act of breastfeeding and it initiates, enhances and encourages the whole process. The research also pointed to the low incidence of SUDI/SIDS in most bed-sharing cultures and the sheer enjoyment that many parents (and all babies) derive from it.

As I said, however, it is not for everyone. No parent should bed-share reluctantly because they have heard it has 'advantages'. The desire to partake in it should be embraced by the mother solely because of an instinctive wish to do it, because to them it feels right. Neither should it be done in desperation and reaction (for instance) to a screaming infant. It is less safe under these conditions.

Formula-fed babies and their parents also have a different set of responses while bed-sharing, both to each other and to sleep itself. Their best sleeping arrangement seems to be with the baby in a cot, next to the parent.

We also have to be a little more careful in the first months with those babies who were born small for their gestational age or who were born prematurely. These babies may not be as capable of keeping their air passages open if their sleeping position is not ideal. It is a good idea for these babies to be put back into an adjacent cot after feeds.

Recent research also emphasises the absolute importance of the safety rules surrounding it. Our sleeping arrangements are not the same as in the Pleistocene era when it evolved, and many modern sleeping comforts and bedroom furnishings are not suitable for babies. In addition it is very important that the parents' minds be clear and not clouded with alcohol, drugs, sleeping pills or fatigue. This is a critical aspect of bed-sharing with safety.

Advantages

- All babies love it. It makes them feel loved and secure, and enhances the bond between baby and parent.
- As breastfeeding is enhanced by night feeds, and babies who bed-share feed frequently, it can really boost the milk supply.
- It seems to encourage mothers to feed their babies until they are older.
- It minimises the baby's crying and unsettledness.
- Some studies from Dr James McKenna suggest that mothers get a better night's sleep than when solo sleeping.
- It feels natural and normal for many parents. The majority of breastfeeding mothers do it because it's more convenient and seems like a natural part of the whole process. Mothers naturally position their bodies in the bed to envelop the baby and make the feeding easier. Many just love it, relishing the feel, smell and taste of their baby.
- Mothers don't have to wake up fully at feed-times and as time goes on they become more skilled at sleep-time feeds.
- Theoretically it ought to decrease the incidence of SUDI/ SIDS. The mother's body automatically tends to envelop and nestle the baby. The presence of the mother's body offers the baby 'arousals' so he doesn't fall into level 3 (deep) sleep, to which babies are poorly adapted. However, in practice this decrease in incidence from bed-sharing has not been demonstrated.
- Some psychological studies point to the babies growing up with improved self-esteem and self-discipline. For more on this subject, see Dr James McKenna's website (https://cosleeping.nd.edu) and book.

Disadvantages

- Regarding the likelihood of SUDI there is no doubt that the margin for error is decreased in bed-sharers, compared to a baby sleeping in a separate cot. In a couple of recent studies, about 50 per cent of the cases of SUDI were in bed with a carer. However, in nearly all of the cases one or more of the preventable risk factors were present. No study has shown that bed-sharing is a risk factor *by itself* but with risk factors present (for example, sleeping on a sofa, or with smoking and drugs) the risk is certainly enhanced. It must be clearly understood by the parents that no sleeping arrangements immunise a baby from SUDI. We can only minimise the risk as much as possible, especially by back-sleeping, and being aware of the other risk factors and rules.

- The bed arrangements need thought and preparation.
- The rules and precautions must be strictly adhered to, and the risk factors known and, as much as possible, removed.
- It is definitely more disruptive to adult sleep patterns.
- It reduces couple time for the parents.
- Many fathers (and some mothers) would prefer to sleep only with their partners.
- Some mothers find bed-sharing too overwhelming and need more time to re-group and reconnect to themselves after childbirth.
- Some babies are noisy or travel around the bed when they sleep.
- Though it is usually easy to change the arrangement as the babies get older, some children do resist going into their own bed later.

Risks, rules and precautions

- No alcohol, drugs, or sedative medications are to be taken, as these induce deep, non-protective sleep.
- Parents should stay in light sleep, with an awareness of their baby. If they feel they sleep too deeply, co-bedding may not be for them.
- No extreme tiredness or exhaustion in parents, as they may fall into a deep sleep in which they will not protect their baby.

- No smoking by either partner at all. After smoking, we exhale a lethal gas (to a baby) for hours. Smoking outside does not help this particular issue (although it does decrease side-stream smoke in the home to some degree).
- Use a large conventional bed – a king size if possible. The baby's side should be up against the wall or a bolster used along the edge to prevent the baby falling overboard and being trapped between the mattress and the sheets.
- Be extra careful with ex-premature or small babies, whose resilience may not be as great as that of full-term babies.
- No overheating, as this can induce apnoea (cessation of breathing), so no waterbeds, doonas, bonnets, excess clothing or heavy bedcovers.
- No soft mattresses. The surface on which the baby sleeps should be firm. Old mattresses can develop troughs that could entrap a baby.
- No soft pillows, toys or bumpers or any other objects that can cover the baby's head and potentially smother them.
- The baby should not be unwell, as he will not be as resilient and there might be a potential for fevers and consequent overheating.
- No toddlers and no animals, as neither can be trusted not to lie on the baby.
- No unconventional sleeping arrangements, especially sofas and couches. These are a particular danger as the baby tends to end up in the cleft between the back and the seat cushions with a potential for smothering. Even mattresses on the floor have been described as a danger. Only large, firm, conventional beds should be used.
- If a parent has long hair they need to tie it back, as it could possibly entangle the infant.
- No gross obesity, as it makes your body less sensitive to your baby's position.

I reiterate that there is no doubt that the safest place regarding prevention of SUDI for the baby is to sleep in a cot next to the parents' bed. This gives a far greater margin for error and a greater scope for good observation than other arrangements.

If bed-sharing with the baby is embarked upon it must be treated with great respect. All the risks must be considered and rules must be adhered to without exception.

Problems may arise when parents are used to sleeping with their baby and it becomes their routine. There is the potential that if they have a couple of drinks they fall into their familiar routine unconsciously, and break the rules, possibly with tragic consequences. This is clearly what happens in many of the cases that end up in the coroner's court.

There are also devices available – cot-shaped areas that can be attached to the side of the parents' bed or low baskets that protect the baby within the family bed. These allow the advantages of bed-sharing with an increased safety margin, and these should be considered.

Bed share? Take care and be aware.

CHAPTER 16

SUDI/SIDS

THE NEWER LABEL OF SUDI (Sudden Unexpected Death in Infancy) is used nowadays to include not only SIDS babies where no cause for their death could be found, but also about 15 per cent of babies in whom a cause – a congenital inborn metabolic or heart problem, infection, suffocation or child abuse – is established by autopsy or death scene analysis.

The sudden, unexpected death of a child under one year of age has to be one of the most devastating occurrences in any parent's life. And this is even more poignant when no reason for it can be found.

Until recently, this happened too frequently. About two to three babies in every 1000 died from this condition. Then some doctors discovered that most of these babies were found on their front (prone) in their cot. They soon showed that when babies were placed on their backs to sleep, the chances of suffering from what was known then as SIDS or 'cot death' was greatly reduced.

What a difference the 'Back to Sleep' campaign made! Quite suddenly the incidence of SIDS was reduced by over 80 per cent in those countries that instigated a public health campaign about it. That was 20 years ago. There have been many studies looking at the risks of SUDI/SIDS since then in an effort to reduce the level still further. The pattern of cases seems to be changing lately – the babies who do die are younger, the peak incidence that was seen in winter seems to have gone and the concern about overheating remains, but seems less important.

Below are the risk factors and how they can be minimised.

Prone sleeping increases risk 3–14 times

I can still remember the days when paediatricians actually encouraged parents to put their babies down to sleep on their front. That was because it was found that premature babies, after feeding, emptied their stomachs quicker in that posture. Also it was noticed that babies slept deeper on their front and it suppressed the 'startle' reflex so they often settled better.

The early 1990s saw a massive beneficial change to that advice so babies are now always put in their cots face up. It is okay for them to be prone under supervision while they get some tummy time, which helps them develop good strength in their neck and also reduces the chance of them getting a flattened back of the head.

Nowadays the most dangerous situation is when babies, who usually sleep on their backs, are put down for the first time on their front – for instance, by a new carer. This increases the risk many more times.

It is not specifically known why the prone position is so dangerous. It is unlikely to be based purely on the smothering aspect where the airway is obstructed, though the diaphragm does not seem to work as efficiently in the prone position as compared to the back-sleeping baby. It could be that the baby re-breathes his expired air or has changes to his breathing drive. As mentioned above, we know babies tend to sleep more deeply when face down, which might be relevant; also the blood flow to the brain seems to diminish somewhat when the baby is face down.

Side-sleeping is not safe either, as a large number of babies when put down on their sides end up on their front.

Many parents are concerned that if the baby is on his back he may vomit and inhale. Many studies have shown that this fear is not justified. Even babies who reflux and vomit frequently are very good at keeping liquids out of their airways. They clear their throat efficiently and keep breathing by turning their heads to the side.

Face covering increases risk 17 times

This is the concern about blankets and soft toys covering the baby's face. Up to a quarter of SUDI victims have bedding material over their faces. It is not certain whether this causes smothering or overheating. A real danger is the doona or quilt, which is light and can easily float up and cover the baby's head during the night. Far safer is a sleeping bag or sheets and blankets with the baby's feet down touching the bottom of the cot so he can't slide lower.

Cigarette smoke increases risk in a dose–response relationship

This is probably the most important factor in reducing the incidence of SUDI. It is possible that up to two-thirds of SUDI cases could be avoided if all smoking in the baby's environment ceased. All the accumulating factors of smoking in pregnancy, mother, father or carer smoking, the number of cigarettes, whether in the same room or not, and the amount of environmental exposure to smoke, are all significant and the less the better. Smokers also tend to breastfeed less than non-smokers and that has an impact too.

Unsafe sleeping environments

As mentioned in Chapter 15 on bed-sharing, care should be taken regarding sleeping surfaces. The mattress should be firm and not saggy, nor too soft. Sheepskins, doonas, pillows, comforters and quilts can overheat or smother a baby. This issue is especially important should the baby be prone.

Cots should conform to the mandatory standard AS/NZS 2172.

There should be a sticker showing compliance – don't buy a second-hand one without the sticker. The mattress should fit snugly into the frame without a gap. Perhaps a new one for a new baby is a good idea.

Allowing a baby to sleep for periods in prams, strollers, bouncinettes and little chairs should be well thought through as they are not designed for the task. Make sure that the baby cannot sag and obstruct their breathing or fall to the side and smother. Better to pull them out and slide them into their cot.

Refer back to Chapter 15 for more detail on the risks of shared sleeping.

Immunisation decreases risk by half

There was a hysterical campaign a while ago suggesting that immunisation leads to an increase in SUDI. This has been comprehensively refuted now with numerous studies showing that immunisation *decreases* the incidence.

Breastfeeding decreases risk by one-third to half

There are a lot of studies all saying slightly different things; however, there is no doubt that any breastfeeding is beneficial to this risk, but exclusive breastfeeding for a longer time decreases the risk more.

Dummies (pacifiers) decrease risk by one-third

Careful studies do seem to show that these might offer some protection against SUDI, as does thumb-sucking. The problem is that the use of dummies can have a negative effect on breastfeeding as babies suck a dummy with their mouth shut and breastfeed with their mouth open. So if you wish to introduce a dummy, do so well after the breastfeeding is established and only if the baby seems to need or enjoy it. Better yet, encourage thumb-sucking, as a thumb can't fall out of the mouth and need you to find it and put it back.

Monitors

Cardio-respiratory or movement monitors for babies do not seem to offer any advantages to prevent the occurrence of SUDI. They also can give parents a false sense of security or conversely cause anxiety by sounding false alarms.

The future

Taken in tandem with the rules about bed-sharing, avoiding the above risks and implementing the helpful factors should theoretically reduce the incidence of SUDI/SIDS to 0.1 in every 1000 babies.

It's up to every parent to be on their guard to prevent this tragedy from happening to their family.

CHAPTER 17

When your baby gets sick

THERE IS LITTLE IN LIFE THAT is as worrying as the possibility that your baby may be unwell. For some reason this usually occurs in the middle of the night, during a public holiday and when your doctor is away. Or you're travelling. Somebody once said that within every child there is a virus that only emerges when you are more than 400 kilometres from home. So true!

Infants and toddlers frequently get viral infections, especially from other little children. When they are in day care, where they have a lot of contact among themselves, the average number of infections is about 14 per year. That, to the parents, feels almost continuous! These infections usually centre on the nose (causing snuffles or runny nose) and throat and lungs (causing coughs, altered voice or stridor, which is difficulty breathing in) or the gut (causing diarrhoea) and are often associated with a fever. Any temperature over 38°C is significant and should be given attention. If it is not easily controlled, medical attention should be sought.

Most of these respiratory and gut viruses will run their course over a few days, usually peaking after two to three days when things improve by themselves. If your baby is over two months old, paracetamol or ibuprofen can be used without medical advice and usually helps to control the fevers and make the baby feel more comfortable. However, research has shown that controlling the temperature with these agents is actually not essential and, in fact, can cause the infection to last slightly longer; but it is reasonable to use them if the baby is uncomfortable. Viruses and their infections are completely unaffected by antibiotics and these should not be used unless the doctor feels that there is a bacterial risk, component or complication to the infection.

Bacterial infections are quite another matter. Usually the temperature is higher and the babies are sicker (although this is not always the case). These infections, whether in the lungs, urinary tract, middle ear, blood or the membranes overlying the brain (meningitis), can be treated successfully with antibiotics, and the sooner the better. Young babies are particularly susceptible to these infections, and as they have less efficient immunity they tend to allow what would be a local infection to enter the bloodstream and infect other parts of the body. It is for this reason that young babies with a fever are frequently admitted to hospital and given a 'septic workup' and treated (see later in this chapter).

It is for a few of these sorts of infections that vaccines are strongly recommended. Mention is made of the HIB vaccine later in this chapter, but the vaccine for pneumococcal infection, that can invade the meninges or lungs, is as important. The incidence of this infection has dropped enormously since the Prevenar vaccine was introduced. Pertussis (whooping cough) is also a preventable bacterial disease with an effective vaccine. Prevention is always better than cure.

WORRYING SIGNS IN BABIES

General

Fever: The safest place to take your baby or child's temperature is under their arm. If the temperature is more than 38°C (101°F), it is significant and you should seek medical advice.

If the temperature is below this, but still elevated, a dose of paracetamol (15 mg/kg body weight) or ibuprofen (10 mg/kg) should be administered in the over two month old to see if this brings it down. In young babies, mild temperatures can be due to over-wrapping if the weather or the room is too warm.

Pallor: If the baby is pale, check whether it is just the face (which, on its own, tends to be less serious), or also includes the tongue, mouth and lips. This would indicate a more important problem with oxygenation or blood pressure; for instance, she may be suffering from a shock reaction or severe stress from a fall or accident. She should be wrapped warmly in a blanket, lying down, and taken to a medical facility for urgent care.

Less serious, but still of importance, is pallor from anaemia. A common cause of this, in infants and toddlers, is iron deficiency, especially as they head towards one year of age. This is made more likely by feeding them normal cow's milk long before one year of age, and in breastfed children who are picky with their food intake and refuse meat and other iron-rich foods. Get your doctor to check the blood for anaemia and iron level.

Blueness (or cyanosis) of the nails or, especially, of the lips and tongue is often a serious matter. This condition is called cyanosis – lack of oxygen in the blood – and it can be caused by heart or lung problems. It may be caused by poor circulation to the tissues, which can occur if the baby has a serious infection. Again, urgent medical attention should be sought.

Refusing feeds in young babies or taking reduced amounts over a number of feeds may be a harmless temporary matter but it could also be the presentation of a serious illness. If it persists or the baby has other worrying signs, it would be worth having her checked before night falls.

Dehydration: Fewer than two wet nappies a day may indicate this. Well-hydrated babies will have at least five wet nappies a day. If their fluid intake is reduced, or they have vomiting and/or diarrhoea they are very susceptible to becoming dehydrated. Such babies need medical attention. Unlike adults and bigger children, babies have very little reserve of fluid in their small bodies. Consequently they will tend to become dehydrated in a very short time if their fluid loss from diarrhoea becomes excessive. In the absence of vomiting it is often possible to maintain adequate fluid balance by giving older babies and toddlers oral electrolyte solutions. Electrolytes are the chemicals sodium, potassium and chloride, which are in high concentration in our blood. In diarrhoea they can be excreted in the stool and this can cause depletion in the blood. Even without vomiting, smaller, younger babies with diarrhoea might still be unable to keep up with their fluid loss orally and need intravenous fluid therapy administered in hospital.

Many people are concerned if the fontanelle (the soft spot on top of the skull) is slightly sunken, and this is sometimes mistakenly interpreted as caused by dehydration. On its own this is not so. When babies are sitting up and relaxed, often the fontanelle is slightly depressed and a pulse may be seen within it. This is normal. If the baby is so dehydrated that the fontanelle is abnormally sunken, there will be other signs present. The mouth will be dry, the skin will 'tent' when a fold is raised, and on gentle pressure of the eyeball behind a closed lid, it will have the feel of the inside, not the outside, of a tomato. Babies who are so dehydrated as to have a sunken fontanelle will be 10–15 per cent dehydrated. It will be obvious.

Excessive crying: Many babies cry excessively (in the parents' opinion), but if this is not your baby's usual pattern it deserves close attention. If the baby continues to feed normally, has prolonged breaks from the crying and has no other worrying physical signs, one can be patient. This is a more important sign in the older infant or toddler if it is out of character for them.

Doesn't 'look right': You know how your baby or child normally looks. After a few days if you are worried by his appearance, get him seen to promptly, and certainly before night falls.

Respiratory

Elevated respiratory rate: The normal rate in babies is 40 breaths per minute and this drops to 20–30 breaths per minute in the first year. Prolonged breathing rates in excess of this are abnormal and may indicate serious respiratory disease.

In the first few months, however, babies may have 'periodic breathing' where the breathing rate alternates between fast (up to 120 breaths per minute) and periods of up to nine seconds apnoea (no breathing). So count the breathing rate over a full minute before making this diagnosis.

Difficulty with breathing:
Breathing in: difficulty drawing in the breath is called 'stridor'. It means there is narrowing in the throat, larynx, trachea or the bronchi; that is, the larger main airways to the lungs. This occurs typically with croup, which is usually caused by a viral infection in these upper airways. Before the vaccine was developed there was also a condition called epiglottitis in which the bacterium *haemophilus influenzae type B* (HIB) caused severe inflammation of the flap at the top of the larynx. This would start with stridor, which rapidly worsened to completely obstruct the airway. These infants would die without intensive care to keep the airway open. The condition has disappeared since the early 1990s after the introduction of the HIB vaccine (in those who are immunised).

Breathing out: difficulty breathing out is called 'wheezing' and it typically occurs with asthma-like illnesses. The narrowing in these diseases is in the small airways of the lung known as the bronchioles. The baby can breathe in easily but then the air is trapped as these narrowed small airways collapse and obstruct the 'out' breath. The trapped air may be seen as 'barrelling' of the baby's chest, which is expanded front to back. Asthma is caused by a narrowing and constriction of the tiny airways or bronchioles in the periphery of the lungs caused by an allergic reaction. It is extremely unusual in babies in their first year. The most common reason for a baby to wheeze at this age is bronchiolitis; that is, inflammation of the bronchioles, usually caused by a virus. The most common virus to cause this is respiratory syncytial virus (RSV), which is highly infectious and causes a copious secretion by the bronchioles. It is the mucus and the swelling of of the bronchiole that causes the obstruction.

Snuffles and blocked noses in babies are common and not usually a serious matter. Many young babies who are breastfed develop severe snuffles as a consequence of syphoning milk up into the nose and the delicate air passages. These produce mucus to protect themselves from this onslaught. It is quite harmless and will run its own course. In the older child it is usually due to viral infection, past or present.

Coughing is especially concerning:

- if it has a barking or 'seal-like' quality. This is usually caused by croup viruses or, as described before, very rarely, inflammation of the epiglottis. It is often repetitive and hacking.
- if it is so intense that it finishes with a vomit. With these two kinds of cough it is necessary to make sure the baby does not have pertussis (whooping cough), which can be a very serious illness especially in babies.
- if it is productive and sounds like a 'smoker's cough'. This is a cough usually caused by the overproduction of mucus often as a consequence of bronchitis, or even more so in bronchiolitis. In bronchiolitis the mucus glands increase in size and number to counteract the presence of the virus. After the virus disappears these glands can continue to overproduce mucus for weeks as they slowly return to their pre-infection size.

Alimentary tract (the gut)

Repeated projectile vomiting: When this occurs in babies in the first weeks of age, a condition called 'pyloric stenosis' must be considered. It presents by a rapid increase in spectacular vomiting over the course of a couple of days. It tends to occur in male babies, many of whom are firstborn. It is caused by a thickened muscle ring around the exit of the stomach, which causes narrowing of the outlet that prevents the stomach contents from draining down into the small bowel. When diagnosed, this needs an urgent surgical operation.

The most common cause of projectile vomiting, however, is still the reflux that occurs in many babies and which can be a constant feature of their early life. In contrast, the vomiting of pyloric stenosis starts suddenly and accelerates to a climax over the course of a couple of days.

Vomiting in combination with diarrhoea: The combination of these two is usually caused by a virus (the most common being rotavirus); however, it can be caused by bacteria. In babies or young infants it can cause rapid dehydration because, as noted previously, babies' fluid reserves are small. It needs urgent hospital attention.

Diarrhoea: Fully breastfed babies, especially in the first few weeks, may produce 20 gassy explosive stools a day and this can be normal. The normal stool is milky and opaque. Diarrhoea, on the other hand, is watery and 'urine-like'. This is usually alongside the baby being generally unwell (though not necessarily) and having a fever. In older babies, oral electrolyte preparations may be used to keep up the child's hydration until spontaneous recovery occurs after a few days. However, in the young baby (under four to five months) medical attention should be sought, as many will require intravenous fluids to stay hydrated and maintain their fluid balance.

Following a bout of infective gastroenteritis, many babies lose the ability to absorb the sugar in milk (lactose). Lactose is the main sugar in milk and if it cannot be absorbed it will hold onto fluid in the gut and this will be passed in the stool and create more diarrhoea. So although the infection has passed and the virus has disappeared, the diarrhoea may continue. Testing the stool shows that it contains a large amount of lactose and this makes the diagnosis. If the baby is formula fed, the feed can be changed to one which is lactose free. If the baby is breastfed it is often best to continue the breastfeeding as long as hydration can be maintained easily.

Blood in the stool: This usually gets parental attention rapidly.

The most common cause is mild irritation of the lining of the large bowel. It is sometimes caused by cow's milk protein allergy (CMPA) but most often occurs for no known reason. The blood is usually in small amounts and is in combination with mucus. The baby should be medically checked but the condition usually will run its course.

What needs to be ruled out is the bloody stool of 'intussusception', which is a serious obstruction due to the small bowel folding in on itself. The stools are typically described as having the appearance of redcurrant jelly and the infant has bouts of severe abdominal pain. This infant needs to go to hospital for radiological and possibly surgical attention.

A fissure or crack in the anus can be caused by the passage of a large, hard stool. Following its formation small amounts of bright blood may be seen coating the stool. This condition needs medical attention and careful treatment with stool softeners to avoid constipation and to allow healing.

Blood in the vomit: This can occur as a consequence of ulcers and inflammation at the lower end of the oesophagus. It can occur in severe reflux or from CMPA and should be investigated by a paediatrician or gastroenterologist.

Bile in the vomit: This discolours the vomit bright green, even a fluorescent colour. Bile is produced in the duodenum beyond the stomach and there is no good reason for it to return to the stomach to be vomited. Bilious vomiting tends to occur when there is an obstruction in the small bowel beyond the duodenum. This needs radiological investigation and surgical attention.

Skin

Increasing jaundice over one week of age: After a baby is born, jaundice normally rises for three to four days, plateaus and then reduces gradually over the next few days. If the level is still increasing, there may be a blood problem of increased red blood cell breakdown, or a feeding problem causing dehydration. It is possibly a serious matter and needs medical attention.

The most common reason for jaundice to remain after a week or so is breastmilk jaundice. This is prolonged, usually mild, jaundice, caused by a substance in the breastmilk that maintains a low or moderate level of jaundice, sometimes for weeks. If this is the cause, it is always harmless, but it can only be diagnosed by exclusion of all the other (possibly harmful) conditions. So if you are not sure, get your baby checked as high jaundice levels can cause serious trouble if left unassessed and untreated.

Generalised rash on trunk: A rash of red and/or raised spots, called an exanthem, may be the consequence of a general viral infection. There is also the possibility of an allergy causing it. It needs medical attention. The most serious rash and one needing immediate attention is the 'petechial' rash. This rash is caused by small haemorrhages within the skin. It is diagnosed by pressing on the skin lesion with a clear glass – and it will not blanch and disappear. It can be related to meningococcal infection, which needs urgent treatment.

Blisters on the skin: These can be caused by an allergic response. However, they can be caused by infections either bacterial or viral. Some of the infections can be very serious so these need to be ruled out. Rarely some congenital genetic conditions can cause severe blistering and need urgent medical attention.

Redness and inflammation around the mouth: Rash developing around the mouth following new foods can be a manifestation of an allergic sensitivity to that food.

Weeping rash with the area greater than 5 cm across: Some bacteria can cause quite serious skin infections that look like burns. They need urgent treatment with antibiotics.

Redness and inflammation around the base of the umbilical cord before it has separated: Occasionally bacteria can enter the umbilical stump and cause serious infections as they invade the baby's circulation. This sign needs urgent medical attention.

Ears and eyes

- Wax from the ears is normal (and means the ears should be dried more thoroughly after bathing); however, discharge, especially with pus, is not normal. Inflammation of the outer ear canal or from a ruptured ear drum from middle ear infection both need medical attention and antibiotics.

- Inability or reluctance to open one eye can occur. A spasm of the eyelid occurs if there is an infection or a foreign body in the eye.

- Sticky eyes or infected blocked tear ducts are quite common after birth. They should be cleaned with saline solution and possibly (after a few days or weeks) treated with antibiotic drops. Some viruses can cause conjunctivitis – the eye is sticky but also the white of the eye is red and has dilated blood vessels. This needs medical attention.

- Squints that come and go are fairly common following birth and for the first three months or so. The baby tends to only use the image from one eye at a time for this period and the other eye's gaze can deviate away. After three months, the eyes should be straight and together in their gaze.

Neurological

Fits or convulsions: These are caused by abnormal electrical discharges from the brain. The most common cause is a 'febrile convulsion' where the brain reacts in this way to a high temperature. However, there are many other much more serious causes and this needs urgent medical attention. If there is any possibility of a seizure occurring, seek medical care.

'Benign nocturnal myoclonia' (Latin for 'harmless, night-time, jerking movements of the muscles) is a fairly common condition, in which the baby's limbs may jerk spasmodically and rhythmically when the baby or child is falling asleep. It is not serious but medical attention should be sought to exclude other, more serious, conditions.

Not moving limbs symmetrically: Clearly it is necessary to find out what is going on in this situation. Following birth some peripheral nerves may be damaged by the birth process, especially in the face or the arm. But weakness caused by brain problems is a possibility and needs investigating.

Baby is floppy: If the baby's muscular tone is reduced and she feels a little like a rag doll, it is necessary to seek medical advice to determine the cause.

Drowsiness, listlessness: This may be caused by a number of potentially dangerous problems, such as infections, general illnesses or inborn metabolic problems. Seek medical help.

If the baby or child exhibits any of the above signs or symptoms, it is a good idea to seek medical advice sooner rather than later. If you are uncertain, it is better to seek medical advice during the day. Everything looks worse at night, and finding a doctor is more difficult. Accident and emergency departments are also more crowded at that time (with worried parents like you).

THE SEPTIC WORKUP (FOR BABIES UNDER THREE MONTHS)

If the doctors suspect an infection in your baby, who is less than three months of age, they will wish to do a 'septic workup'.

This means that following a full medical examination, a sample of blood, urine and cerebrospinal fluid (CSF) will be examined for the presence of germs, and other investigations will also be done to confirm or exclude an infection.

The process is explained below.

Blood

This is taken by a needle in a vein, for:
1. examination of the white cells (type and number) – these increase in number and react in certain ways when challenged by germs in the body;

207

2. a small amount of blood that will be sent for bacterial culture (to see if germs grow in 48 hours); and

3. measuring the C-reactive protein level (this is a specific protein that becomes elevated in the presence of infection).

Urine

This is best taken by a needle into the bladder (it's quite safe when done properly) or catheter so the urine is not contaminated by the baby's skin. It will be sent to a laboratory for examination for cells (type and number) and bacterial culture. Urine collected by a special plastic bag stuck to your baby's skin ('a bag urine') is less reliable.

Cerebrospinal fluid (CSF)

This is obtained by a needle placed between the vertebrae in the lower back into the fluid space surrounding (but much lower than) the spinal cord. It is examined for inflammatory cells and chemical signals that indicate whether the baby has meningitis (either from bacteria or viruses). This is also sent to a laboratory for culture and viral tests. A sample of CSF is vital if meningitis is a possibility (and it usually is considered) as it can give an immediate answer that will alter the treatment options.

It has to be done. As every paediatric doctor is taught: 'If you don't put a needle in it, you'll put your foot in it.'

Chest X-ray

This also may be done if a respiratory infection is suspected. The X-ray dose nowadays is really low (about the same dose as an international trip in an aeroplane) and it can give important information about whether an infection has invaded the lungs.

Once these tests are done, treatment can start without masking the diagnosis. Antibiotics are given into a vein via an intravenous infusion (a 'drip'), not as oral medicine. This is because in babies and young infants, infection can spread quickly as their immunity is not very efficient until they are older. The treatment will be continued until the results from the blood and CSF cultures are ready, which takes at least 48 hours. If the cultures are negative, that means there was no infection or that the infection was caused by a virus. The option is then to stop the antibiotics, which is preferred. However, if the baby is still unwell it may be decided to continue them for other reasons, such as the possibility of complications caused by bacteria.

By then, of course, the baby may be perfectly well. Babies tend to get sick quite quickly, but equally they recover rapidly too. So your hospital stay is not likely to be a long one for a mild viral infection.

CHECKING YOUR BABY'S ILLNESS ON THE INTERNET

A word about Dr Google: unfortunately he's not very good, as he overstates the bad things and understates the good. Remember that people tend to contribute to the information on the internet when things go horribly wrong and the ones who have a good result are so happy they don't bother. Consequently it is easy to read information that will tend to panic you unnecessarily and is likely to be dead wrong anyway.

'Cyberchondria' is a terrible condition. Immunise yourself by staying off the web until you've seen your doctor!

INFECTIOUS DISEASES IN BABIES AND CHILDREN

After the birth, for the first three months or so, the baby is less susceptible to infections than later. In the first trimester of pregnancy the mother transfers antibodies to her foetus that her body developed in response to the infectious diseases she had been exposed to in her life.

This is called 'passive immunisation' and these antibodies fade from the baby's circulation; by six weeks the level has dropped by half, so by three months the level is so low that he is vulnerable. Then it is necessary for the baby to build up his own antibody levels, hence why he needs 'active' immunisation through vaccination. These antibodies can last him for much longer, some for a lifetime.

Babies, however, remain susceptible to some infectious diseases, many of which have no vaccine available or are caused by viruses that mutate and change regularly, such as influenza. Also some vaccines, though effective for most of the population, cannot give complete coverage to everyone.

So, babies remain vulnerable to some infectious diseases.

Let's look at the diseases that are still prevalent in our lives. There is a number of infections that start as a cold- or a flu-like illness then develop a red skin rash. They can all be confused with each other.

Listed in order of increasing severity:

1. ROSEOLA: This usually mild disease is caused by a couple of viruses in the herpes family (HHV6 and HHV7). It starts with a cold-like illness, fever and occasionally diarrhoea. It lasts about two to three days before a faint pink, non-itchy rash emerges on the child's trunk and the fever settles. It tends to affect children under two years of age. Incubation period is ten days; infectious period is three days. Treatment is paracetamol/ ibuprofen only. No vaccine available.

2. FIFTH DISEASE (Slapped cheek): This is caused by a virus called Parvovirus B19. Usually affecting older toddlers, they develop a cold-like illness and fever for a few days until a prominent bright red (slapped cheek) rash occurs on the face. Usually the child is not too sick but improves anyway when the rash appears. It can be followed by a 'lace-like' rash over the rest of the body. Incubation period is from two to four weeks; infectious period ceases when the rash appears. Pregnant women who are not immune to this disease are vulnerable to

it, which can cause damage to their foetus in the first trimester, so beware the pregnant babysitter or childcare worker.

3. RUBELLA (German measles): This is usually a mild disease with most people developing the antibodies without knowing they had the disease (so-called sub-clinical infection). Again, a flu-like illness, fever, sore throat and swollen glands in the neck followed by a fine red rash over the whole of the body three days later. Incubation period from two to three weeks with an infectious period until rash disappears. The most important aspect of this disease is that it can cause serious damage or even death in first-trimester foetuses of unimmunised mothers. It is very successfully prevented by the MMR vaccine.

4. VARICELLA (measles): A potentially serious disease of the same pattern but with a more extensive rash, and also includes ulcers and lesions in the mouth. The rash is prominent, the fever can be high (up to 40°C) and the disease lasts for eight to ten days. The incubation period is from nine to 12 days, and it is highly contagious during this time and the infectious period which continues until the rash has disappeared. Complications are not rare and include diarrhoea, middle ear infection and even brain inflammation. It also has a high mortality in the developing world. Happily it is also prevented by the MMR vaccine.

These are other important infectious diseases:

5. RESPIRATORY SYNCYTIAL VIRUS: This extremely common disease infects almost all infants by the time they are two years old. It also affects many adults who can help its spread as it is highly contagious. In older people it tends to cause a flu-like illness, but in infants and children it mostly causes bronchiolitis. One of the most prominent aspects is that the virus causes the copious

production of mucus by the small airways of the lungs.
The virus only lasts a few days in the lungs but the effects
of the overproduction of mucus can last for much longer
– often for weeks, with the infant coughing like a smoker
(especially at night). Incubation period is two to eight days,
infectious period about five days. Infection unfortunately
does not confer immunity and infants and children can
be infected more than once. Young babies may need to go
to hospital if they are unable to feed adequately because
of the cough and mucus; likewise anyone who also gets
the complicating pneumonia (infection in the lung tissue).
Treatment is symptomatic only. Vaporisers are often used
at home but unfortunately they do not help.

6. PERTUSSIS (whooping cough): This nasty infection is
caused by bacteria called *Bordatella pertussis*. It causes
the production of thick tenacious mucus from the lungs,
which is intensely irritating to the cough reflex but
very hard to cough up. The 'whoop' is the sound of the
in breath after a prolonged bout of coughing that has
emptied the lungs of air. It is particularly dangerous in
young babies, who are very vulnerable as their mother's
antibodies are usually ineffective at protecting them
(or their mother for that matter). As the organism is a
bacterium (not a virus), treatment is with antibiotics,
which is effective at removing the organism but not
necessarily stopping the disease process. Incubation
period is from seven to 21 days with an infectious period
lasting until five days after antibiotics have been
administered. The vaccine is 90 per cent effective and
in the 10 per cent remaining, it lessens the severity of
the disease. The antibodies produced by infection or
vaccination in childhood tend to wear out by adulthood,
leaving older folk vulnerable. Adult vaccination is
therefore vitally important for those in contact with a
newborn baby (parents, grandparents and other carers).

7. CHICKEN POX: Once you've had chicken pox (or the vaccination) you are immune from this disease for life, which is why only children get this disease. It has a long incubation period of up to three weeks and, towards the end of this time, children can pass on the infection but be apparently healthy. They then start with a flu-like illness for a few days, before crops of red, raised spots appear, first on the body, before spreading to the limbs and face. The spots then become blisters with clear fluid in them. The crops can continue to erupt for some days and the child is highly infectious from their respiratory secretions or the fluid from the skin blisters until the last scab of the last spot has separated. The child should be isolated from other children and especially pregnant women who are not immune. A significant percentage of children can also get the virus (which is called *varicella zoster*) into their central nervous system and develop meningitis and other similar complications. These children need to be looked after in hospital. Chicken pox is not always a trivial disease – which is why the vaccine is so strongly recommended. Treatment for the usual disease is symptomatic: paracetamol/ibuprofen for the fever and a soothing lotion, such as calamine, for the spots.

8. HAND, FOOT AND MOUTH DISEASE: This is caused by a group of viruses called enteroviruses (such as the 'coxsackie' virus). The incubation period is from three to seven days. It is a relatively mild disease of a fever followed by the emergence of a blistery rash in the mouth, on the soles and palms and also on the buttocks. It usually lasts only from seven to ten days but is infectious during this time and the child should be isolated from other children. The mouth lesions can be sore and should be treated with soothing oral gels and cool drinks. The rest of the treatment is symptomatic: paracetamol/ibuprofen for fever and local dressings to the blisters.

9. IMPETIGO is also worth a mention as it's one of the most common skin diseases in children. It is caused by a common skin bacterium and is highly infectious between children, and even to adults. It causes sores in little clusters, which weep fluid and characteristically cover with a honey-coloured crust. Antibiotics, especially flucloxacillin, quickly control the infection and allow the spots to heal.

10. ORAL HERPES: Sometime in the first couple of years of any child's life they will come into contact with the oral herpes virus – the one that causes cold sores. The first infection can be completely hidden, where the child just develops the antibodies and never manifests the disease, but in some they can get a nasty oral gum infection, which is quite painful. The gums are covered by a blistery rash that is so sore the child is reluctant to close their mouth or swallow. It clears up in a few days and subsequent cold sores are not common. Treatment is just with soothing oral creams and analgesics. No fun at all.

CARING FOR A SICK INFANT AT HOME

If you have a baby or toddler in the house, this issue is not about if, but when. So think ahead and make a plan. If you have gone back to work you may need some backup if because of the illness your child is not allowed to go to day care. A study by Audrey Vand-enHeuvel of 1500 working families with children showed that 15 per cent of parents of sick children sent them to school or day care because they had no contingency plan. This is an area where grandparents rule, but if they are out of town you'll need a friend, nurse or nanny. You may be lucky and have a helpful employer who will let you either take the child with you to work (if she's not too sick) or take time off. The same Australian study showed nearly half of parents needed to stay off work at some time to look after their sick child.

So let us look at the issues of caring for a sick baby or child. Having established that the child does not need hospital admission or further medical care for her illness, we need to sort her out at home.

Here are some important points:

- Don't make her feel guilty for being sick. Pretend that it's okay for you to be off work and you would love a day with her at home (even if it's hopelessly inconvenient). In fact if you are usually at work, use this period to reconnect with your child and have some fun.
- Don't let her know you are anxious about her. There is a direct correlation between how anxious and depressed a child is about her illness and how worried her parents are about it. So get a friend to comfort and calm you and don't let your little one know you are anything other than bright and breezy.
- The process of looking after a sick child at home is exhausting. As much as you are able, also look after yourself. Get in some help if you can.

Bed rest

This is usually recommended by doctors for adults, but not for children. Tired children will lie down and sleep. Sick children will generally not want to move around much anyway but should not be tied to their bed. For toddlers and older children (but not babies), they might prefer to be under a doona on the sofa instead.

Give them a room with a nice view outside if possible. Studies have shown that people recover faster when they can see the natural world outside, rather than a brick wall.

If the child is distressed, this might be a time to temporarily return her to your bedroom, perhaps on a mattress on the floor. Even independent children become dependent babies again when sick.

Fluids and food

Give them plenty to drink. If they don't want to eat, don't force them. If they are unwell, they will often not eat for days at a time so make sure their drinks are nutritious. Don't worry if your baby or toddler loses a bit of weight; it will be replaced rapidly when she is well again.

Fever

If her temperature is over 38°C, bringing it down with paracetamol (15 mg per kg body weight) or ibuprofen (10 mg per kg) every four to six hours is reasonable. A recent report from the American Academy of Pediatrics outlines that these 'antipyretic' drugs are overused and actually slow the resolution of the infection by a few hours, but it is not significant enough not to offer this comfort to the child.

If the temperature is very high (40°C), placing the child in a lukewarm bath (not cold) might offer comfort and some control to the temperature. If the temperature is that high, of course, the infant or child should get (or have had) medical attention.

Cough

Coughing usually with increased mucusiness is a common symptom with upper respiratory tract infections. It tends to get worse in the night as the child lies down and the temperature of the room falls.

With wet coughs in children, be wary of over the counter drugs such as cough suppressants or expectorants. They don't work very well and the cough may well be useful, bringing up the mucus from the airways of the lungs.

For babies over one year of age, using manuka honey has been shown to decrease coughing and is well accepted by youngsters. For this age group and older if the cough is dry and repetitive a small amount of cough suppressant at night can be helpful.

There is no evidence that vaporisers or humidifiers help at all. They just make your walls damp.

Vomiting

Vomiting is a common symptom and not always associated with stomach infections. It becomes dangerous only when it is copious and accompanied by diarrhoea. In young babies this combination can threaten their hydration and is a reason to take them to hospital for an opinion. Generally older children are more resilient and small amounts of fluid regularly can help, but if the vomiting becomes excessive or continuous, see a doctor anyway.

Diarrhoea

Excessive diarrhoea can be a threat to a baby's hydration, especially if they are also vomiting. This is an indication for hospital admission and possibly for an intravenous drip. If it is mild, the only management necessary is the replacement of the lost fluid and electrolytes. Sachets of replacement electrolytes can be obtained from pharmacists but if it is serious enough to require them, the baby probably needs medical attention.

Never use kaolin (clay) medicines or Lomotil or Imodium medicines for babies or young children.

General points

Here are a few practical tips to help you look after your sick child:

- Make sure the bedroom is well aired and the child is not too hot. Wrapping up feverish children is unhelpful, uncomfortable and potentially dangerous.
- If they have a cough and are hoarse, give them a bell by their bed so they can summon you. Remember to take it away after they're better!
- Tell them the truth about their illness. Explain to them what is happening to them and what may happen in the future; for instance, they may have further fever or vomit again. Be upbeat but honest.
- Ask them how they are feeling and listen to their answers. Then reassure them that all is under control. If it's not, they should be in hospital.

217

- Distract them when they are distressed. Give them a massage, show them an animated movie or play with them. Pretend their teddy is sick and both of you look after him, administering medicines and treatment. Let the child use her doctor's kit to help her dolly, as this helps her to work out her issues with her illness.
- Use rewards and treats, especially after unpleasant medicines or treatment. Generally, within reason, give them what they want.

Looking after your sick child at home for the first time can be a harrowing experience, with long nights on call and numerous demands on your time and energy. It is a time when your anxiety can also prevent you sleeping even when there is an opportunity. So spread the load if you can by getting some help.

Wash your hands constantly if there is infection in the house or you will be next in line for the germs – infections are most commonly transmitted by hands. Have a dispenser of antiseptic hand sanitiser by the child's bed, by the door and in the bathroom, and you and the child should use it frequently but especially after nappy changing or the handling of wet tissues.

You can bet that you won't have the luxury of being looked after when you get the infection next!

IMMUNISATION

I'll keep this brief. All I want to say further on this subject is that I know of no immununologist, infectious diseases special-ist or paediatrician who has not insisted on immunising his or her own children. Tellingly, for the conspiracy theorists, it is not those physicians who do the immunisation. That task lies with the family doctors, so, wild though such a speculation is, there could be no reward or kick-back from Big Pharma to persuade them to get it done.

There is a lot about the cellular chemistry, the molecular biology of immunisation, and the intricacies of manufacturing of vaccines that I know little about, but I do know the basic science and practical paediatric information which convinces me completely.

For these matters I trust my colleagues who specialise in it, like immunologist Professor Sir Gustof Nossol who, among holding many other prestigious positions, was Chairman of the World Health Organization's Vaccines and Biologicals Program. I leave the arcane details to such experts with trust and confidence.

Doing your 'own research' on the internet is a waste of time and energy and will open the door to foolish uncertainty and anxiety.

Just do it.

CHAPTER 18

Your day: using play to connect with your baby

OVER THE YEARS QUITE A FEW mothers have asked me with that slightly panicked look of the swimmer getting out of her depth: 'But what do I DO with her all day?'

They quite reasonably want to know how they can usefully spend what seem like sometimes interminable days with their young babies. They want to keep their babies calm and settled but also help them develop to their full potential and, at the same time, not drive themselves potty with boredom.

There is no doubt that the babies' environment, particularly in the early years when their brains are making so many vital connections, plays an enormous role in how babies interpret the world around them and their particular place in it, and, over time, develop a rounded personality.

The main part of their environment that has the biggest impact on all of this is of course their parents and carers – the people with whom they interact, imitate and use as a model day by day.

The process of learning in babies and children is through play. Play is learning and learning is play: they are inextricably linked.

However, up to the age of 18 months infants need help to be guided to play creatively and to push their little boundaries.

This chapter lays out the fundamentals of the developmental steps babies go through and how we can help them along their path. For the most part parents really only need this information to perhaps reassure them that they're doing okay. Unfortunately almost an inevitable part of parenthood is the feeling of guilt that you are not quite doing it right. This, I suspect, is a fairly modern phenomenon which may well be related to the fact that parents tend to spend less time in the home and with their children than in the past.

The two-income family now seems to be a modern necessity. It is said that the median income in the developed world is much the same now as it was in the 1960s in relative terms. However, in the earlier time this income was earned by only one parent, usually the father.

Governments are starting to realise how vital these early months are to babies' ultimate development. Parental leave programs are beginning to spring up in the developed world. Still too short-term and too paltry, but at least it's in the right direction. Enlightened governments must realise that allowing parents to spend time with their babies and infants is one of the best investments they can make for a stable, happy and productive society in the future.

NEWBORN

The baby uses all five senses to explore the world but for the first few weeks that world is mostly encompassed by her mother – by the sight, smell, taste and feel of her breasts and by her face, hands and body. In the first few weeks, however, all of these senses are one to the baby. They are bombarded with input but cannot define which is which, what is vision and what is hearing; what is inside their body and what is outside. Consequently it is easy to overload them with too many stimuli. So try to keep everything simple.

For instance, if you are going to chat to your baby, try to reduce extraneous noise from TVs, radios or other people around, so the baby can concentrate.

Let's look at the senses and see how we can help the baby expand and enjoy them.

Vision

In these early weeks, your baby is mostly interested in your face, simple objects and light.

Despite their eyes seeming somewhat unfocused, babies see clearly from birth, though they are a little short-sighted, with a focal distance of around 17 to 20 cm. They do not have detailed colour vision to start with. That will arrive later.

Babies take delight in certain patterns; their favourite by far is that of the human face. This tendency to look into the eyes of those around them seems to be hardwired at birth and may relate to the affection and love such a gaze evokes. They also like contrasting patterns and will run their gaze along the edge of stripes, enjoying the contrast of white and black. This is how babies get some depth perception from what they see. By looking at the edges of objects, they can get a sense of foreground and background. They do prefer, however, a pattern of curves rather than zigzags. This possibly relates to the soft features of a face – their favourite object, if it's their mother's.

Play point

To your baby your face is the most beautiful thing in the universe. Let her gaze at you.

It is hard to believe but babies can imitate an expression on your face from early on and they also appreciate, and are amused, when you imitate their facial expression, and right from the start babies have a preference for a smiling face over a glum one. There is also evidence to suggest that laughing babies wire up their brains faster and more efficiently. You can certainly upset her with a frown.

Right from the start she will take delight in bright objects, especially those with faces and big eyes. She will prefer high-contrast images, such as simple black and white picture books or mobiles.

Play point

During her awake and alert time, get her attention and stick out your tongue, then raise your eyebrows and make your mouth an 'O'. Smile at her a lot and make her laugh. Be patient as you wait for her response, as babies' reaction times are quite slow.

Also don't overdo these episodes as your baby is easy to overload. As mentioned earlier, within the womb the foetus experiences a fairly bland view. Because vision is such a powerful medium it is easy to overwhelm babies in the first few weeks with too much visual input. Check that your baby does not become fussy and upset because of this. If she starts to look away, develops jerky movements or starts frowning, decrease the intensity of your interaction.

Hearing

The ear canals of the foetus become unplugged about half-way through pregnancy. From then on she is listening intently to the sounds around her. She very soon gets to recognise her mother's voice, its rhythm and cadence. The loudest and most pervasive sound, though, is that of her mother's heartbeat. As we know, that's why after birth babies are often calmed by such a sound or their bottom being gently patted at the maternal heart rate.

They also have a reflex that allows them to turn their heads in the direction of a sound.

Babies usually have a preference for higher voices over those with a lower frequency; that's why we instinctively raise our voice in 'baby talk'.

Some babies, however, find high-frequency sounds irritating. If you think this is so with your baby, try speaking to her in a low voice.

Play point

Talk to your baby in soothing tones, raising and lowering your voice in an interesting way. You might notice she opens her mouth when you're talking and shuts it when you pause.

She will love you to sing her gentle lullabies, nursery rhymes or other songs you love, and repeating simple rhythmic poems will attract and engage her. Lie on your back and position her on your chest when you do this, as she will love to feel the vibrations as well as hear the soothing tone of your voice.

Touch

Touch is essential to a baby's development. Babies who are not cuddled have difficulty developing in a normal way socially and tend to be anxious.

Even the lightest touch induces pleasurable hormones and brain chemicals such as oxytocin, endorphins and dopamine. These induce beneficial brain connections, which allow us to enjoy close relationships throughout our lives. These hormones are also secreted into a mother's body in response to touch and cuddles from her baby. Oxytocin is a hormone that causes your uterus to contract or your breasts to expel the milk, but it's also a neurotransmitter secreted within the brain. In this situation it induces a feeling of calm and connectedness. Just what a mother needs when looking after her baby! It's also secreted in the father when he spends time with his baby, touching and cuddling.

Play point

So cuddle your baby to calm and soothe her (and yourself). Give her a baby massage with some fragrant oil, remembering to keep the baby warm at all times and provide continuous touch during the massage.

'I get such a buzz from my baby,' said the rapidly talking businesswoman when she was in my office for a consultation. 'But I have no idea what's actually happening to me!'

I smiled at her encouragingly. 'How do you mean?'

'Well,' she said, settling into her seat, gazing briefly at the sleeping baby in the car capsule at her feet, 'I'm a tough cookie. Before I had Sam I worked in a big engineering company, where I fired people for a living. But since I've got him home, I've become a total wet noodle. All I want to do is feed him, and when I'm not feeding him I just want to gaze at him. I'm totally besotted.'

'I think that's great!' I said. 'How's the feeding going?'

'Really well!' she said. 'He feeds brilliantly. But just lately it's started to become a little disappointing. You see, he used to feed every two hours for about ten minutes but now he's reduced his feeds to around six times a day and I was enjoying the frequent feeds so much! Now I just hang around waiting for him to wake up so I can put him back on the breast. When he's feeding it gives me such a wonderful feeling, like an electric charge in my whole body. And I want to be nice to everyone. It's so unlike me.'

I laughed. 'Have you ever heard of the hormone oxytocin, or beta endorphin and prolactin? Because I think you're getting a good dose of all of them, especially oxytocin!'

Movement

For the newborn, most of the body movements are reflexes over which they have no control. They can turn their head to keep their airway open and they have a powerful gag reflex for the same reason.

Babies have a powerful grasp reflex and she will hang onto things placed in her hand. (Such as your hair!) If her head is allowed to drop slightly onto a mat, she will fling her hands out sideways and then bring her grasping hands back towards the midline – the 'startle' or Moro reflex.

They also have a powerful sucking reflex but as this movement is reflexive so they need guidance to latch effectively onto the breast. This process can take a little time for you both to get right and that's why it is a good idea to get professional help in the early days for this if it is proving difficult.

Right from the start babies enjoy the sound of their mother's voice and tend to move to the rhythm of her words. It seems that dance is inborn in humans. Babies like being gently rocked and swung. That's why babies like their dads to play with them, as they tend to interact with their babies in a much more physical way than mothers.

Babies like to be in an upright position and many find it calming. This can be mistaken for the 'need for burping', or even misdiagnosed as 'reflux' when the baby only settles when upright.

Always support your baby's head and neck when you raise her when she is on her back, as she cannot support flexing her head forward at all. However, when lying on her front she can momentarily raise her head and turn it to the side.

Play point

Give her brief episodes of 'tummy time' by putting her on a comfortable surface on her front. Some babies don't like it much but nevertheless persist just a little day by day and she will improve. Use toys and objects that she loves in order to encourage her in this position; lie with her or, if using a raised surface such as a change table, stay at her eye level while you sing and play.

Carry her around the house and show her interesting things, telling her what is going on – baby carriers which allow for baby wearing can be invaluable at this stage. You can gently swing her as you move. Sing softly to her and swing her in the rhythm of the song.

Taste and smell

The foetus in the womb has an acute sense of taste and smell from early on in pregnancy. They can taste the food their mother eats through the food tastes that go through into the amniotic fluid. In this way they learn their mother's taste preferences and they make these preferences their own. So during your pregnancy try lots of different cuisines, and eat lots of good and tasty foods.

After birth, they get the same taste experiences from the breastmilk and this helps them develop an even wider repertoire of food preferences. So while breastfeeding, vary your diet and don't spare the spices! If you're formula feeding, add different tastes to the milk, such as vanilla, nutmeg or cinnamon, and change the formula regularly to give a more varied taste to the feed. (See Chapter 19 for more information on this.)

Play point

When breastfeeding, make sure your diet contains lots of tasty food for your baby to enjoy through your breastmilk.

Don't overdo it . . .

Babies utilise all of their senses to communicate with the world around them and in the early months benefit greatly from the gentle exercise of all their faculties. However, observe your baby carefully to learn what she prefers and which inputs are too intense for her. All babies are subtly different in their capabilities. Some have difficulty dealing with more than mild input from one or the other of their senses, so some cannot handle a lot of bright light and colours, while others find massage and heavy touch too intense.

I wonder if you could help me with my little boy Luke. He is now ten months of age and a lovely little lad. He was born five weeks premature but did well in the neonatal intensive care unit. He has normal development, he is sitting, crawling and has just started pulling up on the furniture, he is babbling and says 'mama' and 'papa'. He was breastfed for four months and then was on formula and solids, and has a good weight and height.

His issue is he hates cuddles and will fight and struggle when we try to hold him close. He has always been like this even when we first got him home, and it really hasn't changed since then. He is otherwise fine with both my husband and me. He likes singing, will dance with us, but won't get in our bed. He will briefly sit next to us on the sofa and that is the closest he is comfortable with. He sleeps well and is otherwise a delight. Where did we go wrong? Was it the early days in the nursery that affected him?

HC: It is very unlikely that his stay in the NICU will have had this effect on your baby. Babies are enormously adaptable and they have no memory of these early days.

Nevertheless there is variation when it comes to the sensitivity of babies to their five senses, therefore variation in the amount of input a baby can deal with. Some babies get easily overwhelmed by sound or visual input. Others, perhaps like your boy, are overwhelmed by too intense tactile sensation. You can help him with this, by taking things very gradually. He needs to be reintroduced to the pleasure of gentle touch. When he is in a quiet relaxed mood, offer gentle touches to his toes with your fingertips, at the same time cooing, talking or singing to him. After a few days of short episodes, move to his feet. If he withdraws, back off for a few days and then restart the process more gently. Once he is used to your gentle touch, then, perhaps a few days later try a soft massage. If he withdraws or gets upset, reduce the stimulation. Over days and weeks, gradually teach him that touch is pleasurable, but don't increase the input too quickly or you will overwhelm him. He should gradually learn to love cuddles. If you are making no progress, see your paediatrician.

FOUR – EIGHT WEEKS

During this period your baby becomes increasingly perceptive about what is going on around her. Also the individuality of the baby starts to emerge as you notice she has a little personality. So while some babies get a thrill out of bodily movement and love to be carried or swung about in the air, other babies are more passive, and are more interested in watching and listening.

Vision and hearing

During this period she gazes more intensely around her and starts to take in the sights and sounds in her environment. At about six weeks of age she starts to smile socially – she does this especially in response to a friendly face and a soft voice.

At eight weeks old, rapid change occurs in the visual (occipital) cortex of the brain (that part of the brain that receives the visual impulses). As a consequence, the baby starts to gaze fixedly at things around her, especially her mother's face. Her mother also finds her baby's gaze magnetic and can't help returning it. Then the baby disengages, looking away to calm herself and, once recovered, re-engages her mother with her eyes. Their gazing becomes an open channel of communication between them, and, with the baby in control, as she becomes more experienced, she has a revelation! She can use her eyes to explore the big outside world, but she can also use the sight of her mother to keep herself calm! Two sides of the same coin.

She takes an increasing interest in the curtain that flaps and tends to watch you as you walk around in front of her, following your every movement.

Play point

Babies start to see colours as their eyes mature so mobiles and books with simple outlines and bright colour can be very attractive to them. You can make your own mobile with simple pictures or cards, or with coloured objects of interest like beads, and even bells so it makes a pleasant sound too. However, if you do make your own, ensure that everything is secured tightly.

You can also start to encourage your baby's eye tracking by moving bright and interesting toys slowly up and down or from left to right in front of her. As her interest in faces continues it is a great time to introduce a mirror at playtime – at this age she won't realise she is looking at herself, but she may become quite entranced by the facial expressions of her new friend.

Movement

Tummy time is now much easier for her. She can keep her head in line with her body and not turn it to the side, and can even raise it to 45 degrees above the horizontal.

When raised from lying on her back she still has little ability to support her head and needs your hand under her neck and head to do this.

She still has little control over her hand movements and the startle reflex still throws her around and upsets her.

Play points

- Explore your baby's preferences and see which experiences produce more smiles. Sing to her, dance with her, chat to her, read to her, carry her around and show her the objects in the room, explaining them as you go, and take her to different rooms in the house.

- At this age it is simple interactions that will best support her development. Try using fabrics of different textures, such as muslin wraps, fleecy blankets, silky hankies or toys, across her hands and over her body. Show her the texture of things. Let her feel velvet, silk, wood and water and talk to her about the sensations she must be feeling as she does so.

- She will enjoy walks outside in a stroller or a sling, and often simple things like watching the wind blow the leaves of the trees will entrance her. But she will still needs lots of cuddles and reassurance, as it is easy to overload your baby's senses by too much, or too intense, input. If she appears to be getting upset, frowning, or developing jerky movements of her limbs, quieten things down and soothe her.

EIGHT – TWELVE WEEKS

It is during this period that babies start to understand that they can influence people and events by their actions. This increases her interest and interaction with things around her. It can also be a difficult period where clinginess or thumb-sucking emerges and over-arousal can occur, so monitor playtime carefully in case things become too intense.

By now you will have figured out that the timing of playtime is something best determined by the baby. When she is ready to play with you and when she is receptive to your input she will indicate this by the intensity of her gaze and arm waving. Do not impose on her if she is concentrating by herself. At the end of playtime she will also indicate this by her movements, frowning and looking away.

Vision

She is so much better at focusing on objects now that her eyes fixate nicely and converge when the object is near. She can follow an object drawn across her field of vision through a wider arc. She likes looking at patterns as she tries to make sense of things around her and she will gaze intensely at faces, studying the facial movements and expressions. This is the first part of learning about conversation and social cues, which influence early language development.

Towards the end of this period she starts to look at her hands, so-called hand regard. This is as definite a developmental step as the timing of its disappearance.

Play point

This is a really great time to focus on simple picture books, with bright images on plain backgrounds, with your baby. Talk to her about what you see in the pictures.

Vocalising

Towards three months she will start chuckling and laughing – possibly one of the most delightful sounds in the universe. She will also start talking to her toys, making little random sounds like 'eek', 'eeh' and 'mm'.

Movement

With tummy time she can now raise her head to nearly 90 degrees from the horizontal and starts to bear weight on her forearms. Lying on her back as she is drawn into a sitting position, her head lag is improving.

The startle reflex that she hated so much is now starting to diminish and disappear and she has therefore more control over her arm movements. She now tries to swipe at her toys and will try to grab them. By 12 weeks she can hold onto a rattle put into her hand and may even jerk it up and down. She will kick out at toys as she now understands her efforts can change things around her.

Play points

- This is an age where they like to see new things, especially household items, so take her around the house and allow her to see, feel and smell the objects in the home.
- Put her under a mobile that is close enough for her to swipe at or make use of play mats and frames.
- As she now perceives patterns, show her some. Show how they get smaller as they recede from her view so she gets an idea of three dimensions. You can buy or borrow from the library lots of books with these – there are even pattern cards you can print from the internet to help you with this activity.

- Her attention span at this age is quite short so change the objects around her regularly. Provide only one toy or object at a time and change it when she appears upset or loses interest in it. Again encourage her to fix and follow by moving objects slowly from left to right or up and down.
- Set her on your lap and chat or sing, varying the rhythm of your words and your facial expression. Give her time to respond.
- Take a bath and shower together and let her splash in the water.

TWELVE – SIXTEEN WEEKS

From 12 weeks onwards your baby is much more able to regulate her mood. She is calmer as she can now withdraw attention from things that overexcite her.

This is a delightful age. Your baby will be much easier to get along with and amuse during your day. She will delight in playing with you, and will make it more obvious to you when she has had enough.

Some babies are observers and some babies are active. So don't worry if your baby appears not to be making progress with her body movements. All babies progress at their own rate and the acquisition of gross motor skills is inherited and does not relate to intelligence.

Vision and hearing

She now loves to be propped up in a sitting position so she can look around and will turn her head quickly to sounds or her name. She is just starting to appreciate that the world has three dimensions and objects appear smaller as they move away from her.

Movement

She now loves tummy time and is up on her forearms with her head at 90 degrees, looking out. Because she can now lift her head independently and for longer periods, she can really explore her environment. When drawn into the sitting position from lying on her back her head comes up in anticipation and she holds it steady.

Her movements are much less jerky now and she is getting more skilful at moving her limbs. She loves trying to grab objects dangled in front of her but is only starting to be able to judge distances, so she often swipes and misses. When she develops a new skill it is repeated often, as she loves to practise.

At this age, babies particularly love their hands, and with their improving spatial perception start to develop hand–eye coordination, for manipulation and exploration.

Play points

- You can now have a real conversation with your baby: she speaks first and you answer. In this way she learns about narrative and how conversations work. She still loves to be imitated and to imitate you, and this can add a new dimension to your conversation.

- It is easier now to make her laugh and as we know that laughing makes babies smarter, a sure-fire laughmaker is the raspberry kiss on the baby's tummy.

- Let her hands explore your face, nose, ears and hair as you explain their names. Offer her toys to knock over and to reach for. Activities where you get your baby to reach out with her hands are great for developing these skills – baby gyms, mobiles and toys that can hang from prams and cots can be very engaging at this stage.

- She is now less shy, and loves new environments and strange places she has not seen before. So you can explore places around you without worrying that she will cling and whinge in an unfamiliar place.

- She will love movement games, such as swinging her on your legs or flying her through the air holding her by the trunk. This is when fathers come into their own as babies appreciate the physicality and greater challenges of daddy play. But if he wants to throw her into the air and catch her, beware of the ceiling fan! (I'm afraid it happens . . .)

SIXTEEN – TWENTY WEEKS

She is now watching everything around her carefully and is fascinated. Sometimes her interest is so intense feeding becomes an issue and she will pull off the breast to see where the dog is going. It is at this age that play gyms start to hold their interest for long periods of time as they click, swipe and feel all the objects in reach. The best activity centre, though, remains her parents and their doings. She loves to watch her father doing the vacuuming and the chores and her mother working at her laptop. (I think I've got that politically correct . . .)

Generally she is crying less; however, as the skills she is now acquiring become more complicated so she can develop some frustration with herself which can make her somewhat fussy and even clingy.

She loves baby talk and will chatter to her toys and to you. And when she finds a performance that is responded to, or especially laughed at, she will repeat it incessantly.

She now starts to take an interest in what you are eating and it is a good time to start her on spoon foods. Also by now she knows when she is full and will stop eating. Do not disagree with her and food force; it is important to allow her to regulate her own food intake.

Vision and hearing

It is at this time that full colour vision arrives and your baby will start recognising and developing preferences for certain colours. Spend lots of time examining objects she is interested in. Touch and look at them, talk about them: their colour, their size, their texture.

She now reacts to her face in a mirror and knows her name. She also recognises tunes and songs that she has heard before.

Movement

She now has excellent head control and even when she is rocked in a sitting position can keep her head steady. Her grasp becomes much more useful; however, it is still 'fisty'. Nevertheless she can now grab an object, examine it carefully, feeling its texture and shape, mouth it to discover its taste and feel, and then discard it. Actually, casting toys and objects away now becomes a favourite activity and she will watch where they go.

She also starts to pass objects from one hand to another. It is not until one year old, however, that she develops a favourite hand for activity.

Hand regard often disappears about now but may last a while longer.

Play points

- Get her a brightly coloured, fun play gym, with lots of different activities to do.
- Prop her up so she can see the family in action.
- Engage her in chats and conversations constantly – they are never boring to her.
- Play peek-a-boo simply, with your hands over your face; try saying 'Where's Mummy?' . . . then when you reveal yourself – 'Here's Mummy!' She can't appreciate the game properly until beyond seven months of age but it will certainly spark her interest! Babies of this age still have object impermanence, so the point of hide-and-seek and peek-a-boo is still lost on them.
- To encourage her to develop her hand–eye coordination and depth perception, place objects at different distances from her but still within her reach.
- Your baby will also now start to recognise photos of familiar people – show her these and talk about these people.
- It has been shown that musical rhymes and songs associated with body movement are a more effective way to

teach literacy than just reading books. Nursery rhymes are always enjoyed, especially if they are accompanied by the actions of the baby's body. Hold her arms and wave them to the words and rhythm of a song. 'Twinkle, Twinkle, Little Star' and 'Heads and Shoulders, Knees and Toes' are popular ones with very intuitive movements.

- Music in all its forms is a great experience for a baby and singing to them teaches them about pitch and rhythm. It can also soothe and quieten them.
- Playing different styles of music to babies can help them develop a liking for music as they grow. Listening to classical music (probably due to its complexity) has been shown to improve spatial reasoning. (For instance, with the older child after listening to such music, jigsaws are easier to accomplish.)
- Babies love water games. They love splashing in the bath.
- Crumpling paper is a sure-fire delight!

FIVE – SEVEN MONTHS

At this age they are starting to become a unique little individual with a definite personality and temperament that you can observe developing month by month. They start to develop opinions and preferences about toys and food, but as things are changing for them so they need familiar objects for comfort; for example, transitional objects such as a favourite blanket or soft toy play a big part in their life. For the same reason, thumb- or finger-sucking is very common at this time.

She discovers how useful an organ her mouth is for experiencing the world, and everything she can grasp ends up in there. New objects are examined carefully using every sense, including gums and tongue. Parents often misinterpret this mouthing for 'teething' but there is no relationship between them.

This mouthing reflex is also utilised in so-called baby-led weaning, as carrot sticks and items of food will end up in the mouth if placed in the baby's hand. For many mothers it is an inefficient and messy way to feed a child. If you are happy with mess and very patient, though, you might want to give it a try. Certainly the babies love it.

If you are breastfeeding, part of your baby's experimentation at this time might be to bite down on your breast and hurt you. She is not aware of how little fun this is, so rapidly and pragmatically detach her and interrupt the feed. This will soon persuade her to desist. A big vocal reaction on your part may just encourage her to repeat the performance, so stoic restraint (in spite of the excruciating pain) is a good idea.

If she is given a cube to hold, and then given another one, she throws the first one away. Towards the end of seven months she will start to hang on to both cubes at once.

She can start to get a little anxious about strangers and will hide her head in her mother's chest if their gaze is too intrusive.

If she isn't getting the attention she feels she deserves, she will make a noise to get it. She will also raise her hands to be lifted up.

Vocalisation

Long conversations of complicated jargon also feature prominently in a baby's day and they love it when people around them join in; they can now make single syllable words like 'Ga', 'Ka', 'Da'.

Movement

Now she gets better at sitting up – but still needs a cushion behind her to help. It gives her a better view of the world.

! Beware the swiping hand around hot drinks.

Now that she is sitting and actively swiping at everything within reach, be especially careful of her sitting on your knee within reach of your teacup. She will have turned it over in no time. She can also pull on the tablecloth and drag the cup towards her.

She can now roll from her tummy to her back and, as seven months approaches, from her back to her front.

She loves being held to stand and this makes her bounce with pleasure.

When placed on her front her body is now supported up on her hands; however, she tends to collapse when one of her hands reaches for an object ahead of her.

Some babies start to try to crawl at this age, but they only succeed in going backwards.

Her grasp is now more competent and she transfers objects easily from hand to hand and bangs them on the table.

Play points

- She loves chatting and talking to her family members and, as earlier, she loves singing and dancing.
- Putting words and actions together in poems or songs is rewarding for both parties. 'This Little Piggy' with the toes is a favourite that will last months.
- Combining music, song and dance is a great way to enhance your baby's language development. Sing with the baby on your lap and hold her hands and wave them to the rhythm of a simple song like 'London Bridge is Falling Down'. Make the words fit the movements and the baby will learn the combination.
- Anatomy lessons – 'This is your NOSE, this is your TUMMY' and so on, or anatomy songs such as 'Heads and Shoulders, Knees and Toes' can be very popular.
- Bath toys and water games are still very much on the agenda.
- Toys that make noises or do unexpected things start fascinating the little mind at this stage. If you can stand the noise, toy drums and xylophones are likely to become favourites.

SEVEN – NINE MONTHS

This is a charming age for the baby, and easy for her doctor, who can examine her without shyness or complaint (unlike at one year).

At this age she is getting mobile, so she is getting into everything and is less interested in playing with her mother. But let Mama try to leave and there may be howls of complaint. Perhaps you shouldn't leave anyway – she's only going to head for the nearest power point to investigate it. (Time to buy those covers for the sockets!)

Indeed, clinginess may recur now that her boundaries are expanding. If there is anxiousness, don't push it too hard as it will soon improve. Make sure you explain to her if you are leaving and talk to her as you go (say, into the kitchen). Do not just disappear.

Many babies now start to appreciate that if they see an object being hidden, it remains in existence even when out of sight. 'Object permanence' is just starting. It helps if they can see a little bit of it sticking out, of course, and they will often forget it if they can't see it at all.

Because of this, your baby will finally get the point of peek-a-boo games and this is a useful technique to get her to be less dependent on your constant presence. Hiding from her briefly will condition her to your non-presence – and is fun at the same time.

Now she understands significant words like 'milk', 'walk' and also responds to 'No', though she often chooses not to hear.

When given two cubes one after another, she now keeps them both and compares them in size, weight and colour, then bangs them together. Such concentration penetrates other activities too and she will develop rapt interest in games and objects. When she concentrates she is liable to slobber.

> **WARNING**
> Now that the baby's mobile, it is critical that you make your house 'baby safe'.
> Use your imagination and recognise that babies are flexible, ingenious and have no common sense at all.
> Make sure every conceivable object that can fall, be pulled, or trap fingers, feet or heads is removed or made safe before the little explorer hits the territory.

Movement

She now sits stably without support and if pushed gently will correct with her body and not topple over. She can even stand with a little help from hand holding and as nine months nears so she becomes able to stand while holding onto the furniture.

Crawling at last goes in the right direction and commences forwards, which intoxicates the infant with the power of mobility. Soon the whole day is one big crawl-fest as she can now also reach objects previously out of reach. Rolling is also attempted and can give even more freedom of movement.

Her grasp is more sophisticated and at nine months she has a pincer grip and is able to pick up small objects and crumbs from the floor. (And put them in her mouth . . . so beware!) She uses both hands to do things but is still ambidextrous.

Vocalisation

She is just starting to connect words and gestures, so pointing with 'Ah', or 'Oops' for a spill, is now part of her repertoire. Some babies start to use double syllables, such as Dadda or Mama, although many will need a few more weeks before such parental reward is available.

Play points

- Peek-a-boo and hiding games create peals of laughter. Hide a popular toy (but let her see you hide it). Hide your head under a cloth and then re-emerge. She's not yet old enough to hide herself.
- In the bath, hide her rubber ducky under the bath foam.
- Hide toys and objects around the living room with a little bit sticking out, and let her explore and find them.
- She will love to empty the rubbish bin, the kitchen cupboards or (alas!) a plate of food from the high chair. She will also try to take gadgets and things apart. So beware of small parts that can be swallowed or can be pushed up little noses.
- A particularly fun game at this age is taking toys in and out of a box – put a collection of small rattles and objects of interest into an ice-cream container.

- Now is the time to buy a box of blocks. They love to build them up and knock them down.
- Continue to have conversations with her and praise her when she answers you. Book reading now becomes a little more satisfying as she listens and tries to turn the pages over while sitting in your lap.
- She is starting to become familiar with the nursery rhymes and will remember the movements and tunes. She will start to get into instrumentation, and will love drums that bang, toys that squeak and keyboards that ding.

Signing language

At nine months babies are starting to link sounds, gestures and meaning. This means from then on they are capable of learning a simple sign language about the common things in their lives. This can enable them to communicate their needs and feelings before they have the ability to articulate speech.

There are standardised signing languages; for example, Sing-along and British Sign Language among others. However, you can invent your own very simply. Here are a few from the British system:

More: Hold your hands open, palms facing towards the body, with one in front of the other. Move the hand in front forward a short distance.

Food: Put your fingertips to your lips.

All gone: Move your hand, palm up, backwards and forwards.

Happy: Draw an exaggerated smile over your mouth with your finger, while smiling.

Hot: Put your hand out and withdraw it quickly.

Where? Shrug your shoulders, with your palms held out.

Car: Steer an imaginary wheel.

Book: Hold your hands flat with your palms up.

I have also heard of success with:

Nappy: Forefinger and middle finger of each hand tapping over the front of hips.

Thirsty: Tipping a bottle into mouth gesture.

Sleepy: Hands together against one cheek.

The secret is consistency and repetition. If every time the appropriate situation comes up the sign is made and then you help the infant make the sign herself, increasingly she will use the sign for herself. This gives the infant a real feeling of satisfaction to at last make her thoughts known to her family. Then increase her vocabulary with invented signs relevant to your family situation. It does not in any way reduce the desire or ability of the infant to start speaking. It enhances their power of communication.

NINE – TWELVE MONTHS

Now our infant teeters on the brink of toddlerhood and her abilities increase rapidly as her development accelerates. If your house isn't baby safe yet, the clock is ticking – so fix it. Now if you can't see her, you really don't know where she has gone. She can move faster than you can believe with her efficient crawl or roll and can spend longer away from you than ever before.

She's now at the age when she recognises that objects occupy different categories, be it in size, shape or function, and the world starts making more sense to her – indeed, she is thinking more like you and figuring out things and problem solving. So she knows that crackers and beans look different but are both food, and horses and cows are both animals. If she is given a pile of mixed objects, such as plastic animals and pencils, she can put them into their own particular boxes, properly sorted out.

Empathy is increasing and she will often cry if another child is crying nearby. She also understands how others think, so she will act charming to get what she wants – 'If she wants to stay up, she can be such a sweetie at bedtime.'

However, when you take her to doctors, they don't get a look-in. She is clingy and shy with strangers and very dignified about her personal boundaries. No examination – I decline, thanks!

At nine months or so she may start waking up at 3 am for some party time. It seems to work, as she can get hours of personal Mummy time this way (although Mummy is a little unenthusiastic, it must be said). The little one needs a short period of unrewarding time at this hour – not abandoned but not played with either – to dissuade her from this course. It will only take a few nights before she's bored – as long as there are no rewards, breasts, bottles, talks or major cuddles. If towards 12 months she appears anxious at night as separation anxiety kicks in, then some reassurance is necessary and wise, but if she's just trying to have fun . . . less is more.

She is so active and mobile now that nappy changing can be a little difficult as she practises the crocodile roll while the nappy comes off. A little wrestling technique and a pin-down can work to finish the job. It is definitely time to be really careful of the change table – never leave the baby on one for even a nanosecond without a steadying hand on her.

Food is found to be not only good to eat but a lot of fun to throw about. Just see my mum run about with a cloth! She can now drink from a sippy cup and maybe drink through a straw as well – all these new skills!

Vocalisation

She now becomes more fluent with her few words such as 'Mama' and 'Dadda' and says one or two words with meaning. However, she understands up to a dozen words and by ten months 'Where's the doggy in the picture?' and 'Where's Daddy gone?' can usually be answered by her pointing a finger in the right direction, as at this age she now recognises what things are and where they belong.

She can repeat words spoken to her and mimic the actions of people around her. She knows exactly what to do with a toy telephone and can have long conversations with her imaginary friends on it. She gets better and better at naming things, and loves picture books to share with Mum or Dad.

Movement

To start with, she commando crawls on her belly efficiently and after a month or so graduates to bear crawling, up on hands and knees. Soon after she starts to pull up on the furniture and by 12 months is taking her first steps independently. Some children, however, are not walking until halfway through the second year, so don't get anxious if your baby remains a crawler. Often these babies had parents who also took their time to walk. The more timid prefer to walk with both hands held in the early weeks but with a little practice they become confident in their balance and soon can even stand on one leg if both hands are held. (This is a good balance game.)

She can now pull herself to sit and go from the crawling to sitting and back again, easily and smoothly. While sitting, she can turn right around to pick up an object behind her without toppling.

Mouthing decreases and then stops, and her hands become even more dextrous. She is able to pass objects over and release them into your hand. And she starts to love 'give and take' games. When she sees an object she wants, she approaches it with her forefinger and her neat pincer grip can pick up anything she wishes, large or small.

A favourite game is to throw objects or drop them for others to pick up and as she now likes repetitive games, this can go on for probably longer than your patience can bear . . .

She can now play 'Pat-a-cake' and anticipate the nursery rhymes and songs she knows. She can pat and kiss her dolly if you ask her to.

Play points

- She can play peek-a-boo with her doing the hiding – though her bottom sticks out from under the blanket. Pretend you can't find her for a while, talking the whole time, totally mystified . . .

- Fill up a large carton with interesting things and let her explore it. Empty one of the cupboards in the kitchen and put things inside that she can play with, like plastic tableware and spoons, tea towels, napkin rings, any small items from the kitchen that aren't sharp or pointed. Let her riffle through things. Favourite objects to play with can be anything from plastic cups and saucers to balls, to noisy pots and pans.

- She loves to go out on trips in a stroller (even more fun if you're up for it!) or backpack to children's farms, markets and shopping centres.

- They love objects they've never seen before – especially if they are complicated shapes with bumps and protrusions. There is nothing so fascinating as a bunch of keys. The child will run her fingers over the smallest protuberances to explore them completely. And, of course they will love to sort items out into categories. These groups may surprise you – rhinos and blocks into one box (they're heavy) and feathers, paper and tissues go into another (light). They love sorting sizes, hence the popularity of the doughnut rings on a stick.

- They love to see how gadgets work and will take things apart if possible – make sure that there are no small parts that can be swallowed (or worse, inhaled) if that happens. Put her in the kitchen and see how she can dismantle everything in sight, empty all the cupboards and mix everything up. It's actually quite a talent, a bit like a human tornado. Pity her mum or dad who has to pick everything up.

- Help her explore textures and new materials. Give her a play box with lots of different materials in it like velvet, silk scraps, wool or felt. Water play continues to fascinate and the outdoors is a vista of new experiences and objects to examine.

- Another firm favourite is you and your face, hair, ears and hands, which she will examine in great detail as she learns anatomy: nose, hair, mouth.

- To help her develop expressive language, repeat the amazing words your toddler is saying and add descriptive words; for instance, 'Ball', 'Yes . . . that's a blue ball.'

TWELVE – FIFTEEN MONTHS

At last they are one year old. She has a brightly coloured birthday cake with one candle and she gets so excited and she puts her foot in it, but does eventually eat a little.

At one year she really now knows she is in a separate body from her mum. With that realisation comes a greater appreciation of things around her. She now recognises that they are separate, and wants them or worries about them. Strangers can be a serious worry for her and she will resist newcomers and cower into her mother's chest if she is under scrutiny.

Pointing with her finger is now a big deal. She points to things she wants and she will look at things that other people point out. If she sees an object she is not sure about she checks to see her mother's reaction to it before she investigates and can gauge from the response whether she wants the object or not. She is also sophisticated enough to copy her mother's actions regarding what to do with the object if she gets it.

This is a major philosophical leap for her – she now has a greater understanding of other people's minds. She comprehends that other people have feelings that maybe she does not, and she can now interpret those feelings and make assumptions about situations. For instance, if she sees her mother look into a box and seem disgusted, she can interpret that what's in the box isn't very nice and she might decide not to look in it herself.

She starts to take an interest in personal grooming and will try to dress or undress herself. She will try to brush her hair and wash her face, and will do all these things to her dolly as well. She will play pretend games with her toys and dolls and doesn't wish to be interrupted in these tasks.

She is very happy to accompany you in household chores and she wishes she had her own vacuum cleaner! I know it takes longer when she helps but she really is learning such a lot when she does, so slow down and help her.

She begins to understand that she can use tools to do things for her. If there is an object she would like on the blanket, she knows by pulling the blanket that she can get it to her, and also knows that if the toy is not on the blanket then pulling the blanket is a waste of time.

She is still putting things into categories but is now even more sophisticated about it, and can spot and appreciate more subtle differences between similar objects.

She is more subtle in playing with objects, also varying her actions with them to see what else they do.

Vocalisation

She now can put together two to three words with meaning. And when asked 'Where is the book?' she will look for it, then go and get it.

Because she is more grown up, parents talk to her in a different way. Mothers will often talk to their babies almost continuously, letting them know what is going on and what they are doing. The parents understand that from here on their baby is a sponge for new words.

At six months all babies can hear and discern all the tones of different languages but by the age of one year babies have integrated into their brain the sounds and tones of only their particular language. For instance, one-year-old Japanese babies can hear only the specific tones of Japanese and can't hear some tones in English. So they can't differentiate between the sounds 'lake' and 'rake', while European babies can. Spanish parents have babies that differentiate the multiple sounds of the 'p' consonant, which can't be discerned by English speakers. So bilingualism starts early.

By 15 months she speaks constantly in jargon with a smattering of translatable words.

Movement

Mobility is everything at this age; from bottom shuffling through bear crawling to rather clumsy walking, one-year-olds want to spend their day covering ground. If there is someone with a helping hand, she is more than happy to walk with her hand held. By 15 months she can pull herself to stand and even creep upstairs carefully, and most babies are by now pretty reliable walkers.

Having asked for an object by pointing and getting it fetched for her, she no longer mouths it but delights in throwing it away. And then asking for it again. Great game for her, less so for the fetcher. But she is so charming by this age, with her incessant chatter, that her family are more than happy to oblige, at least for a while.

At last she is starting to figure out about cause and effect – that doing one thing can lead to another. So she wants to press the button in the lift or ring a front doorbell to make it chime. She also learns how things fit together, so now she can build a tower of two blocks (then kick them down), and really appreciates those toys that have slots which fit various shapes.

She now becomes more adept at feeding herself, though it's still a messy business, and loves to have finger foods to play with, put in her hair, all over the high chair, and even occasionally eat.

Play point

By now you know your baby so well that you know what she likes to do and the games she prefers. Games are definitely a two-way street and she enjoys games where you join in and get involved.

All babies are different and have different talents and preferences. See what your baby likes to do in play: is she an observer, or a doer? Does she like games that involve major body movements or does she like to sit down and concentrate on small objects? Some like interacting with people, not objects. Babies learn things in different ways and you can enhance her early learning experiences by helping her in the way she enjoys best.

However, don't impose on her. Don't interfere if she's trying to figure something out by herself; leave her to do it. Don't jump in and do it for her. Help her if she gets stuck, but let her find out that persistence pays.

Such determination can be a little trying. Try not to get upset if you do something for her (like feed her) and all she does is spit it out unless she puts it into her mouth herself. She's not a rebel and it isn't anything personal, she's just practising her new skills.

She does love hiding and finding games, and these can go on for long periods of time. She'll even hide your car keys and wait for you to find them.

She can now help you round the house, and choose what she wants to wear and help dress herself. To assist with the development of these skills, offer two choices at a time: 'Would you like to wear a skirt or pants?', 'Would you like to wear your red or blue cardigan?' Keep up the commentary as you do things and she can learn so much from this everyday activity.

Singing and dancing games remain favourites and she now knows and can follow the words of nursery rhymes. If you can't remember them, get a DVD and learn them. The DVD is for you, by the way, not the children. While we're on the subject, try to avoid TVs or computer screens until she is two years of age or older. The interaction is too one-sided and tends to make babies passive watchers, rather than active participants. Brief periods of children's programs are okay if that's what it takes to get you some shower time, but keep it as short as possible, especially if she seems rapt in the experience.

At this age push-and-pull-along toys or ride-on wheels are fun, as are shape sorters, pop-up toys and board books to practise page turning. She loves noisy instruments such as drums, and pots and pans, and enjoys sand, buckets and spades, and balls of all sizes.

Toys don't have to be expensive – she will prefer a shoebox with lots of interesting things inside!

EIGHTEEN MONTHS – TWO YEARS

In this era toddlers know that they are not only in separate bodies but that other people have different thoughts and desires from them – separate minds. They can figure out and appreciate that, although they don't like broccoli themselves, their mother is very fond of it.

They are fascinated by the 'What's in other people's minds?' concept and constantly devise experiments to explore it. Hence she will look at you fixedly as she approaches the electrical points because she understands that you obviously don't like it, but she is driven to know whether that remains constant and is repeatable. She isn't being naughty – she is merely trying to find out the size, and depth, of the difference between her mind and yours.

She also has much more insight and empathy at this age. When her parents are arguing, this may cause her to burst into tears, and as she gets nearer to two years of age this empathy may extend to comforting her mother or father.

She can now classify objects not just by their appearance (one-year-olds can do that) but also by function, putting together in groups things that spin, or make a noise when you press a button, or things that can be used for cleaning.

She can play next to other toddlers and imitate their actions, but she will not play with them. That's reserved for when they are over three years of age. Help her to share when playing and teach her about taking turns.

By two, she can use logic to work out fairly complex puzzles and use tools in a much more sophisticated way. If a toy is out of reach, an 18-month-old toddler can work out that a little toy rake nearby can be used to pull the toy towards her.

She now has the ability to plan ahead to achieve objectives. She appreciates that there are a number of ways to succeed but has learned what works best for her, especially when interacting with her parents. Coercion techniques become ever more sophisticated. She might learn to achieve a later bedtime by being charming or mischievous or very, very quiet . . . She will check out various strategies and use the particular one that tends to work best.

She is a great imitator and is watching and observing constantly. If she starts to become aggressive, check where or who that technique was derived from. Many toddlers try this out, just to see how effective it is. She needs to know that in THIS family we are rewarded for being considerate and pleasant!

She can also copy physical actions – climbing, opening doors and escaping outside. Beware the out of sight toddler who you can't hear. Go and check!

She is just becoming aware of toilet issues and some can let their mother know that they have wet pants around this age. If so, toilet training now becomes a possibility.

Vocalisation

During this period she will learn to start joining words together. She can now say that she wishes to 'drink milk' or that she wants you to 'play with me', and she gets more adept at repeating words said to her. She is like blotting paper for new words from here on and many toddlers can acquire new words every day. Some start to talk in short sentences.

She knows how to ask for a drink and can carry out between two and four simple orders such as 'take off your shoes' and 'put this on the table'.

The concept of separateness is extended to her language. By two years she now talks about I, me and you, and beyond the age of two will natter about everything incessantly.

Movement

From 18 months she walks skilfully and can run, and seldom falls. She can climb stairs, holding on to the rail. She can stand on one leg and even walk backwards.

She may practise movements constantly, spinning on the spot, picking up heavy objects, rolling around on the floor, hurling herself to the ground, and is constantly investigating things. She can't walk past a rain puddle without stepping in it, or walk past a door without opening it and looking inside. This is a time for safety gates and locks to keep her safe.

Dexterity is now extended to building bigger and bigger block towers, three at 18 months and up to six or seven by two years. She can turn the pages of her book, firstly two or three at a time, but gradually she will do it more and more delicately, so that at two years she's turning each individual page.

She can also spoonfeed herself, at last with the spoon not being inverted as it goes into her mouth. She can wash her hands (over and over – she still loves to play in water) and can unscrew the lids off containers.

Play point

In this age range children need a lot less supervision for their play, but they love having an adult around anyway so they can perform for them and use them to help. When you're with them let them know how interested you are in what you are both doing. Talk to them constantly.

Everything is new to explore, full of wonder and adventure for little people – they want to imitate what those around them are doing and imaginative play starts to develop, which is the beginning of an exciting journey for you and your toddler.

At this age they love to discover new things, so toy and book libraries are great places to visit – to give them the tools to try new things and develop new skills.

They can also amuse themselves alone for considerable periods of time, as long as the pastime or object they are involved in is interesting to them.

Their newly awakened imagination and dexterity means they can invent scenarios and then act them out, nattering all the time in their own special language.

Below is a list of activities for this age, categorised by the areas of children's development that these activities can encourage and enhance.

Gross motor skills:

- Catching games, especially outside with nice big soft balls.
- Action games using imagination – 'Let's go hunt for a crocodile', 'Let's go on a Bear Hunt'. This can be a great fun space for dads to be silly!
- Exploring – while you may want to go to 'exciting' places with your little one, you will be amazed at how exciting they find the places right around where you are: outside in the garden, at the local park, or inside the house, in cupboards and drawers, or under the bed or the table are all places for the creation of great adventure.
- Hammering pegs into boards – sound, sight and muscular precision (hand–eye coordination).
- Push-pull toys, which they can steer around the floor.
- Swimming lessons – for a highly mobile toddler, they are strongly recommended. These days the content focuses heavily on personal water safety, and at most swim schools, up until the toddler is about three years of age, Mum or Dad go into the pool with them. It is a lovely bonding time, and provides great tips on what to do – and not to do – around water. A surprising example is that you shouldn't teach them to blow bubbles in the water. Instead you should teach them very early on to hold their breath when water hits their face. So if they fall into water, their automatic response is to hold their breath and not blow out all of their air.

Fine motor skills:

- This is an age where fine motor development is involved in many daily activities – turning the pages of board books, linking the carriages of a wooden toy train, then pulling it along, rolling smaller balls along the floor, holding a spoon to eat cereal. These are all ways that your little person is developing the fine motor skills they need for life.
- Painting, free drawing, scribbling – at this age, paintings are not representative, but mostly good practice for hand–eye coordination, as are collage and stamping.

- The simple things are often the best and building blocks, or even various-shaped cardboard boxes, can provide plenty of entertainment. At two years a child can build a tower of up to six blocks. Then usually kick them down!

Numeracy:

- At this age they become interested in the concept of numbers. There are lots of ways to incorporate numbers into what you are doing during the day, such as sharing games: 'one for you and one for me.'
- Counting objects that are part of the daily routine: 'one, two, three plates – one for Mummy, one for Daddy and one for you . . . that's three plates!'
- Abacus – let them slide the beads along the bars and an adult counts as they move them.
- Number games – use five balls (of a size too big to be put in the mouth). Show her the number in two hands: '1 and 4', '2 and 3', '3 and 2' '0 and 5'.

Spatial sense:

- At this age the emerging toddler starts to be interested in large simple jigsaws and puzzles.
- They do lots of experimenting with what sized shapes they can get themselves into and out of (which means they require constant supervision); squeezing through gates and under fences is all part of exploring the space they occupy in the world. Cubbies and boxes can make for hours of enjoyment at this age.
- You can incorporate 'size' concepts into the things you do during the day:

  'Is that your toothbrush . . . no, that's Daddy's toothbrush – it is too big for you!'

  'Can Mummy wear your dress . . . no, it's too small for Mummy!'

  'Does teddy fit on the little train . . . whoops! No, he's too big!'

Memory:

- You will be surprised how quickly memory is developing at this age and at times their memories will more than rival yours. They will often pay attention to things that may not take our focus. Try to ask questions about things you have done earlier in the day: 'What was the name of the boy we met in the park?'
- If you don't think that they remember well, try skipping pages in favourite books and you will soon be told!
- Remembering game: on a small tray of objects, one or more objects go missing. 'What's missing?'
- Show them objects or pictures in books. 'What's that?'

Imaginative skills:

- By two years, children understand that toys can represent people in the real world (that is, they are not just objects) so they can put them into meaningful groups and invent a scene for them to act out. So all the dollies can have a tea party.
- This is the beginning of magical journeys. Providing props enhances toddlers' exploration of their imagination, so keep a pile of containers and boxes that can be made into creations; a box of old clothes is good for dress ups or costumes. Make finger puppets.
- Read lots of fantastical stories to encourage imagination to flourish.
- Make a cubbyhouse out of a blanket over a couple of chairs, or a ship out of an upside-down children's table.

Musicality and dance:

- Singing – children's songs ('Pat-a-cake', 'Ring a Ring a Rosy', 'Incy Wincy Spider', 'Twinkle, Twinkle, Little Star', 'Big Red Car', 'Heads, Shoulders, Knees and Toes' – the list is endless). If you feel you can make up songs about daily activities, it can be a great way to mark routines; for instance, 'Now it's sleep time, now it's sleep time, time for bed, my sleepyhead.'

- Make a drum out of an ice-cream container and bang on it, or make shakers using containers with secure lids (old Berocca tubes are great) and put in rice or other food items to make different sounds.
- Play with instruments – tambourines, triangles, keyboards and xylophones.

Enjoy playing with your child. Childhood doesn't last very long . . .

CHAPTER 19

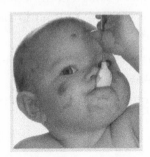

Food for thought: solids and spoon foods for babies and kids

YEARS AGO, WHEN I WAS TAUGHT about how to introduce babies to solid food, it all seemed pretty clear and based on common sense. Firstly, I was told, start at exactly six months. From prehistoric times our species required 'transitional feeding' at about that time, when the all-milk diet could not provide enough extra nutrients, such as protein, iron or vitamin D, for the babies' needs.

Then introduce the spoon foods gradually, one different food at a time. 'If you go too quickly, they'll reject them all,' the dieticians warned. The first spoon food should be 'baby rice', designed especially as a first food as it is iron fortified and tastes very bland. Then use specialised 'baby foods', such as sweetened purees, delicious fruity dishes and high-carb starches.

Be wary of potentially allergic foods, such as peanuts and eggs – delay them at least until after one year of age 'as these foreign proteins can enter via the immature gut and set up a sensitivity reaction'.

And so on and so on. And in the light of new scientific evidence, that advice has turned out to be wrong, wrong, wrong.

Not only is it factually incorrect, but it might have helped create a catastrophic legacy with which we are now having to deal: a generation of kids who prefer hamburgers, sweets and soft drinks to vegetables and other real foods. Children who are seriously overweight and who suffer in childhood, or later in life, from a group of diseases that are related to obesity – hypertension, diabetes and so-called metabolic syndrome – and who, as a consequence of this, will possibly die at a younger age than their parents will.

It is now an unarguable fact that the so-called Western diet is a slow killer. It is this diet that tends to cause its consumers to overeat, become obese and develop insulin resistance in their tissues. This causes diabetes and a whole host of downstream and other illnesses.

The incidence of childhood obesity has tripled in the 30 years between 1967 and 1997, and during the 1980s the incidence of people being overweight doubled, according to the Australian Institute of Health and Welfare. In the United States the situation is even worse, not only among children but adults as well. More than seven out of ten adults in both the United States and Australia are now overweight or obese.

The burning question is why is this occurring? And why is the problem growing, like waistlines, year after year even though the food supply is constant and, in the last several decades, has always been plentiful?

The answer can be gleaned from evidence from those nations that until recently had lived on non-Western diets, especially in Asia where slimness is the norm. Since the introduction of the Western diet, their incidence of obesity has accelerated rapidly, and is now catching up with that of the West.

Which component of the Western diet is causing the harm?

Thirty to forty years ago it was believed that it was the fat content of the diet that caused obesity levels to rise. Let's face it: it seemed logical. Put too much fat into the stomach, and you get too much fat around the waist. As a consequence the food companies rushed to create a new market of low-fat and fat-free foods, and to make these products more palatable, they replaced the fat in the food with more carbohydrate. Sadly, the fat story turned out not to be true. In the last couple of decades the consumption of fat per person in the United States and Australia has fallen by over 25 per cent, but the rate of obesity just keeps increasing as rapidly as before.

It becomes clearer year by year that the problem is, and always has been, the carbohydrate content. It's the sweets, the sugary foods and the sweetened drinks. It is the West's addiction to high-calorie carbohydrate food that has created this weighty problem, both for the individual and for nations.

Primates like us have always liked sweet foods. They are rare in nature and are energy dense so evolution taught us to grab them when we could, stuff ourselves and store the energy in our tissues against a future famine. As we evolved, our attraction to sweet foods wasn't a problem as the amounts available in nature were so small. The fruit went out of season and the honey was hard to steal from the bees, so nature didn't feel the need to develop in us an off switch to prevent the over-consumption of such foods. Instead we had developed the opposite: a powerful incentive system for consuming such high-energy food for storage with feel-good hormones flooding our brain to reward us for such a find.

Nowadays the food supply situation is markedly different from the time of our origins, at least in the West. Thanks to modern food production (and marketing), such foods are available in vast and increasing quantities. But our primordial instincts haven't changed at all. Food scientists and producers know this, of course, and make their foods sweeter to increase our consumption and boost their profits.

But what has this got to do with babies and solids?

A recent study by B.G. Moss and W.H. Yeaton in the United States looked at a cross-section of their baby population and found that 32 per cent or about a third of all their babies were at risk of becoming, or were already, overweight and obese, by nine months of age! Not only that, but by the age of four years, the incidence only increased a little more – to 34 per cent. That is, most of the problem of weight showed up in young babies rather than occurring later. So, it was the babies that were getting fat, not the toddlers and children!

FAT BABIES: PREVENTION AND CAUSES

A good way to prevent inappropriate fatness in babies is to breast-feed them. Breastfeeding has a number of relevant advantages:

- Babies make the decision about how much they will eat, not Mum, so they learn to regulate their own intake and appetite.
- Breastfed babies have to work a bit to get the food. Formula-fed babies just open their months and it pours in.
- Human breastmilk (but not formula) contains a substance called adiponectin, which is an appetite suppressant. It teaches babies to regulate their appetite.
- There are fewer calories and lower protein levels in the breastmilk in comparison to formula, and the babies' tissues produce less insulin in response to the feeding.
- This circulating insulin, and other biological factors in the milk, also seems to have an effect on fat cell production in the body.
- Breastfed babies are often chubby but this extra weight tends to fall off them as they go into the second half of their first year. They tend to slim down as they get more active, especially if they continue to breastfeed.

So what happens when solids are introduced at four to six months? When this occurs, there are really important factors at play.

The 'wisdom of the body'

Even 20 years ago it was taught that young children had an innate and genetically driven desire to eat a healthy balanced diet. It was called the 'wisdom of the body'.

This was demonstrated by studies done in the 1920s or '30s by C.M. Davis that looked carefully at the diets chosen by young children. These children, within the study environment, were offered a large variety of food and were given no guidance about what they should eat. The scientists noted that within a short time, these children would start selecting for themselves a perfectly balanced diet.

What could be more reassuring for parents! It also reassured a generation of paediatricians, allowing them to believe that children would naturally regulate the type of food they ate to keep themselves healthy.

What a pity it was not correct! The studies indeed offered the children a wide variety of food, but all the food was good food, expertly prepared by nutritionists and none of it containing excess salt or sugar. Of course the children ate a balanced diet. They had no choice!

LEARNING GOOD TASTE: THE FIRST YEAR OF LIFE

We now know from many studies of foetuses, newborns and children that the sort of food they like to eat and their taste preferences as they grow up are wired into their brain within their first year. During this time babies will readily accept and enjoy most of the food introduced to them by their parents.

Humans are omnivorous, so they eat a wide variety of foods from many different sources. It makes them adaptable and able to live successfully in many environmental niches but such variety has its dangers. Many apparently nutritious titbits will be poisonous to them. So to protect themselves, humans developed an instinctive resistance to new, unfamiliar foods (food neophobia or 'fear of new foods').

Clearly the safest food available to a human is that eaten by their family. So when they are young, they will accept and enjoy the food offered to them by their parents. This is especially true if the food is given to them in the context of love and content-ment, in a warm, social environment, like a family mealtime.

In summary, children accept and enjoy those foods that are familiar to them.

Evolution also allows for the fact that when these babies become mobile (at about a year of age) they may now wander and explore, and maybe come across strange berries or plants, which might poison them. Hence from that age onwards their food neophobia kicks in to become even more powerful. This explains the reticence of toddlers and older children shown towards unfamiliar tastes.

> Children eat what they like, and they like what they know.

The bottom line is that you have a window of opportunity under the age of one year to establish your baby's taste and food preferences. If this is done successfully, he will grow up liking good quality, nutritious food that will create him a lean, healthy body and give him a long life.

The foetus

Once conceived, the foetus forms then floats in a sack of amniotic fluid. The amniotic fluid is derived from the placental circulation, which is in close contact with mother's bloodstream. Consequently elements (so-called odourants) of the food that her mother eats rapidly transfer into the amniotic fluid that is constantly being swallowed by the foetus. So within a few minutes of her meal the foetus has the same taste experiences as her mother, and being an omnivore she rapidly accepts her mother's taste preferences as her own.

We know foetuses taste. In the animal model, if saccharine is injected into the amniotic fluid the foetus is observed to suck more vigorously. If a bitter substance is injected, the foetus stops sucking.

A nice experiment done in the south of France demonstrated something similar in the human foetus. A group of expectant mothers in their final trimester were given desserts containing anise (which is popular in that area). Another (control) group of mothers had no anise in their desserts. After birth all the babies were confronted with a cloth containing the smell of aniseed. The babies whose mothers had had the anise dessert were attracted to the cloth, but the babies whose mothers had not, did not recognise the smell. Not only that, they turned their heads away and were actually repulsed by the smell.

Therefore, if Mum likes it, even if it tastes unpleasant, babies will accept her opinion and like it too.

If that doesn't give you an incentive to avoid exposing your foetus to certain tastes, like cigarettes and alcohol, what will?

So obstetricians and midwives should be telling their pregnant patients to experience as many different high-quality foods as possible in order to introduce the foetus to the taste of healthy eating.

Such a foetus will develop a large repertoire of taste experiences, which will stand her in good stead for the acceptance of a variety of foods later in life.

The newborn baby

Once the baby is born, he rather misses the taste and smell of the amniotic fluid that surrounded him in the womb. This is why, nowadays, we do not bathe babies straightaway as in the past. Instead we allow them to keep the smell of the familiar amniotic fluid on their skin. This comforts them as it reminds them of their mother and her womb. It also encourages them to suck their fingers and soothe themselves when they are unsettled.

It has been shown that unbathed babies cry less and for shorter periods in the first few days than bathed ones. Smelling and tasting your hand or arm that has the odour of baby wash is not especially comforting!

When breastfeeding is commenced, the milk comes in on day three. As mentioned earlier in this book, when it arrives the milk contains the same odourants and food tastes that the amniotic fluid carried from the mother's diet. This is yet another advantage of breastfeeding. Every time the baby breastfeeds she gets a different taste, and that depends on what her mother has been eating.

So breastfeeding mothers should eat as tasty and varied a diet of good foods as they possibly can. What an opportunity to eat great food from five continents! Both participants can then enjoy the culinary experiences and the baby can broaden his palate.

As mentioned, the main sugar in breastmilk is lactose. Lactose is the primary sugar in all terrestrial mammals' milks. It seems that the amount of lactose in a species' milk is directly related to the size of the brain or the amount the brain has to grow. For the human, breastmilk is serious brain food. It creates galactolipids and other metabolic products, which are directly incorporated into brain tissue. A relevant fact about lactose for this discussion is that it is the one sugar that is not very sweet. On the 'sweetness index', with sucrose (white table sugar) placed arbitrarily at 100, lactose has an index of only 15 (with glucose at 60). How appropriate is that, considering we do not wish to program our babies to like sweet things (any more than it is genetically determined, anyway).

Formula

This is also relevant when deciding which formula to use, if such is the family's decision. The formula Isomil does not contain lactose, but instead is sweetened by sucrose, which makes it very sweet and therefore unhelpful in this context. It has also been noted that sour-tasting formulas, such as the ones containing hydrolysed proteins, tend to encourage babies to enjoy sour and bitter foods later.

While we're on the subject of formulas, it has always been conventional advice that when you find 'a formula that suits your baby, you should stick to it'. Unfortunately this means that your baby gets one taste (similar to wall plaster!) for the first six months of his life. New information suggests that in order to give such babies a wider variety of tastes we should change the formula regularly, alternating with ones that taste totally different – so give him soy formula for a week or two, then perhaps a hydrolysed one before returning to his usual standard one, and add other flavours to the formula, such as alcohol-free vanilla essence, cinnamon or nutmeg.

These extra tastes will make his dietary life more interesting and broaden his taste horizon.

INTRODUCING FOODS:
AT FOUR TO SIX MONTHS

At about six months the milk is no longer sufficient to meet the baby's nutritional needs. In particular he needs more iron, which is barely represented in breastmilk; he also needs more vitamin D and increased levels of protein.

It is about this time or slightly earlier that the baby starts to get very interested in what you are eating. That is the best time to start spoon foods. If he is fully breastfed, it is nice if you can spin him out until he is six months but otherwise, starting him from four months if he is keen is fine.

It really is not necessary to put your baby under pressure to start solids if he is not enthusiastic. The food will only end up on his chin anyway. Wait for him to open his mouth and look expectant when you are eating. Then give him something to try from your plate. You can pretend for this purpose that you really love pureed avocado and have some sitting there waiting!

At this age he has started putting everything he can find in his mouth anyway. Because of that, everyone thinks he's teething – he may well be, but that's not why he is mouthing everything. This is a developmental stage of oral exploration and it will help wean him onto spoon and solid foods.

At around this time he has also started to develop full colour vision. Suddenly the world becomes much more interesting as he gazes around him and takes it all in. It is a delightful time, which you can utilise to help you educate him about good food. Now you can make feeding times a multisensory experience of colour, taste and aroma, all in a context of love and enjoyment.

First foods

We now have six to eight months remaining of his first year during which we must teach him to appreciate wholesome and healthy food. The last thing on the planet we should give our baby at this time is 'baby rice'. Refined, purified, processed white rice flour is as bland, as boring and as manufactured as you could imagine a food to be. Similarly with commercial 'baby foods', processed and altered to be unlike the foods from which they were derived. Precisely the foods that would give him all the wrong messages about what he should really enjoy!

We should give him normal foods from our plate, pureed so he can deal with it, but something recognisable as the kind of food we would eat. If we tend to eat the wrong foods ourselves, now is a good time to try something more healthy in our diet and not pass on our bad habits!

> Don't forget that children eat what their parents eat, so it's time to get your diet in order too.

Ideally this should be something aromatic and interestingly coloured, such as sweet potato, capsicum or green avocado. Make sure it's well pureed as lumps can confuse a baby new to solids and make him gag.

Some first foods

Steamed sweet potato: Washed and peeled, cut into small pieces and microwaved or steamed. Mash with breastmilk (or his formula), or boiled and cooled water (or coconut water for something different) until mushy.

Avocado: A fabulous first food. Mashed without liquid or perhaps with some from lamb, chicken or beef stock (watch the salt level, though).

Banana: Mash with breastmilk/formula/water and add a dash of cinnamon, nutmeg, vanilla or star anise to liven up the taste and introduce him to the spice cupboard's contents.

Brown rice: Much better than baby rice with as much iron as the fortified cereals. Quinoa might be better (it is easy to digest and has more protein than rice). Steam as usual, then put through a blender to puree.

Other fruit: pear and apple are standards but low-sugar alternatives are berries or grapefruit (this would introduce the sour-tasting foods to your baby). Microwaved or steamed until mushy then add liquid (milk or water) until the consistency is right. You can also add some vanilla or nutmeg to this for a change in flavour.

Once you've started, foods could be introduced as rapidly as you like, even three or so new foods a day. Soon add celery or carrot sticks, microwaved to soften and then cooled. Nice finger foods. Then mashed potato or peas, or for a lower sugar alternative, try butternut pumpkin. Other vegetables, especially Chinese cabbage, kale, spinach, broccoli and any others you have to hand.

Start soon on egg (boiled or scrambled) using the white and the yolk, meat (especially steamed or diced breast of chicken), then steamed white fish and lean mince.

Once the baby is used to all these in pureed form, start introducing a bit of texture and see if he copes. If not and he gags, back off and try again in a month. Don't worry if he just can't deal with bits in his food. Sometimes it takes months, depending on how active his gag reflex is.

Soon after that, the baby will be eating pretty much what you are, but in a slightly mushier form. Family meals will engage him and teach him that food is to be enjoyed and meals are taken in a loving, family atmosphere. Such lessons last a lifetime!

Sweet and salty

During the following six months the baby should be introduced to a normal diet of adult-style food. However, an important difference is that it should ideally be devoid of sugar and salt as these do not occur commonly in nature. (I don't recommend your oysters or red wine either!)

Don't give the baby anything that is crumbly, such as biscuits, as they are usually not able to cope with small pieces until after the first year. And never ask the baby to cope with hard pieces, such as peanuts or other nuts, as they can be inhaled.

Baby-led weaning

Just wondering what your thoughts are on baby-led weaning (www.babyledweaning.com) where babies are given soft finger food rather than purees as their first foods. They claim that choking is not as common as we would expect.

I gave a talk at a conference recently and the subject was the introduction of spoon and solid foods to babies. It went pretty well and there were a lot of questions in the Q & A session afterwards. One woman got up at the back and asked her question into the slightly distorting microphone. 'What do you think of baby linguini?' I was stumped! I'd never heard of this special Italian pasta for babies. I asked her to repeat her question, thinking furiously about how to respond. She repeated it more slowly and I got it. What she was asking about was 'baby-led weaning'. What a relief! I had something (actually quite a bit) to say.

There is a growing group of mothers that is really enthusiastic about this approach to feeding their baby solids. The theory is that at six months or so the baby starts to put everything she can get her hands on into her mouth. She uses this new developmental step to explore the world, not only with sight and touch, but also the added dimension of taste and the experience of what things feel like in her mouth. Actually this attribute is a good reason to try to dispense (kindly and humanely!) with the dummy before this tendency arrives. Having a plug in the main sensory organ for this exploration really interferes with its expression!

So babies pick things up and put them in their mouths. Well, let's make it food! We give them food that little hands can grasp, such as small pieces of apple or carrot, or mush like pasta, and transfer into the mouth and consume. Bingo! A self-feeding baby. Mother can sit back and eat her own dinner in peace.

Well, quite. This method is said by its fans to lead to babies who regulate their appetites better and so have less chance of becoming obese later. They also believe that the babies get into and enjoy a greater variety of 'difficult' foods, such as broccoli and, interestingly, they innately tend to avoid foods to which they are (or will become) allergic.

Doesn't that tick all the boxes for you!

What a pity it is that there appears to be no scientific evidence to back up these claims.

That is not to say that it's all rubbish. One part that I really agree with is letting the baby decide how much she wants to eat, rather than have the mother decide for her. It sure works with breastfeeding in which Mum has very little say (and in fact barely knows) about the volume of milk the baby gets.

So if the baby can really regulate her intake once she starts solids, then it follows that this would be something to really encourage.

For some babies the process works well. The little one figures it out and, although there can be a fearful amount of mess, she needs very little help to get enough to satisfy herself (and hopefully her mother). That is as long as Mama is patient and recognises that large amounts of food are not actually necessary in the early months after solids introduction.

Many babies, however, are less competent at the transferral of food into the mouth (and down the throat). Just as some babies walk at one year of age and some take their time until 18 months, so it is with self-feeding. Also quite a few mothers find the process too challenging, both in time spent cleaning up and watching anxiously to see how much ends up inside the baby, and how much ends up on the floor, in the hair or on the cat. And with these baby meals, don't be in a hurry. They can take hours!

Some mothers are also anxious about the baby inhaling and choking on the food. This bit is clear: there is no need to worry. As mentioned elsewhere in this book, babies have an incredible ability to protect their airway and they will not allow food (or even fluids, for that matter) to go down the wrong tube. It is still important, however, to make sure the food you give your baby is not crumbly, or the pieces of food are not too hard to mash with the gums.

The proponents suggest that if one feeds the baby conventionally by spoon that they come to rely on that and lag behind others in their ability to feed themselves later. In essence this is probably true as practice does make perfect, but we're talking only a few months. Does this actually matter?

By ten months most babies want to start feeding themselves anyway, and, indeed, can get quite pushy about it. Sometimes they will start refusing food from the spoon and insist on doing it themselves.

So, like most of these issues, you should try it and see how you and your baby deal with it. Babies are self-regulating by nature. If it works, have fun, but ensure you place a large sheet of plastic under the high chair when you feed her. And if it's not working or you have to get out and pick up the toddler in an hour, use your spoon and don't believe anyone who says that your baby is somehow missing out on something important.

Relaxation around food and its consumption is most important. Food is to be eaten in a cloud of love and contentment. It's neither a task nor a competition!

ISSUES WITH FOOD

Constipation when solids are added

When solids and spoon foods are started, there will always be a change in the stool consistency, frequency, colour and odour. The stools will reflect the new diet. The diet will contain more fibre and non-milk products, which will change the stool accordingly.

It is usual that the stools become less fluid or sticky and can even become putty-like or firm. If this occurs you might try to add some more fibre to her diet. So increase the vegetables, especially green veggies, salads, tomatoes and carrots. Kids love carrots or celery sticks, which they can dip into hummus. Fruit, especially pears and oranges, have a lot of fibre too, but cut out (or never give) fruit juice, which has little.

The old favourite standby in this situation is the prune. Use the juice, diluted with 50 per cent water for babies and infants, and use the fruit mashed, whole or stewed for the child over six months old. It's sweet as well as delicious and has been used in professional mothercraft for decades as a stool softener. Multigrain cereals and even bran additives can also boost the fibre intake. A really good 'superfood' which is very high in fibre is chia seeds, which can be added to soups, casseroles, desserts, puddings and cakes. It's also chock-full of protein and omega acids.

Chia pudding

Here's a delicious dessert to get baby bowels moving. You can play with the amounts depending on how thick you would like the mixture.

¼ cup of chia seeds

1 cup coconut cream

1 cup raspberries

Mix the chia with the coconut cream. The seeds will swell so keep stirring so that all the seeds are separated. Add the raspberries and mix to combine. Place in the refrigerator and allow the seeds to swell some more. Then spoon into your constipated baby's mouth!

Now and again the introduction of solids can lead to true constipation in infants. The stools will become hard, dry and infrequent. Occasionally they can be so bulky as to cause pain and discomfort. If the stool is so large that it over stretches the anus, this can cause a split in the ring at the 12 o'clock position (that is, closest to the front). This is called a 'fissure' and can cause acute pain when the bowels are moved and blood can appear on the surface of the stool.

If this situation occurs the first intervention is to stop those foods that are causing the stools to be hard. Bananas, rice and other low-fibre foods should be ceased completely. More water should be offered to the infant and a trial of stool softeners should be started. If prunes, prune juice (now without water) or chia seeds are not effective, lactulose, which can be obtained from the pharmacy, should be used. The start dose is 5 ml a day but this can be rapidly increased, if no response, to 10 or 15 ml per day. It is fairly palatable and very safe. If the dose is too much it will yield too soft a poo and the dose can then be reduced. The aim should be for the infant or child to produce a soft stool every one or two days. If this is not effective, medical help should be obtained soon.

Occasionally you can get the situation where, after the passage of a hard stool has been experienced, the infant becomes fearful of the accompanying discomfort and she starts to 'hold on', and resist passing a motion. If a fissure has formed, then this problem is even more likely. The hard stool then accumulates in the lower bowel and progressively becomes bigger and harder and even more difficult to expel. The bowel that is overfull and distended with stool over time tends to lose its muscle tone and its ability to empty itself – and this further exacerbates the problem. This can become a vicious cycle, which makes the infant and family very miserable. In these circumstances it is necessary to use more powerful agents, usually containing macrogol (under medical supervision), to be sure that the colon is emptied and stays relatively empty.

It is important to treat this situation seriously and consistently over weeks and months. The aim is to make sure that the bowel is emptied regularly and there is no opportunity for the constipation to recur. Gradually, with a daily soft stool, the bowel wall will regain its muscle tone and its ability to contract, which moves the stool along. But it takes diligence over the diet and often daily medication for months to achieve success.

That is not to say that you should become too obsessed with the quality and quantity of your baby's stools, but it is certainly wise to make sure that it does not stray too far from normal and to take early action if the stool starts to become too firm.

Food allergy

In the past we kept young babies away from foods that tended to cause allergies, such as peanuts and eggs, until they were over a year old. The logic was that their immature gut would allow the sensitising proteins to enter their bodies and sensitise them. We now know that this view was backwards; in fact their very immaturity allows them to develop tolerance, and therefore be less likely to develop a reaction to these allergenic foods.

A study by George Du Toit and Yitzhak Katz comparing Israeli babies with Jewish babies (of similar genetic endowment) in the United Kingdom showed that the incidence of peanut allergy was ten times more prevalent in the United Kingdom than in Israel. The Israeli babies had a lot of contact with peanuts (as a puree) in their early months of weaning (they had a peanut confection for babies called Bamba), in comparison to the babies in the United Kingdom who had no contact at all.

Similarly with eggs, an Australian study by J.J. Koplin and N.J. Osbourne showed that babies introduced to eggs between four and six months of age had an incidence of egg allergy put arbitrarily at 1 on a scale. These were then compared to babies to whom eggs were introduced for the first time at ten to 12 months and who had 1.6 times the incidence of egg allergy, and when introduced after one year, there was 3.4 times the incidence. Clearly the introduction of eggs in the early months gives babies tolerance to the egg protein and this should be encouraged. If your baby was allergic to cow's milk protein or she has a sibling with food allergies, it is still important to introduce these foods at four to six months. Delaying introduction will further increase the likelihood of allergy. But it is logical to do them one at a time.

Picky kids

Occasionally you will find some foods that are rejected by the baby right from the start. The younger the age at which this occurs, the easier it is to overcome. Continue to get them to try the food on alternate days and this will usually have the baby accepting the food within seven days, as long as you persist. A study in 2004 by B.R. Carruth and others showed that most parents tend to give up trying rejected foods after three to five attempts, which is not enough. Such studies show that trying for longer encourages the babies to try it and acquire the taste, and months later the baby still appreciates the once-rejected food. The nearer the baby gets to one year of age, the more attempts the baby requires to accept the rejected food. By one year old, it might be eight to fifteen times before acceptance occurs.

This is an important point. In order to get babies to appreciate more subtly flavoured or sour foods you may need a little persistence. But it is worth it, as the variety of food they will then accept becomes much broader. It is easy for babies to accept sweet foods, so fruit is always accepted much more easily than vegetables.

So it is therefore a good idea to introduce a wide variety of vegetables *first*, and later when they've got the hang of these, then embark upon a little fruit in your baby's diet.

Kids who bolt their food

Do you remember when you were a child, your mother would always tell you to eat more slowly and chew your food properly? Actually, she was on to something. There have been a couple of studies that have shown that children who eat rapidly have an increased likelihood of becoming obese. The difference in eating speed is actually not very great. In one 2010 study reported in the journal *Obesity*, the children who tended towards obesity took a bite every 18 seconds and their meals lasted about 28 minutes, and the ones who were slim took a bite every 25 seconds and their meals lasted about 40 minutes.

Eating more slowly allows the body to adjust to the food load and send satisfaction signals for the brain to switch off the appetite.

Fruit juice

While we're on the subject of fruit, there is a real problem with fruit juice. Fruit juice contains only the sugar fructose. Fructose is very sweet indeed. On the sweetness index mentioned earlier, pure fructose comes out with the score of 137! White sugar (sucrose) is a 50–50 glucose and fructose combination and as mentioned above has a sweetness index of 100; high-fructose corn syrup has slightly more fructose than glucose and this has a sweetness index of 120. These two substances are basically the same – their main difference is that corn syrup is cheaper in the United States than sucrose by a significant margin. In Australia the reverse is true. Anyway, the food companies tend to use whichever is the cheapest when they want to make a food sweeter and therefore more attractive.

Now why would the food companies want to do that? Primates love to eat food that is sweet, so it's a great way to boost sales. Fructose has an added benefit for the sellers of food: it doesn't switch off your appetite very effectively as you eat it, so you tend to eat more.

Fructose is mainly a problem for older children and adults. Babies and toddlers actually don't have the factor that helps the small bowel absorb it – they develop that as they get older. While they are young, fructose tends to give them diarrhoea ('toddler diarrhoea'), as their gut cannot absorb more than small quantities. That doesn't stop them wanting it though; it's still very sweet and they're still little primates.

Sugar and sweet food

What sweet foods, and sucrose in particular, do to children is unsettle them. Ten minutes at a children's party full of soft drink and sugary foods should be enough to convince anyone of this.

Limiting the amount of sugar that children get in the early months and years is the aim of most responsible parents. However, only the strong can survive as the persuasive ability of the toddler who wants a chocolate bar is intense. They also very soon learn the market value of good behaviour and silence as measured in confectionery. Grandparents are often guilty of this as it is an instant method to get attention and devotion from the young.

Supermarkets are also to blame, placing such items at kiddie level near the checkout tills. It is a strong parent who can withstand the pressure of the whining at the same time as the packing and paying for the weekly shopping trip.

Somehow it needs to be resisted as sugar craving is an entity whose downstream effect is obesity and all its ramifications.

Dietary fats

I bet that most of you are eating, and wondering about giving your children, low-fat-diet foods. In a word, don't. Infants and children need energy, and skinny milks and desserts will not give them enough. Always use the full-fat foods for them, unless your doctor specifically says not to.

Full-fat foods are also more satisfying and will curb an appetite more appropriately than the low-fat foods. Our stomach produces a hormone in response to fat that shuts down our appetite. That's why it is easy to overeat the low-fat products.

There is a lot of controversy about which fats are healthier for us but in essence it boils down to avoiding processed foods especially when cooked in fat, like chips. These tend to be cooked in unhealthy omega-6 polyunsaturated fat usually derived from sunflower, safflower or corn oils.

Instead, cook your own in a predominantly monounsaturated fat, like olive oil. Use an extra virgin, high-quality one and don't overheat the olive oil so it smokes or deteriorates. Low and slow is the way.

Unlike omega-6 polyunsaturated fatty acids, omega-3 polyunsaturated fats are very beneficial, especially for the growing brain. Fish oil is loaded with it and having supplements when pregnant or breastfeeding is a good idea, particularly in the face of so much omega-6 oil used in the food industry.

As for saturated fats – the animal fats and coconut oil – they're okay and probably not as unhealthy as was thought in the past, but should be used in moderation.

Remember fats are more 'energy dense' than carbohydrates such as sugar, rice and potato. In fact, per gram they give the body more than twice as many calories. So moderation in all fatty foods is a good idea.

AT ONE YEAR

> I really need some advice. I have a 14-month-old who has become a very difficult eater. Everything I give him, he throws off his high chair. I mean everything. He has never been very good at feeding himself so I may have spoilt him and fed him with the spoon for too long. I've been told to put a meal out for him and if he throws it overboard then to pack up and it's the end of the meal . . . he will eventually eat when he is hungry. We have done this for a day and I thought he would be hungry by now but he's still throwing food. Please help, I'm worried this is just going to get worse.

So here we are at one year of age. You have worked hard and now have a young toddler who will eat anything you give him, and everything you give him is good food. Alas, you can't relax.

I mentioned earlier that once babies start to get mobile, evolution protects them from poisoning themselves by giving them food neophobia or resistance to trying new tastes. So he won't eat anything unless he recognises it from before, and even familiar foods become increasingly suspicious.

Also he now demands to feed himself and won't accept just any spoon sent in his direction. As he becomes more independent he develops a wonderful game. It entails throwing the food on the floor, putting it in his hair or smearing it around the table, rather than eating it. It produces for him a hilarious cabaret of nervous parents wondering whether their baby will starve amid the mess.

This is a seriously slippery slope. All over the Western world there are family mealtimes dominated by stubborn toddlers. These little tyrants quickly discover that there is far more attention to be had by *not* eating than by opening their mouth and accepting what their mother wants to give them. By resolutely keeping the mouth shut, spitting skilfully and generally refusing all food, they can star in an hour-long show and dominate the audience. The families, terrified that their chubby toddler will waste away and die, embark upon the most excruciating series of manoeuvres to try to get the toddler to eat. Distraction methods are common. They put on the TV or radio. Or it's cabaret time! Grandma dances a jig and sings a song, Dad wears funny hats and does a terrible impersonation of Charlie Chaplin, so that the toddler will gape in wonder and Mum manages to slide a spoonful in. The family stops, holding its breath, hoping the food will go down and not be spat out at the cat.

In the 2009 Australian movie *The Boys are Back* there is a wonderful scene where a family is depicted at a mealtime. There is a toddler in a high chair. Strangely the father is not at the table. He's outside on the ride-on mower, going up and down outside the window. As the toddler gazes at him in awe, his mother shovels food as fast as she can into his gaping mouth. You also might notice that the toddler in this scene is quite chubby . . .

Other useless techniques are the parents pleading and wheedling, pretending to cry if the baby refuses the food, extolling the virtues of the food to the baby, telling him how good the food is for him and how if he doesn't eat it he'll never get to university.

The take-home sentence for all of this, and I quote from Professor Illingworth's classic book *The Normal Child*:

No child has ever starved in the presence of food
and
It is never necessary to force a child to eat.

So offer your toddler the food. If he refuses it, give it to the cat and declare the meal over. No discussion, no arguments. Be unruffled and carefree. However, no eating between meals, no snacks, no sweets. He will eat at the next meal. If not, the next. Don't worry.

And never chase a toddler with anything on a spoon!

THE SOCIAL CONTEXT OF THE FAMILY MEAL

This has been mentioned already. If family meals are happy and convivial, then the toddler is likely to be confident in trying new foods that others seem to be enjoying.

Not only that, she learns to derive pleasure from the social gathering of a mealtime where opinions are exchanged, subjects discussed, and the family is seen as a single community bound by loyalty and love. The family mealtime's main function is not the consumption of food but the interchange of ideas and experiences. The conversation also slows down the eating process so that it is enjoyed and savoured more. It also teaches good table manners, which is important in a civilised society not because putting your knife in your mouth is inherently bad (though you may cut your tongue) but good table manners teach you to be considerate of others.

Children also copy the eating habits of those around them, especially their mother. Generally if she likes certain foods her children will copy her. This important factor can help motivate the parents into improving their diet to directly benefit their children's eating habits. Fast food is a lifesaver for busy people but shortens the life of everyone around the table.

Too often nowadays the family meal is disappearing as people eat fast foods at different times and in different places. In certain Western countries you are as likely to consume a meal from a drive-through in a car as in a kitchen. As children get older so the importance of family meals increases. In teenage years the presence of this time of family interaction has been shown to improve their mental health with fewer emotional and behavioural problems occurring.

So make the evening meal a routine in your family.

OTHER FACTORS

There are a few other factors worth noting that relate to whether kids will accept new and unfamiliar foods:

- Marketing people have figured out that children are very amenable to the eating habits of their heroes. 'Superman loves broccoli' is a powerful persuasive slogan, though I am unsure if Popeye ever sold very much spinach to children!

- Giving children food as a reward for good behaviour is fine, as long as that good behaviour isn't actually eating the food. Giving a reward for eating certain foods has a very negative effect. Kids are suspicious that they need bribery to eat a certain food and assume there must be an ulterior motive.

- Another way to turn children off a certain food is telling them that 'it's good for them'. Your mother would only do that about foods that taste awful!

- If you want to make a food attractive, forbid it. There's nothing more delicious than forbidden fruit.

- The food preferences that you nurture in your children over these early months are well worth the time and effort. Unfortunately all your hard work can be extinguished in a moment by a single episode of aversion. If your child's first experience with brussels sprouts happens to coincide with a bout of gastroenteritis with vomiting, it can be very hard to get her to try that food ever again.

MILK AND DAIRY PRODUCTS

There is a fairly vigorous, some would say vicious, fight going on about milk. On the one hand, the dairy industry spends a staggering amount of money convincing us that it is the best and most wholesome food available for everyone, especially for kids. Ask anyone on the street and they will tell you that it is full of calcium and it gives you strong teeth and bones, and makes you taller, smarter, stronger and prettier. Governments around the (Western) world have endorsed this message and subsidised or encouraged parents to feed their children dairy products.

Of late, however, research has appeared that seems to suggest that dairy milk and its by-products are not only irrelevant to a healthy diet but can actually be harmful to the human race.

Cow's milk is biologically designed for the baby cow; indeed all animals' milks are only designed for their specific baby. For the most part, if babies are fed the milk of another species, the infant will not thrive and may die. The human and the domestic cat are the only creatures that not only continue to eat such food beyond babyhood, but also get it from another species. You actually have to train your body genetically to digest it. The enzyme that allows you to absorb the sugar in the milk (the lactose) tends to disappear in most animals after their mother stops lactating and they move on to solid food. From the time in prehistory when we domesticated animals, starting with the buffalo, yak and goat, then finally settled on the cow, the Western diet has trained most of us to maintain that enzyme (called lactase) in our intestine for the whole of our life. However, a healthy proportion of the population remains lactose intolerant. In non-Western cultures almost all of the population is intolerant. Figures from around the world show that about 75 per cent of the world's people can't absorb the lactose, and in those people, it produces bloating, diarrhoea and flatulence.

Milk is certainly a good source of calcium, but only about 30 per cent or so can be absorbed by the gut. There is some evidence that even in the tolerant human, consumption can produce a net loss of calcium from the bones and teeth because the protein from the milk needs to be buffered (that is, the acidity needs to be neutralised) by calcium from the bones. This and other studies are summed up in a petition sent from the Physicians Committee for Responsible Medicine in the United States to the US Department of Agriculture Food and Nutrition Service in 2010. It also shows that the greater the consumption of milk products in a population, the greater the incidence of hip fractures, especially as the population ages. There also seems to be an albeit weak correlation between dairy intake and cancers (of the breast, ovary, prostate and gut). The cancer relationship is clearer in those populations whose milk has the remnants of a hormone called IGF1 (insulin growth factor 1) which is given to cows in those countries to increase their milk output. This is relevant in the United States, but not Australia, New Zealand or Europe, where it's banned.

There is no doubt that kids who are given full cream cow's milk early on in life have a high incidence of iron deficiency (up to 10 per cent) as the milk prevents the iron in their diet from being absorbed and causes the bowel to bleed and lose iron from the body.

What is not generally understood is that an excellent source of calcium for the human body also lies in vegetables. Gram for gram, green vegetables such as kale and especially Chinese vegetables such as bok choy, along with sea vegetables, have more calcium in them than full cream cow's milk. (See p. 284 chart.)

The decision of whether or not to give your child dairy is a balancing act for parents. Dairy is an easy, attractive high-calcium food and our children do need a lot of calcium as their skeletons grow – they need at least 600 mg a day. Some vegetables high in calcium often have to be taken in larger quantities than milk (cup for cup) as sometimes the absorption of these vegetables by the gut is inhibited by substances in the food (oxalates and phthalates). However, soy and almond milk are very acceptable and taste good, and have as much calcium as dairy, and their calcium is well absorbed.

So kids don't really need milk, except human milk. After they are weaned, they ideally should be given real food, not baby food designed for large hoofed quadrupeds with four stomachs. Mind you, you'll have a hard time completely avoiding dairy. The industry is massive and it has its finger not only in many pies but everything else on the supermarket shelf. The foods in which it is included can be delicious and comforting. Cheese in particular is probably single-handedly responsible for more obesity, and all its downstream illnesses, than any other single food.

I was recently in Vietnam. Nowadays most of the population is slim and fit, eating a healthy diet of vegetables, rice noodles and other Asian foods. I was aghast to see a new, vigorous advertising campaign pushing dairy foods such as yoghurt, aimed primarily at parents, encouraging them to feed these foods to their kids to make them smart, healthy and happy. I was even contacted by their dairy board's advertising agency to help them

Chart of foods containing calcium

KIDS NEED PER DAY	600 mg
NON DAIRY SOURCES	**mg**
Sardines (85 g)	371
Orange juice, calcium-fortified (1 cup)	300
Sesame seeds (28 g)	280
Tofu (85 g)	190
Salmon (85 g, canned)	180
Collards (½ cup, chopped)	180
Rhubarb (½ cup)	174
Blackstrap molasses (1 tbsp)	172
Amaranth flour (½ cup)	150
Spinach (½ cup, canned)	136
Figs (5)	135
Artichokes (1 medium)	135
Soybean nuts (¼ cup)	116
Turnip greens (½ cup, chopped)	100
Cereal, calcium-fortified (½ cup)	100–200
Kale (½ cup, chopped)	90
Almond butter (2 tbsp)	86
Beet greens (½ cup, boiled)	82
Almonds (28 g)	80
Bok choy (Chinese cabbage) (½ cup)	79
Okra (½ cup)	77
Tempeh (½ cup)	77
Beans (½ cup, baked)	75
Papaya (1 medium)	73
Orange (1 medium)	50
Broccoli (½ cup, chopped)	47
Okra (½ cup)	77
DAIRY SOURCES	**mg**
Milk (1 cup)	300
Yogurt (1 cup)	450
Cheese (30 g)	200–300
Cottage cheese (30 g)	155

peddle this stuff. When I asked a couple of questions about the details and the evidence for their assertions, the offer was not pursued.

It is so sad. At this rate in 20 years they will be as overweight and unhealthy as we are in the West.

VITAMIN D

Maybe we've believed the message about the danger of exposure to the sun, or maybe it's because we work so hard from dawn to dusk in dark offices, but even in Australia, there's no doubt as a population we're getting deficient in vitamin D.

Our daily requirement for vitamin D is 5–10 μg/day. Most of us, children, adults and the elderly, are lucky to get half that from our diet and sun exposure.

Our skin when exposed to sunlight usually produces most of our needs for the vitamin, but time of year, age, skin colour, time spent outdoors and the use of sunscreens can cause large variations in its production.

The most affected populations are of course the dark skinned among us. The melanin pigment in our skin tends to shield us from the ultraviolet rays from the sun that cause the skin to produce vitamin D, so those with more melanin tend to produce less vitamin D (that's the way the system is designed for those who live in sun-drenched countries). These people are much more likely to develop deficiency unless they spend a lot of time in the sun. This situation also occurs in cultures in which the women are veiled, which also obviously shields their skin from the sun. Both those groups are so much more affected when they get pregnant and have to supply their foetus as well as themselves with vitamin D. Up to 80 per cent of these women can be severely deficient in Australia, as elsewhere.

But the European skinned should not be complacent. Caryl A. Nowson and Claire Margerison reported in the *Medical Journal of Australia* in 2002 that even in young women in Geelong, Victoria, by the end of winter up to 8 per cent were frankly deficient in this vitamin.

It also seems that breastfed babies who have vitamin D sufficient mothers still cannot get enough to meet their needs purely from their diet. Breastmilk has about 22 International Units (IU) of vitamin D/litre. As the baby needs about 200 IU/day minimum, the baby could not drink enough to meet his or her needs from that source alone. It is just not enough. If Mum tried to boost the level in her milk by taking a supplement, say 1000 IU/day, this only increases the level in her breastmilk by about 10 IU/litre.

Formula-fed babies get enough vitamin D from the boosted levels in their diet, however.

Dietary vitamin D is present especially in oily fish such as sardines, salmon, herring and mackerel, and also to a lesser extent in eggs, meat and milk. It is also found in the fat from animals such as lamb, duck or chicken. Do you remember how your grandmother used to cook vegetables in dripping? No wonder they tasted so good, quite apart from boosting your vitamin D levels. Don't worry about the saturated fat in dripping. In moderation, it's healthy.

Governments have been trying to improve our intake by fortifying foods such as milk, margarine and other spreads. Even so, consumption is still inadequate for most.

In the United States there is a blanket recommendation that all people from infancy onward be given 400 IU/day. There is no reason why the situation should be very different in Australia, especially towards the end of winter.

In 1991 the Australian National Health and Medical Research Council recommended that 'pregnant women and young children receive reasonable sunlight exposure; those who are housebound or not exposed to direct sunlight for at least 1–2 hours per week should have a daily oral intake of 10 μg (400 IU) vitamin D'.

In more recent years it is clear that the incidence of deficiency is higher than was realised then, and it is logical that such supplementation should be offered to all.

IRON DEFICIENCY

Iron deficiency is another health issue that has crept up on us lately. We now realise how high the incidence is in our general population. In a 1996 study by Margaret Karr and others of Australian children in Sydney, aged nine to 62 months: 1.1 per cent had iron-deficiency anaemia and 10.5 per cent were iron depleted (that is, with low stores but no manifestations of deficiency yet).

Worse still, if they came from an Arabic background: 6 per cent of children had iron-deficiency anaemia and 23 per cent were iron depleted – nearly a quarter of them!

What determined whether or not the child was deficient was how much iron storage they had at birth (so premature or low-birth-weight babies were at extra risk), how much iron they got in their diet and whether they were losing iron, usually through their bowel (often from drinking cow's milk when younger than one year of age).

Breastfeeding infants after six months of age who had no extra iron-containing foods were at risk, as there is little iron in breast-milk (however, what is there is fully absorbed). Hence the need, at six months or so, to introduce iron-rich spoon foods, such as iron-fortified multigrain cereals, pureed meat, beef and chicken (especially beef or chicken liver) and iron-rich vegetables, such as spinach, broccoli, tomatoes, brussels sprouts, beans, peas and potatoes.

Children need about 10 mg or so of iron each day. It is not hard to achieve this intake with a varied diet rich in the foods mentioned above.

As mentioned before, the early introduction of straight cow's milk, especially under the age of one year, was also a risk factor. The cow's milk binds the iron in the diet and stops its absorption, but also causes the bowel to bleed a little. A slow, steady loss of a little blood every day can rapidly deplete a child's iron stores and cause a deficiency. Children on a high intake of cow's milk even after one year old are also at risk and should be monitored.

So make sure that after weaning you give your children sufficient quantities of good iron-rich foods to supply them with this vital element.

Iron-rich foods

Haem-containing foods (the iron in the blood), the richest source:

- Meat of all kinds – lamb, beef, pork, chicken
- Liver (chock-full!)
- Seafood – shrimp, tuna and other fish.

Non-haem-containing foods (the iron is harder to absorb, but enough if your general vegetarian diet is adequate):

- Legumes – chickpeas and lentils, foods like hommus
- Beans – kidney, baked, lima, black, pinto and soy
- Tofu
- Leafy (especially dark) green vegetables, such as spinach, broccoli, mustard greens, asparagus and brussels sprouts
- Eggs, especially the yolks
- Dried fruits, such as raisins, figs, dates, apricots, and prunes and prune juice
- Peanut butter
- Iron-fortified breads and cereals, porridge oats.

But enough of the theory. Let's eat.

RECIPES FOR A HEALTHY BABY

Remember, babies like to eat what their parents eat. Time for you to try these recipes and leave the processed food in the cupboard.

Thanks to Nina Stabey of the Healing Ingredient for these wonderful recipes. They are all gluten and dairy free to boost your baby's body with vitality and health.

A WORD FROM NINA:

I have been in the food and health industries for over two decades and I never tire of creating new recipes that are easy to follow, are made from simple honest ingredients, taste amazing and are highly nutritious. I especially enjoy developing recipes for babies and children.

I feel strongly that our children need REAL food. Not food that is processed, refined or adulterated. Fast food and poor lifestyle choices are reflected in our nation's health, as nearly 70 per cent of all diseases and illnesses are food or lifestyle related.

Healthy relationships with food begin when the child is young. So you as the parent are bestowed a huge responsibility. It is so easy to let our young children get hooked on sweet foods, flavoured drinks, or processed breads and cereals. When we are busy and under pressure it is a slippery slope to use sweet food rewards to sedate our children.

I encourage you to get into healthy, fun explorations with food to benefit the whole family as your child grows and develops.

Stay tuned for more cookbooks.

Nina Stabey, BHSc Nut Med

Sea vegetable fritters

1–2 tsp olive or coconut oil
½ onion, finely diced
1 tsp garlic, minced
½ tsp chilli powder (optional)
½ tsp black peppercorns
5 g Sea Vegetable Garden Salad* mix, soaked and drained
OR
5 g arame, soaked and drained
2 eggs, whisked

Heat the oil in a non-stick frypan and add the onion, garlic, chilli and black peppercorns.

Gently sauté until golden. In a bowl, combine the eggs, drained sea vegetable mix or arame, and the sautéed onion mixture. Spoon the egg mix into the pan to make fritters and cook each side for 2–3 minutes, or until the egg mix is firm. Serve with slices of avocado or salmon.

*Available from www.thehealingingredient.com.

Salmon dip

415 g can red/pink salmon
1 ripe avocado
5 spring onions, roughly chopped
juice of ½ lemon
cracked pepper

Place the first four ingredients in a blender and blend until smooth. You may need to add a little water just to get the blending going. Garnish with a sprinkle of cracked pepper and serve with vegetable sticks or crackers with avocado, or as a sauce over roasted vegetables.

Variations:
Add wasabi powder, horseradish and/or lemon zest if desired.

Cucumber dip

1 continental cucumber, peeled and grated
1 cup raw macadamia nuts
juice of ½ lemon
¼ cup fresh dill, chopped
2 tbsp fresh chives, chopped
½–1 tsp black pepper, ground
¼ tsp chilli powder (optional)
2 tbsp pine nuts, toasted and crushed

Place the cucumber in a strainer for 10–15 minutes, to drain. Squeeze out as much excess water from the cucumber as you can. Place the first seven ingredients in a blender and blend until smooth. Season to taste and garnish with the pine nuts.

Berry berry bake

6 egg whites
1 cup almond meal
3 tbsp cherry juice concentrate (optional)
500 g mixed berries, fresh or frozen (but thawed)

Preheat oven to 170°C. Beat the egg whites until they form stiff peaks. Fold the almond meal and the cherry juice concentrate gently through the beaten egg whites. Place the berries in an ovenproof dish. Then layer the egg white and almond mix on top of the berries. Bake for 15–20 minutes, until the egg whites are lightly golden and the berries are warm.

Spinach, basil and green pea soup

1 tbsp olive oil
1 brown onion, diced
4 cups vegetable stock*
750 g frozen spinach

500 g frozen/fresh baby green peas
1½ bunches basil leaves, washed and roughly chopped
½ tsp salt
black pepper

Heat the olive oil in a medium-sized soup pot, add the onion and cook until tender. Then add the stock, spinach and peas and simmer for 5–7 minutes. Remove the pot from the heat and add the basil leaves. Allow to stand and cool for 15–20 minutes before blending until smooth, or use a hand-held blender for a chunkier soup. Season to taste and serve hot.

*The stock can be made from a handy soup stock bag available from www.thehealingingredient.com.

Fish chowder

2 tbsp olive oil
½ brown onion, diced
3 cloves garlic, minced
1–2 tsp tarragon, dried
6 cups fish or vegetable stock*
500 g white fish, cut into small cubes (blue grenadier, snapper, basa, etc.)
80 ml coconut milk
pepper (optional)

In a soup pot, heat the olive oil and sauté the onion, garlic and tarragon until the onion is transparent but not browned. Add the stock. Add the diced fish to the liquid and cook until the fish is opaque. In a blender, process the fish soup until smooth. Transfer back to the pot. Add the coconut milk and pepper to taste. Serve hot.

*Fish stock bags available from www.thehealingingredient.com.

Apple jelly

2–3 red apples (medium), washed, cored and chopped
1 cup water
¾ tsp agar-agar powder*

Place the apple in a blender with ½ cup of water and blend until smooth. In a saucepan, boil the remaining ½ cup of water and add the agar-agar. Reduce the heat and simmer for 5 minutes, until the agar-agar is completely dissolved. Pour blended apple into the saucepan with the agar-agar and combine well. Remove from heat and pour the apple mixture into a medium-sized glass or pyrex container and refrigerate until firm. Serve cold.

*Available at your local health food store or Asian store. My recommendation is to purchase the powder, not the bar or granules, as these take much longer to dissolve.

Herbed lamb broth

750 g lamb bones (ask butcher to cut in half), joints or necks
6 cups water
3 bay leaves
1 tsp whole black peppercorns
1 tsp whole green peppercorns
2 garlic cloves, minced
½ bunch coriander, washed and chopped
½ bunch Vietnamese mint, washed and chopped
1–2 tsp chilli paste (optional)
2–3 tbsp fried shallots

Place the first six ingredients in a large soup pot or slow cooker. Simmer for 4 hours. Drain the liquid from the bones, then discard the bones. Lamb stock can be stored in the fridge or frozen. (If the stock sets to a jelly in the fridge, it's a sign of a good quality stock.) Serve with fresh herbs, chilli and fried shallots as desired.

Roasted red capsicum sauce

2 red capsicums
1 handful fresh parsley, roughly chopped (optional)
1 tbsp olive oil infused with garlic*
3 spring onions (green part only), chopped
pinch black pepper

Preheat oven to 180°C. Place the capsicums on a baking tray, brush with some olive oil and bake for 25 minutes or until charred. Remove the capsicums from oven, place in a plastic bag and leave for 20 minutes until cool enough to handle. Take the capsicums from the bag, peel the skin off, remove seeds and roughly chop. Place capsicum, parsley, garlic olive oil, spring onions and pepper in a blender and blend until smooth. Season to taste.

Variations:
Add chilli (flakes, paste or fresh) and fresh herbs, such as basil, thyme or oregano.

*Available from supermarkets.

Cherry jelly with star anise

1 cup cherry juice concentrate
3 cups water
1 star anise
1½ tsp agar-agar

Place the cherry concentrate, water and star anise into a medium-size saucepan. Bring to the boil and then reduce heat. Add the agar-agar and stir for 5–7 minutes until all the powder is dissolved. Pour the cherry juice liquid into an appropriate mould, allow to cool for 10 minutes and place in the fridge until firm.

Spicy lentil pâté

425 g can lentils, rinsed and drained
1 tbsp tahini
½ juice lemon
½ stick celery, roughly chopped
½ carrot, roughly chopped
1 clove garlic, minced
¼ red onion, roughly chopped
¼ tsp chilli flakes
¼ bunch parsley, washed
pinch of black pepper

Place all ingredients in a blender and blend until smooth. Season to taste.

Fennel fritters

1 fennel bulb, coarsely grated
2 eggs, lightly beaten
1–2 tbsp coconut flour
½ red onion, finely diced
2 tbsp fresh dill, chopped
2 tbsp fresh mint, chopped
½ tsp turmeric powder
½ tsp ground black peppercorns (optional)
1 tbsp coconut oil

Gently combine the grated fennel, eggs, coconut flour and red onion in a bowl. Add the herbs and spices, and season with pepper. Lightly oil a non-stick frypan and place spoonfuls of the mixture in the hot pan (you can make them as big or small as you like). Cook until lightly golden on each side, then drain on absorbent paper.

Avocado and arame dip

2 g arame*
¼ red onion (or 1 spring onion), finely diced
1 avocado, mashed
¼ cup celery, chopped
pinch of pepper

Soak a handful of arame in a bowl of water for 5 minutes and then drain. Combine all the ingredients in a bowl and season to taste.

Variations:
Add diced cucumber, celery, green beans, grated carrot, etc., toasted sesame seeds, chilli/garlic, sliced black olives or chopped basil.

*Spiral brand, available from the health food store.

Nut milk

You can use nut milks on breakfast cereals, in cakes, bakes, pancakes and muffins, or for making your own ice-cream or nut milkshakes.

1 cup any nuts or seeds or a mix of both
3 cups water
1 tsp vanilla powder*

Place the nuts into a blender and blend until a nut meal. Add the water and vanilla powder. Blend until smooth.

Variations:
Add spices, such as cinnamon, anise, nutmeg, cardamom, and fruit, such as blueberries (fresh or frozen), raspberries, banana, etc. You can also include carob-orange oil, carob-peppermint oil or banana-coconut oil.

*Available from www.thehealingingredient.com.

Carrot chips

½–1 cup coconut oil or grass-fed lamb fat
3 carrots, cut into very thin discs or curls using a vegetable
     peeler or Japanese Mandolin slicer
½ tsp sea salt
1 sheet toasted nori paper*

Heat the oil or fat in a frypan on high. Fry the carrot chips until golden brown. Remove from the frypan and drain excess oil on paper towel. They will be a little soggy when still hot, but they crisp up as they cool. Sprinkle with a little salt and crumbled nori paper.

Variations:

You can make chips using a variety of vegetables, including butternut pumpkin, beetroot, eggplant, choko, swede and sweet potato.

*Available from the Asian section of supermarkets.

Chicken skin chips

500 g organic chicken skins (ask the butcher to collect them
     for you)
1 tbsp ground turmeric
1 tsp dried rosemary
1 tsp dried parsley or chives

Preheat the oven to 180°C. Cut the chicken skins into 3 cm strips, place them in a bowl, and lightly sprinkle with turmeric and herbs. Line a baking tray with greaseproof paper and arrange the skin strips side by side. Bake for 15–20 minutes or until the skins are golden brown and crunchy. Remove the skins from the tray and allow to cool before serving.

Variations:

Add oregano, rosemary, black pepper, etc. You can also add garlic paste when coating the skins.

Nut crème

1–1½ cups any nuts or seeds or a mix of both
1 cup water
1 tsp vanilla powder*

Put all ingredients into a blender and blend until smooth. Serve over fruit salad, grated apple or pear, or in between rice cakes and dusted with carob powder.

Chicken mince nuggets

500 g chicken mince
1 tsp turmeric powder
¼ tsp paprika
2 eggs, whisked
1 cup nut meal or coconut flour
1–2 tbsp oil of choice: olive, chicken fat, coconut

In a bowl, combine the mince, turmeric and paprika well. Form little balls and squash them to form desired nugget size. Dip in the egg and then lightly coat in the nut meal/coconut flour. Fry in oil in a non-stick frying pan until golden brown.

Sunflower snack

1 cup sunflower butter (sugar free)
1 tsp honey, maple syrup (optional)
½ tsp turmeric powder
1 tsp baking powder (gluten free)
1 egg

Preheat oven to 170°C. Line a baking tray with baking paper. Place all ingredients in a bowl and combine well. Spoon the mixture onto the baking tray, leaving plenty of room in between each snack as they will spread. Bake for 15–20 minutes or until golden brown and cooked in the middle. Remove from tray and allow them to cool before serving.

Pumpkin and macadamia soup

1 tbsp olive oil
½ brown onion, diced
3 shallots, roughly chopped
750 g butternut pumpkin, peeled, seeded and cut into
    small cubes
5 cups water or vegetable stock
½ cup whole macadamia nuts
1 tsp pepper
fresh parsley, chopped (optional)
¼ cup flaked macadamias (optional)

In a large soup pot, heat the olive oil and sauté the onion and shallots until transparent. Add the pumpkin and cover with 4 cups of the water or stock. Bring to the boil, then simmer for 10–15 minutes or until the pumpkin is very soft. Using a hand-held blender, blitz the pumpkin until smooth.

In a blender, blend the whole macadamias and the remaining cup of water or stock till smooth. Add this macadamia 'milk' to the pureed pumpkin. Stir well, season to taste and reheat. Serve with parsley and flaked macadamias if desired.

Coconut pancakes

3 eggs, whisked
¼ cup coconut milk
4 tbsp coconut flour
1 tsp vanilla powder*
½ tsp baking powder (gluten free)
2 tbsp coconut oil
pureed berries, to serve

Combine the eggs, coconut milk, coconut flour, vanilla powder and baking powder thoroughly to form a lump-free batter. Heat a non-stick frypan on medium-high and add the coconut oil. Spoon the batter into the frypan and cook the pancakes for 3–4 minutes, then flip over. Serve warm with pureed berries, or apples or sugar-free jam.

*Available from www.thehealingingredient.com.

CHAPTER 20

The relentless toddler

YOUNG BABIES CANNOT BE SPOILT. For the first few months they rely on their carers so completely that it is hard to imagine a baby being cared for too much. The baby's the boss and needs absolute security in all aspects of his life, and there is no danger in him learning 'bad' habits.

As one year approaches the baby's brain has doubled in size, under the weight of all the new brain connections. Through the previous months he has acquired the basics of security, self-worth and communication from his parents and carers. Now he embarks on the exciting journey of mobility, dexterity, language acquisition and more. He will learn how the world works, and his place within it.

As he stands on the threshold of mobile toddlerhood he starts to recognise his own individuality. To find that he is not actually part of his mother's body and is, in fact, a free agent is wildly exhilarating and terrifying in equal measure. As a consequence his behaviour starts to oscillate between reckless exploration and bouts of anxious timidity, which cause him to beat a retreat to familiarity, warmth and love.

He requires this safe haven of security to recharge his emotional batteries and regroup, before returning, re-energised, to his forays. At this time he critically needs an outer boundary of reasonable, consistent limits beyond which he cannot pass. He needs them to keep him safe, to slow him down long enough to develop some experience of the world and to define his frontiers. Without a designated perimeter he has no idea how far his power extends. And he is driven to find out.

THE NEW TODDLER'S PROFESSION

Parents are usually staggered by how busy their toddler is. Every waking moment is filled with the need to acquire as much information as possible from his environment, his body, family, and home and all the objects in it. All these make up his experimental laboratory.

Toddlers acquire information by exploration, experimentation and, like any good scientist, dogged repetition. For instance, he discovers that if he approaches an electrical socket in his house with a fork in his hand, his parents get very excited, take the fork from him and move him away. How interesting . . . He tries it again and gets the same response. Even more interesting. After five or six attempts to electrocute himself with the same result, he has learned something consistent and valuable about his world, so he finally gives up, stores this knowledge away and starts the next experiment. Let's see if spoons fit into the DVD player . . .

It is this relentless pursuit of experience and information that can make living with members of this age group so tiring for both him and his family. But this process of trying to fill in the gaps in his world is a critical part of his development.

While the fork/electrical socket is an extreme example, clearly there are limits that must be imposed to keep the child safe and to make life liveable for other members of the family. Not only that, starting from about six months of age, infants and children derive inner satisfaction and confidence from having limits imposed on their activities and structure given to their lives. Without them, life becomes boundless and uncertain and with so little attention paid to how they live, they wonder if anyone cares about them. This then creates another experiment, to find where the limits are.

Toddlers and separation

No matter how big and brave your toddler appears to be, he is still a baby, who is still part of his mother. He will remain essentially part of his mother's orbit until he is more than four years old. Only then will he be content to be apart from her for some hours. Before that age, he will count the minutes he is away from her.

Studies looking at the behaviour of toddlers separated from their mothers are heart-wrenching. As a species we are not designed for solitude, or the company of strangers, and separation from our loved ones causes almost life-threatening panic.

Typically after a short time of maternal absence the infant starts to protest, wailing and crying in an effort to get their mother to return to them. This phase goes on for hours, in fits and starts. Now and again they stop crying and collect themselves, and seem to buoy themselves up, starting to look hopefully and optimistically at each person who comes into the room, expecting each to be their mother. But after a while they sink again into misery.

This situation may be alleviated by others who offer the child love and affection. This does not stop the searching for the mother figure, but can minimise the effects of this stage and it evolving to the next. These loving figures, however, must continue to remain committed and in contact with the infant in order to prevent further disappointment and their return to the despondent state.

After days in the absence of carers, the child gives up. This is the phase of despair. They continue to cry but there is no element of hope within it. They may talk quietly to themselves and look around with a dull and hopeless gaze, but they no longer look at newcomers expecting familiarity.

Later still they develop detachment. They feel abandoned and lost. They have given up the hope that they will see their mother again. They stop crying and can appear relaxed, although they remain miserable. Even if she then returns they are likely to ignore her. They have been hurt too deeply and do not wish to commit themselves further. Recovering from such an episode can take time and, depending on the length of the absence, recovery may never be in full.

These observational studies summarised by Peter Cook in *Mothering Matters* (2011) were done under the circumstances of children in the past being admitted to hospital without their parents, or situations where the mother herself needed admission and had to leave her child. Nowadays the circumstances are less common as, for instance, toddlers can visit their mother in maternity and other hospitals.

However, this information is useful if you are planning day care or a trip away from your little one. It is most important to transfer your infant to another familiar, affectionate carer. This person must be known and loved by the infant. The infant must feel that their mother likes this person and is confident about her care.

TODDLER CHARACTERISTICS (AND HOW TO DEAL WITH THEM)

Like every other biological variable there is a wide range of toddlers. Some are easy kids and some are difficult; most of them, happily, lie somewhere in the middle of the range. Even so, studies show that over 90 per cent of parents have difficulty at toddler time and, at some time or another, feel they need some professional help. Even professionals need professionals!

However, there are some characteristics that to some extent are shared by all older infants and toddlers.

No common sense

Toddlers have absolutely no common sense whatever and as they are just getting mobile, this is a potentially dangerous combination. Domestic animals will not approach an open fire or a pot of hot water on the stove, but the human toddler will blunder in, hands first, to see what's going on. This is a time when sensible parents childproof their house, put all saucepan handles pointing to the rear of the cooktop and are careful where they put their cup of hot coffee to avoid swiping hands.

Self-centredness

Another important aspect of the older infant's mind is its complete self-centredness. From being a part of his mother's body, now he finds he is an island and needs to develop independence in a vast new world. It is no wonder he relates everything to himself and his survival. He has no time for thoughts other than about himself, and the task at hand.

Short attention span

Although some can concentrate on a picture book for several minutes, generally toddlers have a relatively short attention span. We can't fill them up with love and attention and then expect the recharge to last very long. After a long session of playing and closeness your toddler seems contented, but within minutes of you moving away, he starts to feel unnoticed and needs more time and love. And the game you were playing before is now boring and he needs something new. Toddlers need a lot of your time.

Get used to it.

Toddlers need time.

Stubbornness

However, this short attention span can be used to your advantage. All toddlers tend towards stubbornness. What they eat or won't eat, what they want to wear or don't. Luckily, their specific desires don't last long and distraction works a treat. Having removed the fork from his hand, give him something else interesting to use (perhaps something that doesn't conduct electricity . . .) and he will soon lose interest in what he originally had in mind.

Contrariness

This is related to the previous attribute. Almost as soon as they can talk babies find that their favourite word is 'NO'. They are not just being negative (although toddlers do tend towards that state); they also find that it produces a very gratifying response in the adults around them. From the age of ten months or so, one of the developmental markers of this age is 'repeating a perform-ance laughed at or given attention', to quote again from Professor Illingworth. No wonder this magic word is overused. Try to avoid reacting and confronting, as you'll only make it worse.

Impulsiveness

Toddlers also tend to act impulsively, without thought for the outcome of their actions. Their minds have not wired up the 'cause and effect' aspect. So tipping milk out of the cup onto the floor seemed like a good idea at the time, and they're often surprised that you get upset about such things. Telling them off or asking them to think is a fool's game. Just clean up the mess and next time give them a sippy cup that can't be tipped over.

Assume a 'worst-case scenario' whenever there's a toddler about. That also means making your house incredibly safe, with nothing around that can trap little fingers, or that little people can fall out of, drag on top of themselves or get caught in. Especially beware of the reversing car and never assume that your toddler is with your partner inside the house. Get reversing cameras and doors that lock automatically, and anti-toddler devices on all the drawers in the kitchen.

Liable to tantrum

The occasional tantrum is a normal part of being a toddler. It occurs for a number of reasons but is usually not a premeditated event in the young toddler (under 18 months), and usually the younger the child, the shorter the tantrum lasts. Most often it is an expression of sudden frustration or anger. The toddler has a burst of emotion that she is unable to control; neither does she recognise what she is feeling. Children of this age are not able to identify or label their emotions, and in this, they need to be helped by their parents. They do not understand the difference, for instance, between anger, jealousy, discomfort or frustration, and need an older person to teach them. When in the throes of a tantrum the carer should hold the older infant closely and consolingly, and speak low and slowly. This, combined with a matter-of-fact attitude, will allow the child to regain control, calm themselves and retain their dignity. There should be otherwise minimal reward.

With the toddler of two years or more, especially if the tantrums are becoming part of a routine, walking away and denying them an audience can stop the tantrum cold. Difficult to do in the super-market, I know, but sometimes it's the only way not to reward the exhibition. Then they get a nice cuddle after it's all over.

Doesn't understand rules

It is important to understand that laying out rules and timetables or plans for them is of little help, as they don't understand rules and can't remember what the plan is for.

TODDLERS: CREATING LIMITS AND BOUNDARIES

Moulding the behaviour of young children is not an easy matter but we have two cards up our sleeve.

Love and reassurance

These are needed above all. Children need to know that, although things have changed, your love for them has not, and it is available at all times in quantity; just as important, its presence is constant, no matter how they behave.

Now is the time you start to get dividends from all the love and reassurance you gave your baby in his first year. He is now secure in your love and cares deeply about you. He also cares about what you think of him and will try to please you if he can. This can be used to influence his behaviour and help him recognise and remember the boundaries you set.

A look of disappointment and disapproval from someone he loves can be a powerful motivator to change his behaviour. In the first year he sought love from those around him. In the second, he seeks their approval. It is this desire to please loved ones that motivates the child to start to suppress his basic desires and learn self-control.

The child who has been unloved or ignored in his first year has little investment in his carer's response and will only suppress his impulses in the face of punishment. This does not teach the child how to develop a conscience or self-control. It will teach him only to change his behaviour through fear.

It is the former that internalises compassion and caring in the child; the latter just teaches him how to avoid trouble.

Attention

The currency of toddlerhood, the only commodity in which they deal, day by day, is attention. They need to constantly reconnect and catch the notice and gaze of their source of security, love and safety. This is driven by their anxiety about their newly found separateness. They will expend vast amounts of energy to get it from parents and carers. And any attention is good attention.

Using these as rewards will allow you to get a toddler to do your will. Moulding his behaviour is more easily achieved this way than by using force and old-fashioned discipline. If you want him to behave 'nicely', give him high-voltage attention when he is behaving nicely and very little when he is behaving in a way not to your liking.

For this behaviour, you give him a neutral response, a frown, and minimal or no attention.

If he hits his little sister, throws his food on the floor and then tries to throttle the cat, the action is only as rewarding as the response you give him, and, if your response is negative, it's still better than nothing. To get his mother to stop what she was doing, have her point her finger and say 'What a bad boy!' is vastly better than playing quietly by yourself, being a good boy and being totally ignored.

Many parents reward their toddlers more for performing what they call 'naughty' activities than those the parents would call 'nice'. They ignore their little girl sitting in the living room playing with her toys, but give full eye contact and absolute rapt attention to her when she pulls off her nappy and pees on the carpet.

Pick your battles

If what your toddler is doing is not ideal, but not doing him or the house any harm, perhaps it would be better to leave him to it until he gets bored with it. Let sleeping dogs lie. Developing tunnel vision and hearing is often the best option if the alternative is a pitched battle, which would leave you both scarred. Prioritise the discipline for when it is truly necessary, and make sure that if there is to be a standoff that the outcome is worth it. So if your two-year-old wants to use a black felt pen on the living room wall or ride her scooter full speed down the hallway, explain that this is non-negotiable. Even if it means a period of time in her bedroom until she changes her mind. Just calmly introduce the time in her room as 'thinking time', not as a punishment. When she comes out, see what she thinks when she gets her cuddle.

Appropriate expectations

Many parents have inappropriate expectations of their little ones. A study of toddlers by Christine Mosier and Barbara Rogoff in 2003 in Guatemala and the United States showed that the incidence of 'terrible twos' in Guatemala was much lower than in the United States. It seemed that the American mothers expected their two-year-olds to behave like four-year-olds and share their toys, play with other children nicely, and understand rules and ethics. The Guatemalan mothers, however, had no such expectations and treated their two-year-olds as babies, which immediately reduced the level of conflict for them and increased the contentment for the little ones. Let's face it – if you can't behave like a two-year-old when you're two, when can you?

Consistency

But above all, give the child consistency, along with love. This is one of the essentials of good parenting – that the carer is predictable and reliable, not making one rule one day, and another the next. This is the only logic a toddler can deal with.

Feeling the mood of the home

Babies, and even more so toddlers and children, are supremely sensitive to the 'mood' of their environment. If there is conflict and tension within the household, the baby will sense it immediately. You can pretend you are relaxed and happy to your older friends and have them fooled, but your little one will see through it in a second. How strange it is that we are aware that our dog knows this aspect of life, but we deny it in humans.

So if you have had a row with your partner, your infant knows this, even if he was out of earshot. It worries him and worried toddlers need even more reassurance to tell them everything is okay. This is at precisely the time when you are not in the mood to deliver it.

Explain their feelings to them

When toddlers feel bad, to them that's all there is. They are not able to differentiate between their negative emotions. When they are in floods of tears about an unpleasant situation, they do not know whether they are angry, jealous, stressed, frustrated, hungry or just having a bad day.

The parent or carer needs to help them understand the difference between these feelings and so deal with them constructively and positively.

'Darling, you're crying now because you're angry with your big brother because he's taken your toy truck.'

Sitting down quietly with them, getting them to calm down and offering them a simple, warmly expressed explanation can give them an emotional vocabulary on which they can draw more and more as they get older.

THE 'SPOILT CHILD SYNDROME'

Spoilt kids are those who don't know the extent of their power because they have not had defined limits enforced in their lives.

- Some parents just check out at this stage and let the kids run free. They embark on a program of 'discipline by negotiation', attempting to engage the child as if he was an adult. These parents desperately want their kids to like them and be their friend. They don't realise that, as long as they are not actually neglected, children love their parent however the parent behaves. To feel secure the children need a consistent, reliable and sometimes non-negotiable base at home.

- Another group of parents just don't care and don't give the child what he needs most: time, and lots of attention. This usually makes the child sad and angry, and his toddler behaviour is derived from that negative emotional state. No wonder he becomes a 'Terrible Two'.
- Often the parents, in an effort to protect their children against the normal frustrations of life, have shielded them and cocooned them in an unreal world of constant positivity.
- Perhaps they have showered them with gifts and caved in to their demands even though their behaviour has not justified reward.
- Occasionally the children are just following the behaviour of their parents, who demonstrate self-centred, inconsiderate and manipulative behaviour in their own lives.

Without clear guidance these children become increasingly concerned that the family relies upon them to set their own limits and, innately, they know that situation is untenable. They will keep on pushing till they find something concrete on which they can rely. Unfortunately for the indulging or ignoring parents, that can be when the toddler's behaviour becomes so extreme as to be intolerable. We then have a situation of angry, overbearing children and demoralised, beaten parents.

DIFFERENT TOTS WITH DIFFERENT SPOTS

There are as many variations of personality and temperament in toddlers as in any other age group. They also change and develop at an alarming rate so if a particular stage is tiresome, be patient and don't despair because there's a different one coming soon.

It is important to remember that babies and children are people like you and me. They have their personal dignity, which can be easy to affect, so do not humiliate them. Watch what you say about them in front of other people, as they are listening and, although you may use long words, they can discern the meaning behind your remarks. Equally, don't impose on them unnecessarily; for instance, don't interrupt them when they are engrossed in a game or task unless it is for a good reason.

Like you and me, they also have their up and down days, sometimes they are stressed, tense, hungry or uncomfortable and this affects their mood and their behaviour. Try not to over-react to a brief tantrum or burst of temper and keep the bridges of communication open. You're the adult in the relationship, so you should be the reasonable one.

THE NEW BABY

After a new baby comes home, no matter how much preparation toddlers have had, it is always a shock and an affront. Not surprisingly about 85 per cent of toddlers regress significantly towards babyhood. So they forget their toilet training and need a daytime nappy, they unearth their old dummy from the bottom of the toy box and they want to start drinking from a baby's bottle.

Let's face it, what could be more reasonable? Being a baby in this house seems to have distinct advantages and they work towards getting as much attention as they had before. It usually takes about three months to adapt to the presence of the new baby. Until then you have to remain patient, relaxed and smiling. Telling the toddler off and pointing the finger, as mentioned earlier, is precisely what they are working towards, so stay neutral and understanding until the storm blows over.

There is a nice technique for this problem. Before the baby comes home, the grandmother or father should help the sibling decorate and arrange the new baby's room. When the baby comes home the big responsible brother or sister will be then able to proudly show their new baby their handiwork and be involved in the whole process. The toddler can also have their baby duties outlined, such as arranging the nappies or tidying the baby's toys up, so that they continue their involvement.

However, it is never a good idea to leave a new toddler in the same room as a baby without supervision. (See above: 'no common sense'!)

TODDLERS AND PARENTS

Like all relationships, the one between a toddler and his parents is a two-way street. If the parents are anxious or stressed, it is easy for them to be short-tempered when dealing with a stubborn toddler, and such situations can rapidly go pear-shaped unless they retain some perspective. Fatigue always affects a parent's ability to deal with such difficulties and, as the fatigue is often caused by the toddler's sleep problems, this issue tends to self-perpetuate. (See Chapter 14 for some solutions.)

Occasionally some children evoke in a parent hidden, negative feelings from their past. In this, the parent must recognise they are dealing with their personal ghosts, try to take responsibility for these feelings and avoid letting it affect the relationship with their child.

But above all it is good to keep in mind that the toddler years do not last long. When, at the age of four, the child starts developing empathy, the ability to delay gratification and some sense of responsibility, your little troublemaker will cease to exist. He will be transformed into this other child and, believe it or not, you'll miss him!

TOILET TRAINING

As toddlers can now perceive when their nappy is wet, parents can start considering toilet training. In general children do not like having a wet or soiled nappy so once they get the connection between this feeling and its solution, they will respond to toilet training.

There are a few principles that are worth considering:

- Start changing her nappy only in the bathroom soon after she is 18 months, not the living room or next to her bed. She will soon associate the bathroom with bathroom functions and this is an important early step.

- Until your toddler's spinal cord has wired up the nerves to achieve bowel and urinary control, it is no use pursuing toilet training. These connections are laid down at different times in different babies and cannot be hurried. It is the same as some babies walking at ten months and others not until 18 months.

- There is a reflex called the 'gastro-colic reflex'. Fill the *gastros* (stomach), and the colon (bowel) wants to empty. So straight after a feed it is more likely, than at other times, that the bowel will empty and fill the nappy. That would be a good time to put the child on the potty and possibly be rewarded. If it works, it is a time for celebration and praise. A silver-star sticker on the fridge, for instance.

- Some mothers use this reflex and become adept at predicting when their young babies of a few months old will move their bowels or empty their bladder. This is called 'elimination training'. With a sensitive, observant mother it is possible to achieve good results; however, it is the mother who is the one who is trained, not the baby. Before the nerves are connected, it is not possible for the baby to feel when she needs to go or to control this urge. It can certainly save nappies if you want to give it a try but this discipline isn't for every mother to learn.

- About 18 months is the earliest a child starts to understand the process but many, if not most children, wait until after two. The first intimation that things are moving in this sphere is when she realises she is wet or has a soiled nappy. Give her praise that she told you before you noticed, and change her (in the bathroom).

- Following this breakthrough the next part is for the child to understand that there are warning signals before she wees or poos in the nappy. This realisation usually happens gradually over the following few months. As time goes on the warning time lengthens so it can be of some use, and the child can get help to go to the toilet in time or be put on a potty.

- When this process works, then it is time for more major celebration and praise and another star on the fridge. It is worth a reward as it takes a fair amount of concentration and presence of mind for the child to repeat this trick.

- The most important aspect for the parent is no pressure. Lots of buoyant encouragement but no negative looks or remarks. Most children really want to be big and dry and will work hard towards this end unless, of course, there is an advantage to not cooperating. If you reward the accidents with lots of attention, concern and disappointment then, for a toddler, it's really much more fun and more attention to just keep missing. So accidents should be ignored and dealt with dispassionately.

- Putting small children on the potty regularly without their cooperation, or their suggestion there is something to do, is usually a fruitless exercise. Keep it for when they think there might be a result. Regular potting after a meal, as in elimination training, can still work but the reflex used before becomes less powerful after voluntary control takes over. Nevertheless your experience will guide you as to whether it is likely to succeed and a few empty potties are no big problem.

Epilogue

IN THESE PAGES I HAVE TRIED to explain how the early life of the infant provides the template upon which the child, and later the adult, structures his relationships with himself, his world and the people around him.

The most important aspect of our lives is how we handle our encounters. Each moment of each day we have to make a choice about our actions, words or motivations. We can choose to respond in a loving, open and non-judgmental way, or we can choose the opposite.

As time goes by our life increasingly becomes the sum total of all of these choices. We can live a full life infused with love and acceptance or one stunted in defensiveness and cynicism.

An American travel writer called William Least Heat-Moon once suggested that we meet and engage with about 100,000 different people in our lifetime. Some of the relationships are brief, some long-term and intimate, but the quality we bring to them has the power to affect or transform each encountered individual.

They in turn engage with thousands more, radiating out. One loving word or action can potentially affect millions.

In this way the loving connection you have with your children teaches them to play their part to change the world for the better.

You can change the world, one baby at a time.

Acknowledgements

FOR THOSE OF US WHO WORK in the world of babies, who each day see them emerging wet, pink and screaming from their mother's womb, it is easy to forget that, for the uninitiated, they can appear strange and frighteningly vulnerable. Cute and heart-melting for sure, but a real enigma.

This book grew out of the acceptance of my previous volume *Baby on Board* by parents who wanted something easy to read but evidence-based to unravel this mystery and help them enjoy the journey through babyhood. My thanks to them for their many encouraging remarks and references to their 'bible'. All deeply appreciated.

This book has a broader sweep and is about infants of all ages from newborn to toddlerhood and beyond. I have continued to make an effort to impart the information lightly and without jargon.

During the book's long gestation, many people helped me with specific subjects. As in *Baby on Board* my good friend and Fellow of the International Lactation Consultant Association Joy Heads helped me significantly with the breastfeeding chapter. The illustrations from Rebecca Glover are very clear and a delight.

The Play Therapy Department at Sydney Children's Hospital and, in particular, the manager Janet Burke, helped me with Chapter 18 on using play to connect with babies. I am very grateful for their many suggestions.

I consulted the very experienced Dr Barry Duffy who made some important observations in Chapter 17 on when your baby gets sick. Dr Meredith Ward, neonatologist, neuro-scientific researcher and mother read the draft and taught me much about the difficulties of combining career and parenting. Dr Lee Sutton, a developmental paediatrician, critiqued the toddler information. I thank them all for their time and help. I did filter their remarks so I hasten to add that any errors and omissions remain completely mine.

I took on board many comments and insights based on the experience of numerous mothers and fathers. I would like to make special mention of Emmalee Benhayon, Paula Hanson, Robyn Jones, Anna Karam, Felicity Latchford, Deborah McInnes, Sally Scott, Toni Steenson and Katie Walls, who responded to a questionnaire about parenting in lucid and enlightening ways.

Thanks also to the many parents who have spent time with me in the consulting room and hospital. I still get a charge from them and their babies, and never cease learning from them.

I have learned much from Serge Benhayon, especially about parenting from the heart and 'gentle breath' meditation, and Neil Ringe brought clarity to my suggestions about 'being there' and meditative practice. Thanks to Nina Stabey for her terrific recipes.

Many thanks to the team at Pan Macmillan – Jo Lyons for a detailed, skilled edit and lastly Ingrid Ohlsson, who approached me to write this book and then supported and encouraged me. She made many suggestions about the direction of the book and gave me invaluable insights into the big picture.

Finally, thanks too to my daughter and midwife Georgina Dowden who made some really astute observations and taught me that pizzas are delivered, not babies.

Without my beloved Tamara's support and encouragement, of course, I would never have been motivated to start.

Notes and references

CHAPTER 2   BREASTFEEDING: YOUR BABY MADE ENTIRELY OF YOU

Cox, S. (2006) *Breastfeeding with Confidence: A practical guide*, Meadowbrook, New York. This is an excellent how-to guide for breastfeeding. Buy it with confidence.

Hale, T. (2012) *Medications and Mother's Milk*, 15th edition, Hale Publishing, Amarillo, Texas. This is the excellent standard text on drugs and medication in breastmilk.

Minchin, M.K., J.W. Maher and P.J. Minchin (1998) *Breastfeeding Matters: What we need to know about infant feeding*, Alma Publications, St Kilda South, Victoria, Australia. A quite dense but very readable account of breastfeeding and the politics and marketing of formula feeding. Not for the faint-hearted (or the pro-formula-feeding lobby).

CHAPTER 4   BABY BRAIN 101

Schore, A.N. (2001) 'Effects of a secure attachment relationship on right brain development, affect regulation, and infant mental health', *Infant Mental Health Journal*, 22(1–2): 7–66. A very dense and academic review of the neurodevelopment of the maternal infant bond and its ramifications.

CHAPTER 5   THE NEW
BABY'S TASKS

Gerhardt, S. (2004) *Why Love Matters*, Routledge, New York. Written by a psychotherapist, this book lays out a clear narrative about the underpinnings of infant mental health. Parents and anyone involved in infant care should read this.

CHAPTER 6   THAT'S THE
'HOW' – NOW LET'S TALK
ABOUT THE 'WHO'

Belsky, J. (2002) 'Quantity counts: Amount of child care and children's socio-emotional development', *Journal of Developmental and Behavioral Pediatrics*, 23(3):167–170. This is the report of the network research group that the US government set up to investigate the effects of commercial childcare and a commentary by one of its members.

Cook, P.S. (2011) *Mothering Matters*, Freedom Publishing, Balwyn, Victoria, Australia and the previous edition, *Mothering Denied* (2008), ebook, Peter S. Cook, Queenscliff, NSW. (downloadable from www.members.optusnet.com.au/pcook62/090424MDA4.pdf.) A very well-researched and influential book. Foreword by Steve Biddulph, who also wrote the lucid and illuminating book *Raising Babies: Should Under 3s Go to Nursery?* Thorsons, HarperCollins (2006). A book about day care published in the United Kingdom and available online.

Gopnik, A. (2010) *The Philosophical Baby: What children's minds tell us about truth, love, and the meaning of life*, Picador, New York. Gopnik's book is totally absorbing, fascinating and easy to read – a real page-turner. It outlines the latest neuroscience research to probe the mind of the baby and its implications, and will expand your view about babies forever!

National Institute of Child Health and Development: Early Child Care Research Network (2002). 'Early child care and children's development prior to school entry: results from the NICHD Study of early child care', *American Educational Research Journal*, 39(1): 133–164.

——(2007) 'Are there long-term effects of early child care?', *Child Development*, 78(2): 681–701.

CHAPTER 8   ATTUNEMENT
TO YOUR BABY

National Institute of Mental Health (2001), 'Teenage brain: a work in progress', fact sheet. 'Teenagers whose childhoods were secure and loving tend to get through this difficult time of adolescence with more ease than those whose early days were difficult.'

CHAPTER 9   BEING THERE
AND STAYING CALM

Gopnik, A. (2010) *The Philosophical Baby: What children's minds tell us about truth, love, and the meaning of life*, Picador, New York, pp.187–8. 'For the parents whose childhoods were difficult, how they deal with this when they have children seems to depend on whether they have thought about and processed the reasons behind why it didn't go well.'

CHAPTER 11   FATHERS:
A SPECIAL RELATIONSHIP

Gottman, J.M. and J. DeClaire (1997) *The Heart of Parenting: Raising an emotionally intelligent child*, Simon & Schuster, New York. Both parents should read this.

CHAPTER 12   THE UNSETTLED BABY,
PART I: MYTHS AND MAKING SENSE

Brazelton, T.B. 'Crying in infancy', *Pediatrics*, (29): 579–88. Dr T. Berry Brazelton was one of the early paediatricians who reported that perfectly normal babies cry or fuss for fairly long periods of time as part of their normal development. This graph was exactly replicated with bigger numbers of normal babies by Dr Ronald Barr and others. Dr Barr has also developed an excellent resource for the anxious parents of unsettled babies called 'The Period of PURPLE Crying'. For more details, see purplecrying.info.

Lucassen, P., W.J. Assendelft, et al. (1998) 'Effectiveness of treatments for infantile colic: systematic review', *BMJ*, 316: 1563–69. A group tries to bring some order and sense into a difficult subject to treat.

McKenzie, S. (1991) 'Troublesome crying in infants: effect of advice to reduce stimulation', *Archives of Disease in Childhood*, 66(12): 1416–20. This paper makes absolute sense to me with a clean result, though the numbers of babies are small and the study fairly simple.

Phaire, T. (1544) *The Boke of Chyldren*. Full text reprinted (1981) *Pediatrics*, 68(2): 182. This is the first paediatric textbook in English and lists many childhood conditions in addition to 'colyke', such as 'small pockes and measles', 'pyssing in the bed', 'terrible dreames' and 'stiffenes of limmes'. It went through seven editions in its lifetime of over 50 years.

St James-Roberts, I., M. Alvarez, et al. (2006) 'Infant crying and sleeping in London, Copenhagen, and when parents adopt a "proximal" form of care', *Pediatrics*, 117(6): 1146–55. This excellent paper compared three groups of parents: a 'London' group (standard British parents), proximate (or close attachment) group and a 'Copenhagen' group (of clearly very sensible parents). They all kept detailed diaries of how much their babies cried and how they handled, fed and looked after them, with interesting results.

Vandenplas, Y., H. Goyvaerts, et al. (1991) 'Gastroesophageal reflux, as measured by 24-hour pH monitoring, in 509 healthy infants screened for risk of sudden infant death syndrome', *Pediatrics*, 88(4): 834–40. This shows how often the normal baby refluxes gastric contents into the oesophagus. Answer: very often!

Wessel, M.A., J.C. Cobb, et al. (1954) 'Paroxysmal fussing in infancy, sometimes called "colic"', *Pediatrics*, 14(5): 421–34. (The Yale rooming-in project.) This paper is the standard text that tried to delineate a standard definition for what constituted 'colic'.

CHAPTER 13 THE UNSETTLED BABY, PART II: THE MEDICINE

Hassall, E. (2012) 'Over-prescription of acid-suppressing medications in infants: how it came about, why it's wrong, and what to do about it', *Journal of Pediatrics*, 160(2):193–8. This paper and the Merwat and Spechler article below are salutary reminders that sometimes we can lose control of medical diagnoses and, under pressure from parents and media, over treat it.

Heine, R.G., B. Jordan, et al. (2006) 'Clinical predictors of pathological gastro-oesophageal reflux in infants with persistent distress', *Journal of Paediatrics and Child Health*, 42(3): 134–9. This is the go-to paper on GORD by the leading Australian gastroenterologist on this subject.

Merwat, S.N. and S.J. Spechler (2009) 'Might the use of acid-suppressive medications predispose to the development of eosinophilic esophagitis?', *American Journal of Gastroenterology*, 104: 1897–902.

Orenstein, S.R. MD (2008) 'Crying in infant GERD: acid or volume? Heartburn or dyspepsia?', *Current Gastroenterology Reports*, 10(5): 433–6. A very good review on GORD from the United States.

Ryan, P., M. Lander, et al. (1983) 'When does reflux oesophagitis occur with gastro-oesophageal reflux in infants? A clinical and endoscopic study, and correlation with outcome', *Australian Paediatric Journal* 19(2): 90–3. Gastroenterologists describing their investigations into GORD and the fact that all babies with inflammation of their oesophagus from reflux acid were irritable.

Vandenplas, Y., M. Brueton, et al. (2007) 'Guidelines for the diagnosis and management of cow's milk protein allergy in infants', *Archives of Disease in Childhood*, 92: 902–8. A complete medical guide to cow's milk protein allergy diagnosis and treatment.

CHAPTER 14   QUIET NIGHTS

Anders, T.F. and M.A. Keener (1985) 'Developmental course of night-time sleep-wake patterns in full-term and premature infants during the first year of life', *Sleep*, 8(3): 173–92. This article describes the normal sleep patterns in babies.

Anders, T.F., L.F. Halpern and J. Hua (1992) 'Sleeping through the night: a developmental perspective', *Pediatrics*, 90(4): 554–60. Further useful information on the subject of sleeping patterns as children grow.

France, K.G. and N.M. Blampied (2005) 'Modifications of systematic ignoring in the management of infant sleep disturbance: efficacy and infant distress', *Child & Family Behavior Therapy*, 27 (1): 1–16. An exploration into which extinction (controlled crying) techniques worked best with explanations why.

Nikolopoulou, M. and I. St James-Roberts (2003) 'Preventing sleeping problems in infants who are at risk of developing them', *Archives of Disease in Childhood*, 88: 108–11. From the same team that brought us the crying/fussing diary accounts of the three groups of mothers. This is excellent and is a method to help very young babies to sleep for longer at night.

St James-Roberts, I. (2007) 'Infant crying and sleeping: helping parents to prevent and manage problems', *Sleep Medicine Clinics*, 2: 363–75. A summary by the leader of the above group.

Sunderland, M. (2008) *The Science of Parenting*, Dorling Kindersley, New York. A really excellent, strongly recommended book on the neuroscience of various styles of parenting and their results.

Teng, A., A. Bartle, et al. (2012) 'Infant and toddler sleep in Australia and New Zealand', *Journal of Paediatrics and Child Health*, 48(3): 268–73. A large recent study from Australasia. The data was obtained from parents who filled in a detailed web questionnaire.

van Sleuwen, B.E., A.C. Engelberts, et al. (2007) 'Swaddling: a systematic review', *Pediatrics*, 120(4): 1097. A thorough review of swaddling through the ages to the present day. It is definitely worth a read.

CHAPTER 15   SHARING SLEEP: TALKING ABOUT THE RISKS

McKenna, J.J. and L.T. Gettler (2008) 'Cultural influences on infant sleep biology and the science that studies it: toward a more inclusive paradigm, part II', in Loughlin, G., J. Carroll and C. Marcus (eds) *Sleep and Breathing in Children: A developmental approach*, Vol. 2, Marcel Dekker, New York, pp. 183–221. This is one of the important references regarding the bed-sharing baby and his mother.

Mother–Baby Behavioral Sleep Laboratory, https://cosleeping.nd.edu. This is Dr James McKenna's website, which I thoroughly recommend. You will find here anything that you would like to know about bed-sharing with your baby.

CHAPTER 16   SUDI/SIDS

American Academy of Pediatrics Policy Statement from the Task Force on Sudden Infant Death Syndrome, 'SIDS and other sleep-related infant deaths: expansion of recommendations for a safe infant sleeping environment', published online 17 October 2011. doi: 10.1542/peds.2011–2284.

Center of Disease Control and Prevention Report on Sudden Infant Death Syndrome (SIDS) and Vaccines, 'Comprehensive review from the

AAP on SIDS: risk factors and recommendations', http://www.cdc.gov/vaccinesafety/Concerns/sids_faq.html Includes all the relevant references. No question but the data suggests strongly that vaccines reduce the incidence of SIDS by up to 50 per cent.

CHAPTER 17   WHEN YOUR BABY GETS SICK

Sullivan, J. and H. Farrar (2011) 'Fever and antipyretic use in children', An American Academy of Pediatrics Clinical Report, *Pediatrics*, 127(3): 580. We use too many drugs to force down the temperature of children when they are feverish. This actually slightly prolongs the illness (but if the child feels better it is a judgement whether it's still worth it).

VandenHeuvel, A. (1993) 'Missing work to care for sick children', *Family Matters*, 34: 52–5. It needs to be updated, but this report is a comprehensive review into the difficulties families face with sick children and how many deal with it.

CHAPTER 19   FOOD FOR THOUGHT: SOLIDS AND SPOON FOODS FOR BABIES AND KIDS

Berkowitz, R.I., R.H. Moore, et al. (2010) 'Identification of an obese eating style in 4-year-old children born at high and low risk for obesity', *Obesity*, 18(3), 505–12. Detailed papers about the subjects in the title. Read them to get all data and statistics.

Birch, L.L. (1999) 'Development of food preferences', *Annual Review of Nutrition*, 19: 41–62. Standard text on the science of taste preferences.

Carruth B.R., P.J. Ziegler, et al. (2004) 'Prevalence of picky eaters among infants and toddlers and their caregivers' decisions about offering a new food', *Journal of the American Dietetic Association*, 104: S57–S64.

Davis, C.M. (1928) 'Self-selection of diet by newly weaned infants: an experimental study', *American Journal of Diseases of Children*, 36, 651–79.

——(1939) 'Results of the self-selection of diets by young children', *The Canadian Medical Association Journal*, 41, 257–61. These two Davis papers and the Galef article below relate to the 'wisdom of the body' concept of children self-selecting an appropriate diet. Davis recognised that the papers had created the wrong impression on the paediatric world even before it was pointed out by Galef.

Du Toit, G., Katz, Y. et al. (2008) 'Early consumption of peanuts in infancy is associated with a low prevalence of peanut allergy', *Journal of Allergy and Clinical Immunology*, 122(5): 984–91.

Galef Jr, B.G. (1991) 'A contrarian view of the wisdom of the body as it relates the self-selection', *Psychological Review*, 98(2): 218–23.

Greene A. (2009) *Feeding Baby Green: The earth-friendly program for healthy, safe nutrition during pregnancy, childhood, and* beyond, Jossey-Bass, Wiley imprint, San Francisco. No question but the best book about feeding your baby solids available today. Buy it and read it carefully.

Illingworth, R.S. (1991) *The Normal Child: Some problems of the early years and their treatment*, Churchill Livingstone, Longman Group UK Ltd. It's hard to get this book anymore but it is chock-full of useful advice about common and obscure medical conditions in babies and children.

Kaitz, M., A. Good, et al. (1987) 'Mothers' recognition of their newborns by olfactory cues', *Developmental Psychobiology*, 20(6): 587–91.

Karr, M., G. Alperstein, et al. (1996) 'Iron status and anaemia in preschool children in Sydney', *Australian and New Zealand Journal of Public Health*, 20(6): 618–22.

Karr, M., M. Mira, et al. (2001) 'Iron deficiency in Australian-born children of Arabic background in central Sydney', *Medical Journal of Australia*, 174(4): 165–8. Surprising results about the blood iron status of a broad Sydney population of children.

Koplin J.J., Osborne N.J. et al. (2010) 'Can early introduction of egg prevent egg allergy in infants? A population based study', *Journal of*

Allergy and Clinical Immunology, 126(4): 807–13. Early challenge with peanuts and eggs decreases the incidence of allergy in children to these foods.

Lustig, R.H. 'Sugar: The bitter truth', *UCSF, Mini Medical School*, YouTube, 30 July 2009. See this on YouTube and weep for our children.

Maier, A., C. Chabanet, et al. (2007*)* 'Effects of repeated exposure on acceptance of initially disliked vegetables in 7-month old infants', *Food Quality and Preference*, 18(8), 1023–32.

Moss, B.G. and W.H. Yeaton (2011) 'Young children's weight trajectories and associated risk factors: results from the early childhood longitudinal study – birth cohort.' *American Journal of Health Promotion* 25(3): 190. A broad study of a large population of US children – and how they are changing over time.

Nowson, C.A. and C. Margerison (2002) 'Vitamin D intake and Vitamin D status of Australians', *Medical Journal of Australia*, 177(3): 149–52. Despite our bright sun the incidence of vitamin D deficiency is still surprisingly high in Australia.

Petition from the Physicians Committee for Responsible Medicine to the USDA Food and Nutrition Service, 1 July 2012. This petition was designed to persuade the US Government to remove milk from the National School's Lunch Program.

Rapley, G. 'Baby Lead Weaning', www.babyledweaning.com. A technique where babies are given soft finger foods to feed themselves.

Schaal, B., L. Marlier and R. Soussignan (2000) 'Human foetuses learn odours from their pregnant mother's diet', *Chemical Senses*, 25(6): 729. Wonderful information that fits with what mothers have been telling us for years.

CHAPTER 20   THE RELENTLESS TODDLER

Mosier, C., and Rogoff, B. (2003) 'Privileged treatment of toddlers: cultural aspects of individual choice and responsibility', *Developmental*

Psychology, 39: 1047–60. Apparently no 'Terrible Twos' in Guatemala because they treat the two years olds like babies, unlike the United States where they treat them as four year olds.

EPILOGUE

Heat-Moon, William Least (1999) *Blue Highways: A journey into America*, Back Bay Books, New York.

Contacts

AUSTRALIA

Australian Breastfeeding Association – Lactation Resource Centre

Ph: 1800 686 268 (1800 MUM 2 MUM)
Email: info@breastfeeding.asn.au (head office)
  Website: www.breastfeeding.asn.au

Drug information

For specialised independent advice and information on drugs in relation to lactation or for children, contact the Drug Information Service in your state. These are based at a Women's or Children's Hospital, whose telephone numbers are:

ACT   02 6244 3333
NSW   1800 647 848

NT   08 8922 8424
QLD   07 3163 2417
SA   08 8161 7555
TAS   03 6222 8737
VIC   03 9594 2361
WA   08 9340 2723

For information on recreational drugs or drugs of addiction, contact the Alcohol and Drugs Information Service in your state.

Early childhood health clinics

These are listed under 'Early Childhood Health Centre' in your local telephone directory.

Hospital websites

The website of your state children's hospital is a good resource:
Mater Children's Hospital, Brisbane www.mater.org.au

Princess Margaret Hospital for Children, Perth www.pmh.health.wa.gov.au

Royal Hospital for Women, Melbourne www.rch.unimelb.edu.au Sydney Children's Hospital, www.sch.edu.au

The Children's Hospital, Westmead www.chw.edu.au

Women and Children's Hospital, Adelaide www.wch.sa.gov.au

Mothercraft centres and their helplines

Tresillian Family Care Centre: 02 9787 0800 www.tresillian.net
Karitane: 1300 227 464 www.karitane.org.au

Mothersafe

Phone: 612 9382 6539 (Sydney metropolitan area)
Phone: 1800 647 848 (non-metropolitan area)
www.mothersafe.org.au

Poisons Information Service

Available in all states on 13 11 26

Smoking Quit line

13 7848 (13 QUIT) www.icanquit.com.au

NEW ZEALAND

Plunketline (a 24-hour parents' advice line) 0800 933 922

Hospital websites

Canterbury District Health Board www.chl.govt.nz

Christchurch Women's Hospital www.chl.govt.nz/cwh

National Women's Hospital, Auckland www.nwhealthinfo.co.nz

New Zealand Paediatric Hospital: Starship Children's Hospital
www.starship.org.nz

Breastfeeding

www.lalecheleague.org.nz

Maternity Services Consumer Council

www.maternity.org.nz/

NZ Medicines Safety Authority

www.medsafe.govt.nz

Index

What Makes a Life Worth Living

Hugh Mackay

Hugh Mackay
The Good Life

No one can promise you that a life lived for others will bring you a deep sense of satisfaction, but it's certain that nothing else will.

Hugh Mackay has spent his entire working life asking Australians about their values, motivations, ambitions, hopes and fears. Now, in *The Good Life*, he addresses the ultimate question: what makes a life worth living?

His conclusion is provocative. The good life is not the sum of our security, wealth, status, postcode, career success and levels of happiness. The good life is one defined by our capacity for selflessness, the quality of our relationships and our willingness to connect with others in a useful way.

Mackay examines what is known as the Golden Rule through the prisms of religion, philosophy, politics, business and family life. And he explores the numerous and often painful ways we distract ourselves from this central principle: our pursuit of pleasure, our attempts to perfect ourselves and our children, and our conviction that we can have our lives under control.

Argued with all the passion and intelligence we have come to expect from one of Australia's most prolific and insightful authors, *The Good Life* is a book that will start conversations, ignite arguments and possibly even change the way we live our lives.

David Gillespie
Free Schools

**Bestselling author David Gillespie shows parents how to choose the
best school for their kids, how to avoid fees, and how to make a
less-than-perfect system better.**

David Gillespie has six kids. Like many parents, he and his wife
faced some tough decisions when it came to choosing a high school.
He calculated that sending his kids to a private school would cost
him $1.3 million. A businessman at heart, he thought it worth doing
some research to find out what he'd get for his money. In other words,
would his kids get better results? The answer was no.

Intrigued, David continued his research, only to discover he was wrong
on most counts – as are most parents – when it comes to working out
what factors deliver a great education. Among other things, he found
out that class size doesn't matter, composite classes are fine, fancy
buildings and rolling lawns are a waste of money, the old-school-tie
network won't cut it in the new industries and NAPLAN is misread
by everyone so is largely meaningless as a measure of quality.

Taking on an entrenched system of vested interests – the unions, the
government, our own sense of worth, privilege and entitlement –
this book is both a practical guide to getting the best for our kids
and a provocative overview of why the system is struggling.

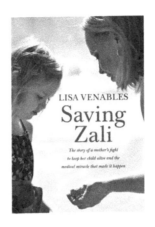

Lisa Venables
Saving Zali

Saving Zali **is a mother's account of every parent's worst nightmare: a diagnosis of cancer with a shocking prognosis.**

In 2009, Lisa and Andrew Venables were told that their eighteen-month-old daughter Zali had Langerhan's cell histiocytosis, or LCH, a cancer resistant to chemotherapy and almost impossible to treat. Zali was given six weeks to live.

It was the beginning of a journey of heartache and bravery as Zali battled daily for her life in Sydney's Westmead Hospital, with Lisa by her side at every step.

Although Zali survived her original prognosis, her condition worsened dramatically. Her medical team ran out of options. Lisa and Andrew were told their daughter had hours to live. But then a controversial treatment was proposed, a treatment never before used for Zali's condition. What happened next was a medical miracle that proved that the extraordinary is possible.

Heartfelt and beautifully told, this is the story of medical dedication, a child's tenacity and a mother's love.